Lab Manual

Gregory L. Moss

Purdue University

A Design Approach

DIGITAL SYSTEMS

Principles and Applications

FIFTH EDITION

Ronald J. Tocci

Monroe Community College

PRENTICE HALL
Englewood Cliffs, New Jersey 07632

Editorial/production supervision: *Alan Dalgleish*
Manufacturing buyer: *Mary McCartney*
Ed O'Dougherty

Printed in the United States of America

10 9 8 7 6 5 4 3 2 1

ISBN   0-13-213190-0

Prentice-Hall International (UK) Limited, *London*
Prentice-Hall of Australia Pty. Limited, *Sydney*
Prentice-Hall Canada Inc., *Toronto*
Prentice-Hall Hispanoamericana, S.A., *Mexico*
Prentice-Hall of India Private Limited, *New Delhi*
Prentice-Hall of Japan, Inc., *Tokyo*
Simon & Schuster Asia Pte. Ltd., *Singapore*
Editora Prentice-Hall do Brasil, Ltda., *Rio de Janeiro*

CONTENTS

EQUIPMENT LIST

Laboratory Equipment

Digital breadboarding system
Power supply (5v, 500ma)
Logic probe
Digital voltmeter
Oscilloscope (dual-trace minimum, preferably 4-trace)
Frequency counter
Signal generator
PLD (or universal) programmer
Personal Computer (IBM or compatible)

Digital Integrated Circuits

2	74LS00	Quad 2-input NAND
1	74HC00	Quad 2-input NAND (CMOS)
2	74LS02	Quad 2-input NOR
2	74LS04	Hex INVERTERS
2	74LS08	Quad 2-input AND
2	74LS10	Triple 3-input NAND
1	74LS14	Hex Schmitt-Trigger INVERTERS
2	74LS20	Dual 4-input NAND
1	74LS27	Triple 3-input NOR
1	74LS32	Quad 2-input OR
2	74LS47	BCD-to-7-Segment DECODER/DRIVER
1	74LS83A	4-bit Binary FULL ADDER (or 74LS283)
1	74LS85	4-bit MAGNITUDE COMPARATOR
1	74LS86A	Quad 2-input EXCLUSIVE-OR
1	74LS90	Decade COUNTER
2	74LS112A	Dual JK Negative-Edge Triggered FLIP-FLOPS
1	74LS138	3-line-to-8-line DECODER/DEMULTIPLEXER
1	74LS148	8-line-to-3-line Priority ENCODER
1	74150	1-of-16 MULTIPLEXER
1	74LS151	1-of-8 MULTIPLEXER
1	74LS160A	Synchronous Decade COUNTER
1	74LS164	8-bit Serial-In Parallel-Out SHIFT REGISTER
1	74LS166A	8-bit Parallel-In Serial-Out SHIFT REGISTER
1	74184	BCD-to-Binary CONVERTER
1	74LS190	Synchronous Up/Down Decade COUNTER
1	74LS221	Dual MONOSTABLE MULTIVIBRATOR
1	74LS244	Octal 3-State BUFFER
1	74S260	Dual 5-input NOR
1	74LS373	Octal D-type LATCH (PIPO REGISTER)
1	74LS393	Dual 4-bit Binary COUNTER
2	2114	Static RAM (1K x 4)
1	GAL16V8A	Electrically Erasable Programmable Logic Device

Linear Integrated Circuits

1	NE555	Timer
1	AD557	8-bit Digital-to-Analog Converter
1	ADC0804	8-bit Analog-to-Digital Converter

Miscellaneous Components

2   MAN72 (or equivalent)
Common-Anode 7-segment LED Display

Resistors (1/4 watt) -- 330 (20 parts), 1K (10 parts), 3.3K, 10K (2 parts), 27K, 33K, 47K, 68K, 82K ohms

Capacitors -- 10μ, 0.01μ (3 parts), 0.001μ, 0.0047μ, 150p farads

Potentiometers -- 10K, 50K ohms

SPST switches -- optional

Pushbutton -- optional

LEDs -- optional

Software

P/C-SILOS by Simucad

LC9000 by Programmable Logic Technologies

text editor or wordprocessor with ASCII output

PREFACE

This laboratory manual was written for students in an introductory digital electronics course that emphasizes logic circuit analysis, applications, and design. The manual is divided into 25 major topical units with each unit containing several laboratory projects. The sequencing of topics primarily follows the manual's accompanying text, *Digital Systems: Principles and Applications, 5th Edition*, by Ronald Tocci. The manual, however, is designed for flexibility in that it is possible to resequence many of the projects to fit a particular course.

The manual is designed to provide an extensive selection of projects for a two semester introductory digital course sequence. Multiple projects are provided in each manual unit to allow variety and flexibility in the assigning of student laboratory experiences. The author does not expect that any course would have sufficient time for any student to perform all of the laboratory projects in most of the units. Rather, the instructor may select appropriate projects to assign for their particular course needs. Additional projects may be selected for student enrichment activities.

The applications-oriented lab projects are designed to provide beginning electronics technology students with extensive experience in the analysis and design of digital logic circuits. The lab assignments consist of circuit projects that range from investigating basic logic concepts to synthesizing circuits for new applications. The projects are intended to challenge all students and to provide them with some directed laboratory experience that develops insight in digital principles, applications, and techniques of logic circuit analysis and design.

Personal computers with circuit analysis and design software are having a significant impact in industry today in the way digital systems are designed and developed. These new tools need to be included in the educational experience of future electronics personnel. Fortunately, relatively inexpensive hardware and software are available to provide this kind of experience. In addition to extensive application of standard medium scale integrated logic devices, the manual provides laboratory experience with standard computer tools used by industry in logic circuit design and development. One of these areas is computer logic simulation. Logic simulation is introduced to students using an easy to use but extremely powerful text-based simulator. Another new and rapidly expanding technology area is electrically erasable programmable logic devices. The custom implementation of logic circuits using programmable logic devices is included in several lab projects throughout the manual. Both of these areas of technology, while very important in industrial practice today, may be treated as optional projects for digital courses that do not currently utilize computer applications and may be replaced with other standard logic circuit design projects which are also included in the manual.

A list of laboratory equipment, integrated circuits and other necessary components is found in the Equipment List in the front of this manual. The standard parts that are used in this manual may be obtained from LEARNING SYSTEMS, INC., P.O. Box 2132, West Lafayette, IN 47906 as well as from many other electronics suppliers. Manufacturers' data sheets for all ICs in the Equipment List are found in Appendix B of this manual.

Gregory L. Moss

UNIT 1

LAB EQUIPMENT INTRODUCTION

Objectives ===

(1)   To be able to describe the function and operation of a typical digital breadboarding and testing system.
(2)   To be able to perform fundamental personal computer operating system tasks.

Tutorial ===

Digital Test Equipment

Breadboarding and testing equipment used with digital circuits generally include the following functions:

Power supply
>   The power supply provides a regulated +5v DC voltage to be used to power TTL integrated circuits. Note that some units may also contain additional fixed voltages or a variable DC power source for other types of circuits.

Lamp monitors
>   The lamp monitors indicate the voltage level at various points in the digital circuit being tested. The lamp monitors will light when a digital "high" voltage is applied to them.

Logic switches
>   The logic switches input either of the two logic levels (voltages) to the circuit being tested. A switch in the "down" position will provide a logic

1

"low" voltage, while a switch in the "up" position will provide a logic "high" voltage.

Pulsers or pushbuttons
A pulser provides a "bounce free" logic input to the test circuit.

Clock
The clock provides a variable frequency pulse waveform which can be used for the timing control of some digital circuits.

Breadboarding sockets
Breadboarding sockets are convenient devices on which circuits may be constructed for testing purposes. The socket contains a matrix of contacts that are used to interconnect the various components and wires needed to construct the digital circuit. The socket holes are small and only #30 to #22 solid "jumper" wires should be inserted into them. A typical breadboarding socket is illustrated in Fig. 1-1.

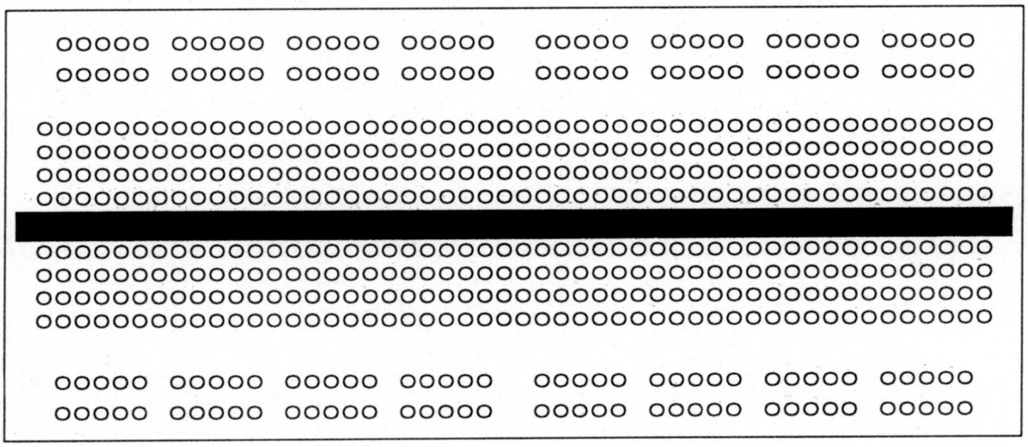

Fig. 1-1 Typical IC breadboarding socket

Measuring Voltage with a DVM

The potential difference or voltage between the + and - terminals of a battery or power supply connected to a circuit will cause current to flow through the circuit. The basic unit to measure potential difference is the volt (v). A potential difference or voltage drop occurs across the various devices in a circuit when current flows through them. The magnitude (and polarity with respect to a reference point in the circuit) of a potential difference is measured with an instrument called a voltmeter. You must be extremely careful when making voltage measurements since the measurement is made on a "live" (powered) circuit. The voltmeter test leads (probes) are placed across (in parallel with) the device or power source whose voltage is to be measured. The procedure to measure DC voltages using a typical Digital Volt Meter is:
(1)   Connect the test leads to the DVM
(2)   Set the function switch to measure DC voltages
(3)   Set the range switch for the maximum voltage anticipated

(4)   Connect (or touch) the black test lead to the reference point of the circuit (or component)

(5)   Connect (or touch) the red test lead to the point in the circuit where you wish to measure the voltage

(6)   Read the voltage on the digital display

(7)   Readjust the range setting if necessary for a proper reading

Ask your lab instructor if you have any questions concerning the use of the DVM.

Measuring Logic Levels with a Logic Probe

The logic probe is an extremely handy and easy to use piece of digital test equipment. It is used to detect and display the logic levels at various test points within a circuit. To use the logic probe to test TTL circuits:

(1)   Connect the alligator clip leads to the power supply for the circuit being tested (red to +5v and black to ground or negative)

(2)   Set the logic family switch to TTL

(3)   Carefully touch the probe tip to the circuit node (chip pin) to be tested (do not short any nodes together in the process)

(4)   Note the logic level present at the test point by which LED (HIGH or LOW) is illuminated

(5)   If neither HIGH or LOW is indicated, the proper logic voltage is not present at the test point

Some logic probes additionally have a pulse detector (LED) feature to indicate that the logic level at the test point is changing. Ask your lab instructor if you have any questions concerning the use of the logic probe.

Personal Computers and Fundamental MS-DOS Operation

Disk Operating System

A Disk Operating System is a program which supervises and controls the operation of a computer. DOS must first be loaded into the computer before the various commands it contains can be utilized. The process of loading the operating system into the computer is called booting the system. A "cold boot" is performed by turning on the computer with the power switch. A "warm boot" is performed by holding down the Ctrl and Alt keys while pressing the Del key. The computer is "booted up" from either a hard disk or a "system disk" placed in drive A:. A system disk is a floppy disk that contains the necessary DOS files for booting the system. Once the operating system is loaded, you may either use the operating systems utilities or load another application program to be run by the computer. DOS indicates that it is ready for the user to give it a command by displaying the DOS prompt which will look like either:

	C:\>	or	A:\>
[booted from:	hard disk		floppy disk]

The prompt indicates to the user which drive is the current (or default) drive. The prompt may also be set up to indicate which subdirectory is currently being used.

Drive specification

Disk drives are specified by two characters, the drive letter followed by a colon. To change the default drive, type the new drive specification following the DOS prompt and press ENTER. For example, to change the default drive from the hard disk drive C: to the floppy disk drive A: type the following boldfaced information after the C:\> prompt and press ENTER.

C:\>**A:**

The system prompt will then change to the following to indicate to the user that the new default drive is A:

A:\>

Filenames

All files (data or program) stored on a disk are referred to by a drive specification plus a filename and extension. A period is used to separate the filename from the extension. An example file specification might look like this:

A:\TESTCKT.DAT

The filename TESTCKT with a file extension called DAT can be found on the floppy disk located in drive A:.

Filenames can be as long as 8 characters and the extension can be as long as 3 characters. The filename and extension cannot be duplicated (within a subdirectory) on a single disk.

Subdirectories

DOS allows files to be stored in an organized system of directories and subdirectories on the disks. This allows related or similar files to be stored together within the same subdirectory, making the files easier to locate and to use. The main directory (the one not below any other directories) is called the "root directory". The root directory usually contains only special files, such as those associated with DOS, and a list of the next level of directories. Within the various directories are other files and subdirectories which may contain even more files and subdirectories. Due to the large amount of file storage space found on a hard disk, it is extremely important to take advantage of the orderly structure of directories and subdirectories in order to make the hard disk more manageable. When using a disk with subdirectories, the complete file specification is more complicated. To specify the file EXAMPLE whose extension is DOC located in subdirectory REPORTS under directory WORDPROC on drive C:, use the following:

C:\WORDPROC\REPORTS\EXAMPLE.DOC

Specifying the drive and directories in which a file is stored is called the file's path. This provides directions to the computer on how to locate a desired file. In the above example, C:\WORDPROC\REPORTS is the path to the file EXAMPLE.DOC.

Changing subdirectories

To change directories, use the DOS command CD. For example, to move from the root directory on the C: drive to the subdirectory REPORTS under the directory WORDPROC located on drive C:, type the boldfaced information following the prompt below and press ENTER. The computer will respond with a new prompt indicating the current default subdirectory.

C:\ >CD WORDPROC\REPORTS

C:\WORDPROC\REPORTS >

To return to the root directory from a subdirectory, type the boldfaced information following the prompt below and press ENTER. The computer will then indicate the current default directory with a new prompt.

C:\WORDPROC\REPORTS >**CD **

C:\ >

Listing files
To display the names of files that are stored on a particular disk or in a specific directory, use the DOS command DIR. Typing DIR after the system prompt and pressing ENTER will display the filename and extension, file size, and the date and time that the file was last saved for all files contained in the default directory. Also displayed will be any subdirectory names under the default directory and the amount of free disk space left. Directory listings for other directories or disk drives (other than the default) may also be obtained with the DIR command by specifying the desired drive and subdirectory path and then pressing ENTER. For example, typing the following boldfaced information and pressing ENTER would list the files contained in the directory LETTERS on the disk in drive A:. Note the space after DIR.

C:\ >**DIR A:\LETTERS**

If the file listing is too long and some of the information scrolls off the top of the screen, use either the /P or /W option switch with the DIR command. DIR /P selects the Page mode directory listing and will display only a screen-full of directory information and then prompt the operator to press any key to display the next screen. DIR /W selects the Wide display option in which only the filenames (up to five files per line) and not the other file information is displayed.

Copying files
To copy files from one disk to another, use the DOS command COPY. At the system prompt type COPY, the source file specification (including the drive and directory path if other than the default, the filename and extension), the destination file specification (including drive and directory path and filename/extension only if different than the original), and then press ENTER. There should be a space after COPY and also after the source file specification. The following example will copy the file CIRCUIT1.DAT from the current default directory, DIGITAL on drive C:, to the floppy in drive A: using the same file name (CIRCUIT1.DAT). Note the space after COPY and after the source filename/extension.

C:\DIGITAL >**COPY CIRCUIT1.DAT A:**

Deleting or erasing files
To delete or erase a specific file from the disk, use the DOS command DEL or ERASE. At the system prompt type DEL (or ERASE), followed by the file specification of the file to be deleted (including the drive and directory

5

path if other than the default, the filename and extension), and then press ENTER. The following example will delete the file CIRCUIT1.DAT from the disk in drive A: (root directory). Note the space after DEL.

C:\ > **DEL A:\CIRCUIT1.DAT**

Renaming files

To change the name of a file that is stored on a disk, use the DOS command REN (or RENAME). At the system prompt type REN, the file specification of the file to be renamed (including the drive and directory path if other than the default, the filename and extension), the new name and extension of the file, and then press ENTER. The following example will change the filename of EXAMPLE1.DOC in the default directory DIGITAL on drive C: to EXAMPLE2.DAT. Note the space after the REN command and after the old filename/extension.

C:\DIGITAL > **REN EXAMPLE1.DOC EXAMPLE2.DAT**

Displaying DOS version number

To determine which version of DOS is currently being used by the computer, use the DOS command VER. At the system prompt type VER and then press ENTER. The computer will then report which version and revision of DOS is currently in operation on the computer.

C:\ > **VER**

Printing files

To print a text (ASCII) file stored on a disk on a printer connected to the computer, use the DOS command PRINT. At the system prompt type PRINT, the file specification of the file to be printed (including the drive and directory path if other than the default, the filename and extension), and then press ENTER. If this is the first time since booting the computer that the print command has been used, the computer will prompt the operator for the name of the printer port to be used. If the default printer port (named LPT1) is to be used, just press ENTER to respond, otherwise supply the appropriate printer port name (LPT2, COM1, or COM2) and then press ENTER. The following example will print the file CIRCUIT1.DAT from the disk in drive A:. Note the space after PRINT.

C:\ > **PRINT A:CIRCUIT1.DAT**

Formatting data disks

To initialize a floppy disk to accept DOS information and data files, use the DOS command FORMAT. A new disk cannot be used by the computer to store information until it has been formatted. Caution: the FORMAT command will erase all previous information stored on the disk, so you must be sure that you wish to FORMAT a disk before doing so! At the system prompt type FORMAT, the drive specification in which the unformatted disk will be inserted, and then press ENTER. The computer will then prompt the operator to insert the new disk and to press ENTER again. After the formatting is completed, the computer will ask the operator if another disk is to be formatted. Respond with a Y (Yes) or N (No). The following example will FORMAT the disk in drive A:. Note the space after FORMAT. Be careful!

C:\ > **FORMAT A:**

Checking disk/memory status
> To display a report on the status of a specified disk drive and the system memory, use the DOS command CHKDSK. The report will include the total amount of disk space, the amount of disk space used, the amount of disk space available (not currently being used), the total amount of system memory, and the amount of memory that is currently free. At the system prompt type CHKDSK, the drive containing the disk to be checked (if not the default drive), and then press ENTER. The following example requests a status report on the disk in drive A: and the system memory. Note the space after CHKDSK.

C:\ > **CHKDSK A:**

Task	Command	Example
Change Default Disk Drive		A:
Change Default Disk Directory	CD	CD C:\EDITOR
List File Names on Disk	DIR	DIR A: /P
Copy Files from one Disk to another Disk	COPY	COPY CIRCUIT1.DAT A:
Delete Specified Files from Disk	DEL	DEL A:CIRCUIT1.DAT
Rename Specified File on Disk	REN	REN PROB1.BAK PROB1.DAT
Determine DOS Version Number	VER	VER
Print Specified File from Disk	PRINT	PRINT A:CIRCUIT1.DAT
Format Disk in Floppy Drive	FORMAT	FORMAT A:
Check Disk and Memory Status	CHKDSK	CHKDSK A:

Table 1-1   Fundamental MS-DOS Commands

Running a program
> Files which have an file extension of .EXE or .COM are executable (i.e., programs which can be run on the computer). These programs can be started by typing the program's filename (you do not need to provide the file extension) at the system prompt and then pressing ENTER. There are many different types of computer programs available including:
>> Text editors
>> Wordprocessors

> Spreadsheets
> Data base managers
> Graphics
> Circuit analysis
> Schematic capture (Computer Aided Drafting)
> Programming language assemblers/compilers
> Logic assemblers/compilers

The programs generally require the user to supply appropriate information and commands from the keyboard. Most programs provide some type of menu or help screen of possible command options available to the user. Programs are typically terminated with commands such as QUIT or EXIT. Upon terminating a program the computer should return to the operating system and the DOS prompt should reappear. A program that gets "hung up" or "crashes" usually can be terminated with a Control-Break (hold down the Ctrl key and press Break). If the computer fails to return to the operating system, do a "warm boot" (Ctrl-Alt-Del).

Laboratory Projects

1.1 Digital test system operation

(1)   Investigate the features of the digital breadboarding and test system available in the laboratory by performing the following tasks with the unit. Carefully plug it into the AC outlet and turn on the power. Consult your lab instructor if you have any problems or questions concerning the laboratory procedures or equipment operation.

(2)   Measure and record the TTL power supply output voltage (with respect to ground) using a DVM. Remember that one of the most important safety precautions to observe in electronics is to avoid contact with any voltage source or component in a "live" circuit. Make sure that you are reading the TTL supply voltage if the unit has more than the single output supply. The TTL supply voltage should be between +4.75v and +5.25v DC. If you are unfamiliar with the use of the DVM, refer to the "Voltage Measurements with a DVM" section of this lab assignment.

(3)   Measure and record the voltage (with respect to ground) from a logic switch when it is placed in each of its two positions (up and down). In TTL logic, a "low" voltage will be approximately 0v and a "high" will be approximately +5v (actually anywhere from +2v to +5v).

(4)   Record your observations when a logic probe is used to test the output from the logic switch when it is placed in each of its two positions (up and down). If you are unfamiliar with the use of the logic probe, refer to the "Logic Probe Operating Instructions" section of this lab.

(5)   Record your observations of the operation of the lamp monitors by connecting a jumper wire from one of the logic switches to a lamp monitor and then moving the switch between the two logic levels (high and low voltage). In positive logic, a high voltage is referred to

as a "1" and a low voltage is referred to as a "0". How does the lamp monitor result compare to the logic probe's?

(6)   Note the operation of a pulser or pushbutton by connecting it to an unused lamp monitor and then pressing and releasing the button. If your unit has pulsers with two complementary outputs available, connect each of the outputs to a separate unused lamp monitor and then press and release the button. Pulsers on some systems provide a very brief change in the logic level of the pulser output (narrow pulse).

(7)   Note the operation of the clock output by connecting it to an unused lamp monitor with the clock set at its lowest frequency. If your unit has a clock with two complementary outputs available, connect each of the clock outputs to a separate unused lamp monitor. Describe the lamp action when the clock frequency is increased.

1.2 Personal computer operation

(1)   Identify the type of computer system (dual floppy or single floppy/hard disk) and then "boot-up" the computer accordingly.

(2)   Use the appropriate DOS command to determine which version of DOS is installed on your computer.

(3)   Check the root directory on the disk used to boot the computer and determine the amount of disk space remaining.

(4)   Change to the DIGITAL subdirectory and identify the names of the subdirectories located there.

(5)   Print a hardcopy of the EDITOR.DOC file for your personal reference.

(6)   Run the editor program stored in the DIGITAL subdirectory. Use the screen editor program to edit the data file STUDENTS.LST (also located in the DIGITAL subdirectory). Refer to the EDITOR.DOC print-out for instructions on using the text editor provided in the lab. Add the following information to the end of the existing STUDENTS.LST file:
        Your name
        Your answers to the 4 questions:
                1.   "Do you have any prior experience with Electronics?"
                2.   "Do you have any prior experience with Digital Circuits?"
                3.   "Do you have any prior experience with personal computers?"
                4.   "Do you have any prior experience with MS-DOS?"
        Exit (& resave) the STUDENTS.LST file.

UNIT 2

CONSTRUCTING COMBINATIONAL LOGIC CIRCUITS

Objectives

   (1)   To be able to construct simple combinational logic circuits from a schematic.

   (2)   To be able to test simple combinational logic circuits to determine the functional operation of the circuits.

   (3)   To be able to identify common logic functions produced by various circuit configurations by the resulting truth table.

   (4)   To be able to connect various gates together to create simple logic functions.

Tutorial

Combinational Logic Circuits

A logic gate is the simplest device used to construct digital circuits. The output voltage or logic level for each type of gate is a function of the applied input(s). Various types of logic gates are available (including Inverters, ANDs, ORs, NANDs, and NORs), each with its own unique logic function. Logic circuits are constructed by interconnecting various logic gates together to implement a particular circuit function. The logic function for a single gate or a complete circuit using many gates can be easily represented in a logic truth table or a logic expression. The layout for 1 and 2 input truth tables is given in Fig. 2-1 below. Note: L = low logic level voltage and H = high logic level voltage.

11

A		X
L		
H		

1-input (A)
1-output (X)

A	B		Z
L	L		
L	H		
H	L		
H	H		

2-inputs (A & B)
1-output (Z)

Fig. 2-1 Truth tables showing possible input combinations

When constructing logic circuits, care should be taken to insure that the parts are not damaged while breadboarding the circuit. Carefully insert the integrated circuit (IC) into the breadboarding socket so that the IC is straddling the center groove on the socket. Make sure that both rows of pins are correctly lined up with the holes in the breadboard, but be careful to avoid bending the IC pins any more than is necessary. The ICs can be safely removed by prying up each end with a screwdriver (or similar tool) or an IC puller. Do not insert or remove ICs with the power applied to the circuit.

A notch or dot at one end of the IC package is used to locate pin 1 of the chip and the pin numbers, then increase in a counterclockwise direction around the device as viewed from the top (see Fig. 2-2). Inserting all ICs with the same orientation for pin 1 will facilitate circuit wiring and troubleshooting.

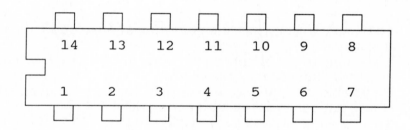

Fig. 2-2 IC pin numbering (top view)

Determine the pin-out information for <u>each</u> chip by consulting a data book or data sheet for the logic devices used. Notice that power and ground, inputs, and outputs are sometimes located on different pins for different part numbers. Label the pin numbers for each device on a logic circuit schematic to aid in wiring the circuit and in troubleshooting it later if necessary.

Wiring errors are the most common source of circuit failure in breadboarding circuits. Systematically and carefully wire the circuit with the power off. The jumper wires should only have about 1/4 inch of the insulation stripped from each end of the wire to avoid inadvertently shorting the wires together. Using <u>short</u> jumper wires will facilitate troubleshooting later if necessary. Double check the wiring against the schematic diagram.

Verify that the correct voltage from the power supply is connected to the circuit before turning it on. Then, and only then, should you turn on the power to the circuit. Check to see if the circuit is operating properly.

If the circuit does not function properly or if an IC gets very hot or starts smoking, turn off the power and all signals to the circuit immediately. Recheck the following items to troubleshoot the circuit:

Do the parts used in the circuit match the schematic?
Have the pin numbers been identified correctly in the schematic?
Are the parts inserted correctly in the breadboard?
Is the correct voltage supply being used to power the circuit?
Is the power properly connected to each chip?
Are there any wires shorted to one another?
Is the circuit wired correctly?
Has the circuit been analyzed correctly?
Has the circuit been designed correctly?

Laboratory Projects

Determine the logic expression for each of the following simple logic circuits. Analyze each circuit to predict its theoretical operation. Draw the schematics for each circuit and annotate the schematics with appropriate component part numbers and pin numbers. Then construct and test each circuit to verify your predictions. Give the theoretical results and test results for each circuit in a logic truth table. Identify any common logic functions produced by the given circuits. Reconcile any differences between the predicted and test results.

2.1   Constructing logic circuits using 1 chip

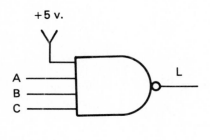

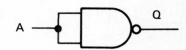

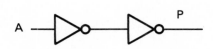

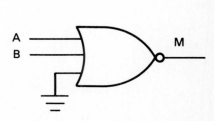

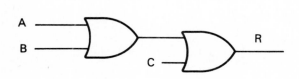

2.2 Constructing logic circuits using 2 chips

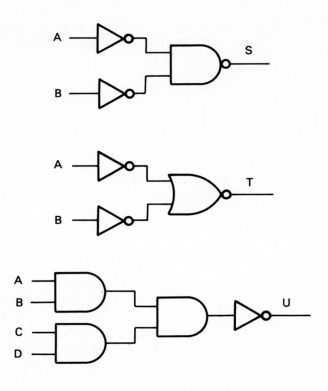

2.3 Constructing logic circuits using 3 chips

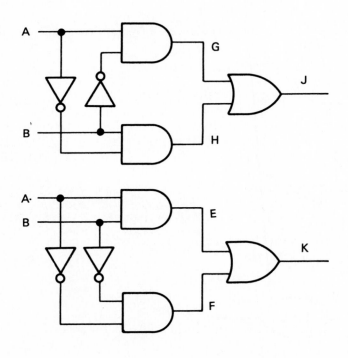

UNIT 3

ANALYZING COMBINATIONAL LOGIC CIRCUITS

Objectives ==

   (1)   To be able to analyze combinational logic circuits to predict their operation.

   (2)   To be able to construct and test more complex combinational logic circuits.

Tutorial ==

Circuit Analysis Techniques

The theoretical operation of a combinational logic circuit can be predicted by analyzing the circuit's output for every possible input combination. The circuit analysis for each input combination is performed by determining the resultant output of each gate, working from the input side of the circuit to the output. We will later discover shortcuts to speed up the analysis process.

Different logic circuits may perform the same function (i.e., their logic truth tables are identical) but be constructed from entirely different logic gates or interconnected in an entirely different manner. In fact we will find that often a complex logic circuit can be replaced with a much simpler one that performs the identical function.

Circuit analysis example

Determine the truth table for the circuit in Fig. 3-1.

15

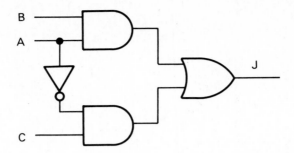

Fig. 3-1 Schematic for circuit analysis example

A truth table (see Table 3-1) listing all 8 combinations that are possible with three input variables is constructed. The resultant output for every gate in the circuit can then be determined for each of the 8 input combinations. This information is added to the truth table.

A	B	C	$\overline{A}$	A·B	$\overline{A}$·C	J
0	0	0	1	0	0	0
0	0	1	1	0	1	1
0	1	0	1	0	0	0
0	1	1	1	0	1	1
1	0	0	0	0	0	0
1	0	1	0	0	0	0
1	1	0	0	1	0	1
1	1	1	0	1	0	1

Table 3-1   Truth table analysis for example circuit

Laboratory Projects

Predict the theoretical operation for each of the following logic circuits. Draw and label circuit schematics with appropriate part numbers and pin numbers. Then construct and test the circuits to verify their operation. List both theoretical and test truth table results. Note any observations.

3.1   Combinational circuit analysis & testing

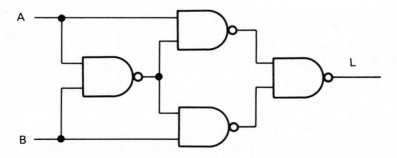

16

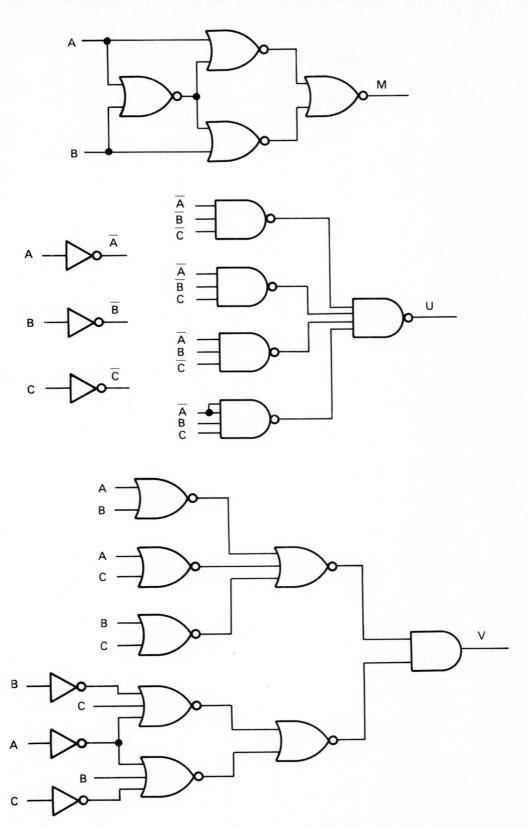

UNIT 4

LOGIC SIMULATION OF COMBINATIONAL CIRCUITS

Objectives

(1) To be able to create a computer simulation source file for given combinational logic circuits.

(2) To be able to simulate a combinational logic circuit from a given schematic.

Tutorial

Computer Logic Simulation

A logic simulator is a computer software tool that uses a circuit's electrical description, input signal conditions, and models of the various logic elements to produce a sequence of output states (or waveforms) that show how the circuit will behave under the input conditions provided. Instead of breadboarding a circuit design and then verifying its functionality on the test bench, using logic simulation on a computer allows the designer to quickly and inexpensively test the design even through the various stages of its development.

There are various types of software available to perform logic simulation. Some use a graphical schematic entry technique to describe the circuit to be simulated while others use a text-based description of the circuit. P/C-SILOS by Simucad is an example of the latter using an ASCII source file (created with a standard text editor) to describe each circuit node, the gate type producing the node signal, the inputs to the gate, and the overall input conditions to be analyzed. The simulator's output provides truth tables and timing diagrams of the desired circuit nodes for the given input conditions. Any of the circuit's source file information (the circuit description, the input states to be evaluated, or the output nodes to be monitored) can be easily and quickly edited and the new circuit conditions can then be re-simulated.

P/C-SILOS DETAILED PROCEDURES

(1)   Create the logic network description file using a text editor. Use the P/C-SILOS instructions & data keywords to describe the logic circuit to be simulated. Save this file as "filename.DAT".

(2)   Type "PCSILOS" and press ENTER to start the program.
The P/C-SILOS screen prompt is "Ready:"
NOTE: On-line help with P/C-SILOS commands, instructions, and keywords is available by entering "HELP xxxx", where "xxxx" represents the topic.

(3)   At the "Ready:" prompt, type "INPUT filename" (include the drive specification but you can leave off the .DAT extension) and press ENTER to input the circuit data file for simulation. For example:

Ready: **INPUT A:\CIRCUIT1**

If the program reports errors in your source file, enter "TYPE ERRORS" to display the errors on the screen. Any errors in your source file must be corrected before you can obtain the simulation output. Exit P/C-SILOS and edit the source file. If no errors are encountered in your source file, the simulation session can be continued.

(4)   P/C-SILOS commands can be given either directly by the user from the keyboard or may be imbedded in the source file to be invoked automatically (see the example source file).

To instruct P/C-SILOS from the keyboard to simulate the logic circuit for a specified number of time units enter: "SIMULATE t1". Substitute the length of time desired for the simulation for t1. The simulation will begin at time equal to zero and continue for the specified length of time.

(5)   The command to display the simulation's output data on the computer screen may be entered on the keyboard or may also be given automatically from within the source file. P/C-SILOS' command to display data on the screen is "TYPE". The two kinds of output data are truth tables and timing diagrams.

Display the circuit's truth table on the screen by entering "TYPE OUTPUTS ON CHANGE". If the length of data displayed is too long and scrolls off the screen, enter "TYPE OUTPUTS FROM t1 TO t2 ON CHANGE" to break up the truth table results. Substitute the desired beginning and ending times to be displayed in the truth table for t1 and t2.

Display the circuit's timing diagram on the screen by entering "TYPE GRAPH". Press <CR> to obtain the graphing menu.

(6)   The commands to store the simulation data on disk for later use can also be entered either from the keyboard or from within the source file. The output file reports can be edited and output on a printer after exiting P/C-SILOS.

20

An output file for the current circuit simulation can be stored on your disk by entering the following sequence of commands:

"DISK A:\CIRCUIT1.OUT"   <-- identifies drive and output filename

"NSTORE NETWORK"   <-- stores circuit network description

"NSTORE OUTPUTS ON CHANGE"   <-- stores circuit truth table

"NSTORE GRAPH"   <-- stores circuit timing diagram

(7)   Terminate the program or do another simulation. To exit the program & return to DOS, enter "EXIT". To reset the program for simulating a new circuit, enter "RESET ALL" and repeat the procedures starting with step 3 above.

INSTRUCTIONS

.TITLE   defines a title header for the simulator's output
.MONITOR   defines the signals to be monitored & output during the simulation
.TABLE   creates a truth table for the listed circuit nodes
.GRAPH   creates a timing diagram for the listed circuit nodes

DATA

.PATTERN   list of input combinations to be applied to circuit for simulation
.EOP   indicates the End Of Pattern list

.AND   \
.OR |
.INV |
.NAND   > standard logic gate devices
.NOR |
.XOR |
.XNOR   /

.AOI   AND-OR-INVERT gate configuration (set of inputs to each AND is separated by /)

.DLA   device in which the output follows the input after a specified delay (can be used to simulate a wire connection)

.GND   represents a fixed low logic level
.VCC   represents a fixed high logic level

.GDEF   defines the operation of a user-defined gate
.GATn   user-defined gate (must be defined in .GDEF)

Table 4-1 P/C-SILOS source file keywords

21

Logic Simulation Software Example

Use P/C-SILOS to analyze the logic circuit in Fig. 4-1 for the given input sequence. Use the labels given for each gate to name the output nodes.

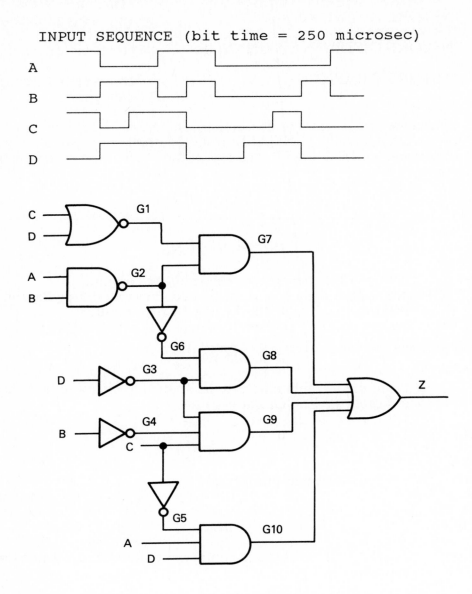

Fig. 4-1 Simulation Example Circuit

First, each gate output in the circuit must be assigned a name. Use the signal names identified in the schematic where appropriate and define arbitrary names for the remaining output nodes. Gate output node names in P/C-SILOS must start with a letter or an underline ( ) and cannot contain embedded blanks. A source file then is created to describe the circuit and the input sequence to be analyzed. An example source file named CIRCUIT1.DAT is given on the next page. Comment lines in the following source file are indicated by a "$". Source file lines may be continued by beginning the continuation line with a "+".

```
.TITLE   CIRCUIT1 SIMULATION EXAMPLE

$   Name:   G. Moss   (use your name for documentation)

$   The .PATTERN statement gives the bit time and the
$   input variable names.
$   The input sequence to be analyzed is listed after
$   the .PATTERN statement.

.PATTERN   250     A B C D
                   1 0 1 0
                   0 1 0 1
                   0 1 1 1
                   1 0 1 1
                   1 1 0 0
                   0 0 0 0
                   0 0 0 1
                   0 0 1 1
                   0 1 0 0
                   1 0 0 0
.EOP

$   .EOP means End Of Pattern list.
$   Next, the circuit netlist is given.
$   Each line describes a gate output node:
$    name     type     delays    inputs

     G1      .NOR      0 0       C    D
     G2      .NAND     0 0       A    B
     G7      .AND      0 0       G1   G2
     G8      .AND      0 0       -G2  -D
     G9      .AND      0 0       -D   -B    C
     G10     .AND      0 0       -C   D     A
     Z       .OR       0 0       G7   G8    G9    G10

$   Note:  a - can be used to invert inputs.
$   The simulator instructions identify which circuit
$   nodes to monitor and how to output the results.
$   Both the circuit's truth table and timing
$   diagram are to be created for this example.
$   The semicolons provide spacing control for the data
$   output.

.MONITOR   A; B; C; D;; Z
.TABLE     A; B; C; D;; Z
.GRAPH     A  B  C  D  Z

$   Simulator commands can be invoked from within the
$   source file by preceding the command with a !

!SIMULATE 2500
!DISK A:\CIRCUIT1.OUT
!NSTORE NETWORK
!NSTORE OUTPUTS ON CHANGE
!NSTORE GRAPH
```

Note that the simulator's output can be stored in a text file on disk as directed by the commands in the previous example source file or just viewed on the computer screen.

The output file created by the previous circuit simulation contains the following data.

$ P/C-SILOS 3B.1 * NETWORK 09:05:24 Apr 14, 1989

$ CIRCUIT1 SIMULATION EXAMPLE

```
****************************
   N E T W O R K    D A T A
****************************
```

UNIDIRECTIONAL GATE FUNCTIONS (7 total) -

NAME	TYPE	RISE DELAY	FALL DELAY	GATE INPUTS			
G1	.NOR	0	0	C	D		
G10	.AND	0	0	-C	D	A	
G2	.NAND	0	0	A	B		
G7	.AND	0	0	G1	G2		
G8	.AND	0	0	-G2	-D		
G9	.AND	0	0	-D	-B	C	
Z	.OR	0	0	G7	G8	G9	G10

$ P/C-SILOS 3B.1 * OUTPUTS 09:05:26 Apr 14, 1989

$ CIRCUIT1 SIMULATION EXAMPLE

TIME	A	B	C	D	Z
0	1	0	1	0	1
250	0	1	0	1	0
500	0	1	1	1	0
750	1	0	1	1	0
1000	1	1	0	0	1
1250	0	0	0	0	1
1500	0	0	0	1	0
1750	0	0	1	1	0
2000	0	1	0	0	1
2250	1	0	0	0	1

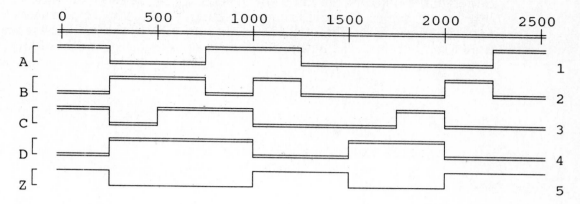

Laboratory Projects

Perform a computer simulation of each of the following circuits for the given input conditions using P/C-SILOS.

P/C-SILOS LOGIC SIMULATOR PROCEDURES

(1) Create the circuit's source file.
(2) Run PCSILOS program.
(3) INPUT source filename.
(4) Simulate circuit for desired input conditions.
(5) Display desired circuit output data.
(6) Store simulation data on disk.
(7) Exit program or continue with another circuit.

4.1 Code conversion circuit
A code conversion circuit which has multiple outputs is defined by the Boolean expressions listed below. Simulate the 4 outputs for all possible inputs.

$$W = D C + D B A$$

$$X = \overline{C}\, \overline{B} + \overline{C}\, \overline{A} + C B A$$

$$Y = B \overline{A} + \overline{B} A$$

$$Z = \overline{A}$$

note: W & D are the most significant bits
(i.e., list inputs in the order DCBA and outputs in the order WXYZ)

25

4.2 Multiplexer chip analysis

Simulate the following circuit using a 74LS153 for the input conditions listed in the table. Create the source file netlist using the equivalent circuit logic diagram for the 74LS153. Note that only half of the 73LS153 is being used and, therefore, the netlist does not have to include the other half.

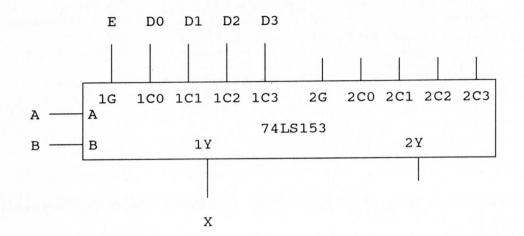

Input conditions for simulation:

B	A	E	D0	D1	D2	D3
0	0	0	0	0	1	1
0	1	0	0	0	1	1
1	0	0	0	0	1	1
1	1	0	0	0	1	1
1	1	1	0	0	1	1
1	1	0	1	0	1	0
1	0	0	1	0	1	0
0	1	0	1	0	1	0
0	0	0	1	0	1	0
0	0	1	0	1	0	1
0	1	1	0	1	0	1
1	0	1	0	1	0	1
1	1	1	0	1	0	1
0	0	0	0	0	0	0
0	0	0	1	1	1	1

4.3   Decoder chip analysis
Simulate the following circuit using a 74LS138 for the input conditions
given in the timing diagram. Create the source file netlist using the
equivalent circuit logic diagram for the 74LS138. List the circuit inputs in
the order G1 C B A and outputs in the order Y0 Y1 Y2 Y3 Y4 Y5 Y6 Y7.
Check the timing diagram (GRAPH display) and note that not all of the
waveforms are displayed. The remaining output waveforms may be
displayed by panning down while in the (TYPE) GRAPH display mode (see
graph menu). Then performing another disk store command will save the
additional waveforms for later editing with the original graph display
waveforms.

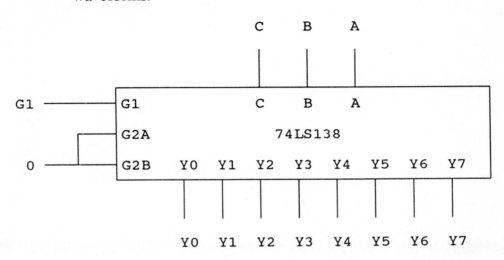

Timing diagram of inputs for simulation:

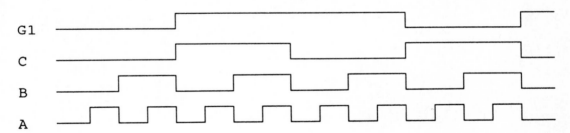

27

UNIT 5

DESIGNING WITH SOP/POS CIRCUITS

Objectives ==

(1)   To be able to implement SOP logic expressions using standard AND/OR and NAND/NAND circuit designs.
(2)   To be able to implement POS logic expressions using standard OR/AND and NOR/NOR circuit designs.

Tutorial ==

SOP/POS Expressions

Sum-Of-Product and Product-Of-Sum are standard expression forms that can be quickly written from a truth table and are easily implemented using a two-level (not counting inverters which may be needed) gate network.

The Sum-Of-Product expression is obtained by identifying all of the minterms (product terms) whose outputs are high and then ORing them together. The SOP expression form can be directly implemented with either AND/OR or NAND/NAND circuit designs.

The Product-Of-Sum expression is obtained by identifying all of the maxterms (sum terms) whose outputs are low and then ANDing them together. The POS expression form can be directly implemented with either OR/AND or NOR/NOR circuit designs.

One of the most common procedures used in the design of combinational logic circuits is to first develop the truth table that defines the circuit's desired function and then from it write the appropriate SOP and POS expressions. The two expressions are simplified using various techniques (such as Boolean Algebra) and then the circuit design which requires fewer components (or is cheaper) is implemented.

SOP/POS Circuit Design Example

Design a combinational circuit which will indicate the majority result of 3 individuals voting.

First define the problem in a truth table as shown in Table 5-1.

A	B	C	V
0	0	0	0
0	0	1	0
0	1	0	0
0	1	1	1
1	0	0	0
1	0	1	1
1	1	0	1
1	1	1	1

Table 5-1   SOP/POS circuit truth table

Next write both the SOP expression and the POS expression for the function now defined in the truth table and simplify each expression.

SOP:

$$V = \overline{A}\,B\,C + A\,\overline{B}\,C + A\,B\,\overline{C} + A\,B\,C$$

$$= B\,C\,(\overline{A} + A) + A\,C\,(\overline{B} + B) + A\,B\,(\overline{C} + C)$$

$$= B\,C + A\,C + A\,B$$

POS:

$$V = (A+B+C)\,(A+B+\overline{C})\,(A+\overline{B}+C)\,(\overline{A}+B+C)$$

$$= [\,(A+B+C)\,(A+B+\overline{C})\,]\,[\,(A+B+C)\,(A+\overline{B}+C)\,]\,[\,(A+B+C)\,(\overline{A}+B+C)\,]$$

$$= (A+B)\,(A+C)\,(B+C)$$

Design circuits to implement **each** of the **simplified** expressions. The simplified SOP expression can be easily implemented with a NAND/NAND circuit arrangement using 2 chips (7400 & 7410). The simplified POS circuit can be easily implemented with a NOR/NOR circuit arrangement also using 2 chips (7402 & 7427). Since each circuit design uses the same number of chips, either choice may be satisfactory. See the circuit schematics in Fig. 5-1.

30

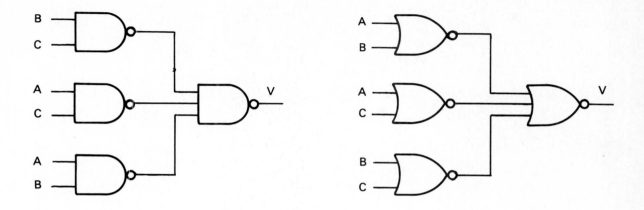

Fig. 5-1   Schematics for SOP and POS solution

Laboratory Projects

Design simplified circuits to perform each of the following functions. Define the problem with a truth table and write the SOP and POS expressions. Simplify the SOP expression to a reduced SOP form and the POS expression to a reduced POS form. Draw and label schematics for your simplified designs. Construct and test one simplified circuit design (SOP or POS) for each problem.

5.1   Two-input multiplexer
Design a circuit whose output (Y) is equivalent to one of two possible data inputs (A or B). A control input (S) selects either the data on the A input (if S is low) or the data on the B input (if S is high) to be routed to the single output line. Attempt to simplify your design using Boolean Algebra. Hint: Pair the terms in the SOP expression and "factor out" the common variables.

5.2   Three-bit equality detector
Design a 3-bit equality detector circuit that will output a low whenever the 3 input bits are <u>all</u> at the same logic level. Note: The POS expression cannot be simplified.

5.3   Elevator control
Design an elevator control system for a large building that has 5 elevators. Four of the elevators are turned on all of the time, while the fifth is only activated (to save energy) if a majority of the other 4 are being used. The control system will have an input for each of the 4 primary elevators to indicate that that elevator is being used (with a logic "1"). A high output from the control system will activate the fifth elevator for its use. Hint: In Boolean Algebra, an existing term can be "re-used"

5.4   Greater than 9 detector
Design a circuit whose output will be high if the 4-bit data input is a value greater than 9.

31

UNIT 6

MINIMIZING CIRCUIT DESIGNS WITH BOOLEAN ALGEBRA

Objectives

(1) To be able to simplify logic circuits using Boolean Algebra techniques.
(2) To be able to determine the minimum number of logic chips needed to implement a logic function.

Tutorial

Boolean Algebra and Logic Circuit Minimization

The various laws and theorems of Boolean Algebra can be systematically applied to logic expressions in order to manipulate and/or simplify the expressions. Of course, extreme care must be exercised to correctly apply the laws and theorems or the resultant expression will not be equivalent to the original function. There are often many alternative Boolean Algebra techniques that can be applied in the process of logic circuit simplification.

While manipulating a given logic expression into different equivalent expression forms, the corresponding circuit implementations of each expression can be analyzed to determine the quantity of chips necessary for the circuit construction. The design which uses the minimum number of available chips may be selected as an optimum design choice (based on the amount of board space required by the circuit, the cost of the needed parts, etc.). This process generally requires some "trial and error" in order to determine the minimum chip solution.

Logic Circuit Minimization Example

Redesign the circuit in Fig. 6-1 so that its function may be implemented with a minimum number of chips.

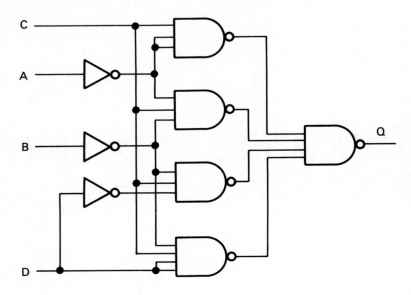

Fig. 6-1 Logic circuit for example

First determine the original circuit's logic expression and then, using Boolean algebra techniques, reduce the expression to an equivalent simplified form. Determine the necessary chips for implementation of the simplified expression. Continue manipulating the expression and selecting appropriate chips for implementation until a minimal design is found.

$$Q = \overline{\overline{\overline{A} \, C} \cdot \overline{\overline{A} \, \overline{B} \, C} \cdot \overline{\overline{B} \, C \, \overline{D}} \cdot \overline{\overline{B} \, C \, D \, D}} \quad \longleftarrow \text{ original circuit expression (requires 3 chips)}$$

$$= \overline{A} \, C + \overline{A} \, \overline{B} \, C + \overline{B} \, C \, \overline{D} + \overline{B} \, C \, D$$

$$= \overline{A} \, C + \overline{A} \, \overline{B} \, C + \overline{B} \, C \, \overline{D} + \overline{B} \, C \, D$$

$$= \overline{A} \, C \, (\, 1 + \overline{B} \,) + \overline{B} \, C \, (\, \overline{D} + D \,)$$

$$= \overline{A} \, C + \overline{B} \, C \quad \longleftarrow \text{ possible solution?}$$
(needs 3 chips - 7404, 7408, & 7432)

$$= \overline{\overline{\overline{A\ C}} \cdot \overline{\overline{B\ C}}}$$ <---   possible solution?
                     (needs 2 chips - 7400 & 7404)

$$= \overline{A}\ C + \overline{B}\ C$$ <---   try another route from here

$$= C\ (\ \overline{A} + \overline{B}\ )$$ <---   possible solution?
                     (needs 3 chips - 7404, 7408, & 7432)

$$= C\ \overline{\overline{A}\ \overline{B}}$$ <---   possible solution?
                     (needs 2 chips - 7404 & 7408)

$$= C\ A\ B$$ <---   possible solution?
                     (needs 1 chip - 7400) <u>best solution</u>!

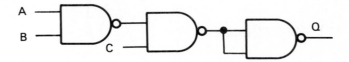

Fig. 6-2   Minimized circuit solution

**Laboratory
Projects**

6.1   Circuit reduction
Redesign the following logic circuits so that a minimum number of
available chips will be used to implement the logic functions of each circuit.
Compare the number of chips required for the original circuits with your
new equivalent designs. Construct and test your simplified designs.

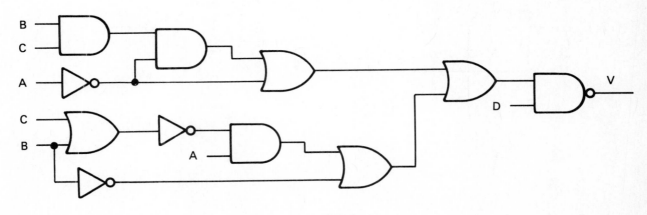

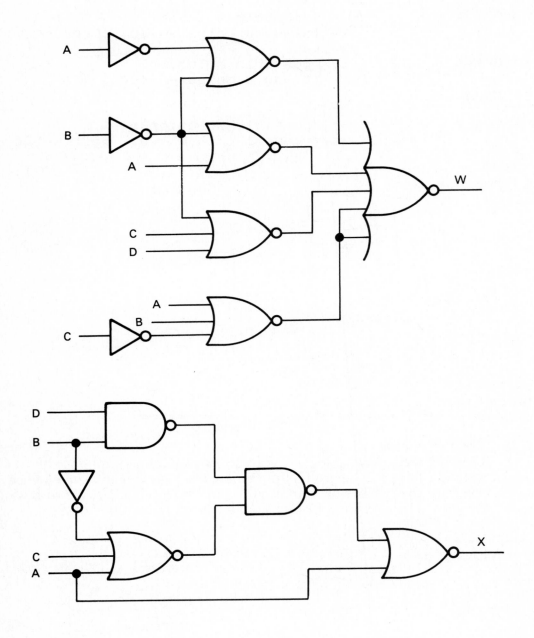

6.1   Circuit reduction (continued)

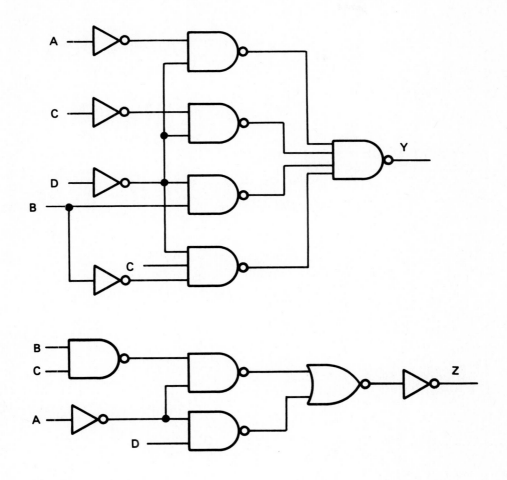

6.2   Circuit simulations

Analyze the <u>original</u> circuits given in lab project 6.1 using the logic simulator software to determine the truth tables and compare your designed circuits with them. Note: A single simulation source file can be created to analyze all 5 circuits simultaneously.

UNIT 7

CIRCUIT DESIGN WITH KARNAUGH MAPPING

Objectives

(1)   To be able to implement simplified SOP and POS logic expressions using Karnaugh mapping techniques.

(2)   To be able to design a combinational logic circuit that will perform a stated task by first developing the truth table for the logic problem and then using Karnaugh mapping to simplify the design.

Tutorial

Karnaugh Mapping Techniques

Karnaugh mapping can be used to simplify SOP and POS standard logic functions and, therefore, reduce the implemented circuit's complexity and cost. The technique starts with the truth table that defines the desired function. The output conditions are transferred to the Karnaugh map and the function reduction is accomplished by identifying common term groupings of either ones (SOP expression) or zeros (POS expression). This relatively simple and fast design technique can best be applied to functions with 5 or fewer input variables.

SOP/POS Design Example

Design a simplified logic circuit to implement the function V defined in the following truth table. Select the standard form expression (SOP or POS) which requires the least number of available chips for circuit implementation.

A B C D	V
0 0 0 0	0
0 0 0 1	1
0 0 1 0	1
0 0 1 1	1
0 1 0 0	0
0 1 0 1	0
0 1 1 0	0
0 1 1 1	0
1 0 0 0	1
1 0 0 1	1
1 0 1 0	0
1 0 1 1	0
1 1 0 0	0
1 1 0 1	0
1 1 1 0	0
1 1 1 1	0

AB \ CD	00	01	11	10
00	0	1	1	1
01	0	0	0	0
11	0	0	0	0
10	1	1	0	0

The output produced for the function V is plotted in a Karnaugh map as shown above. Then appropriate groups are formed with the K-map. Groups of ones are used to create the SOP expression and groups of zeros are used to create the POS expression. The SOP and POS expressions for V are:

SOP:

$$V = \overline{A}\ \overline{B}\ C + A\ \overline{B}\ \overline{C} + \overline{A}\ \overline{B}\ D$$

$$= \overline{A}\ \overline{B}\ C + A\ \overline{B}\ \overline{C} + \overline{B}\ \overline{C}\ D$$

--> either answer requires 3 chips

POS:

$$V = \overline{B}\ (\ \overline{A} + \overline{C}\ )\ (\ A + C + D\ )$$

--> answer requires 2 chips (7404 & 7427)

The best design would be to implement the POS form.

Laboratory Projects

Use Karnaugh mapping to design simplified logic gate circuits to perform each of the following tasks. Determine which implementation (SOP or POS) uses the least number of available chips and construct, test, and verify the operation of your design. Remember to define each problem in a truth table first.

7.1 Two-bit comparator
Design a comparator circuit to compare two 2-bit numbers (A1 A0 and B1 B0). The circuit will have two output signals, GE and LT. GE will be high to indicate that the 2-bit A value is equal to or greater than the 2-bit B value. LT will be high if A < B.

7.2   Alarm circuit
Design an alarm circuit to be used in a process control system.
Temperature (T), pressure (P), flow (F), and level (L) of a fluid are
monitored by sensor circuits that produce a <u>high</u> logic output signal for each
of the following indicated <u>physical</u> conditions:

high fluid temperature
high fluid pressure
low fluid flow rate
low fluid level

The alarm circuit output (A) should be <u>high</u> if any of the following <u>physical</u>
conditions exist in the system:
(1) the pressure is high when the flow is low
(2) the temperature is high when either the
      pressure is high or the level is low
Be sure to identify the correct physical conditions for the alarm in the logic
truth table.

7.3   Prime number detector
Design a 4-bit prime number detector circuit. The 4-bit input will allow the
binary numbers for 0 through 15 to be applied to the circuit. The output
should be high only if prime numbers (1, 2, 3, 5, 7, 11, 13) are being input to
the detector circuit.

7.4   Multiplier circuit
Design a multiplier circuit that will output the product of any 3-bit input
number (0 through 7) multiplied by the constant 3. Note that this circuit
will have several output bits and that each output will have to be mapped
<u>separately</u>. Each output bit represents a circuit that must be constructed.

UNIT 8

COMBINATIONAL CIRCUIT DESIGN USING PROGRAMMABLE LOGIC DEVICES

Objective

(1)   To be able to design and implement combinational logic circuits using Programmable Logic Devices by first identifying the appropriate Boolean equations, assemblying the equations into the standard programming code, and then programming the chips.

Tutorial

Programmable Logic Devices

With programmable logic devices (PLDs), logic circuit designers can go from a conceptual design to customized functional parts in a matter of minutes. A PLD is a digital IC which is capable of being programmed to provide a specific logical function. The PLD family of devices consists of a wide variety of different device architectures and configurations. The three principal types of PLDs (programmable read only memory - PROM, programmable logic array - PLA, and programmable array logic - PAL devices) are internally based on the familiar AND/OR logic gate array. These combinational circuit configurations differ in whether it is the AND gate or the OR gate inputs that are programmable. The programmable AND/OR gate configuration is used to implement Sum-Of-Product functions and, since the SOP form can be used to express any Boolean function, PLD designs are only limited by the number of terms available in the arrays. A wide variety of PLD input/output formats is available. The programmable flexibility of PLD devices typically allows circuit designers to replace many different standard SSI/MSI chips with a single PLD package. PLD devices are available for either one-time-only programming (PALs) or are erasable and reprogrammable (EPLDs and EEPLDs).

The Lattice GAL16V8A is an example of an electrically erasable PLD. The GAL16V8A is quite versatile. This device can be programmed for a maximum of 8 outputs or a maximum of 16 inputs (although not that many of each simultaneously). The GAL chip has an output structure called an output logic macrocell. The output logic macrocell allows for a number of options to be programmed into the device. The outputs may be programmed to be active high or active low, to be combinational or registered, and to be tri-stated or not.

The GAL16V8A is a CMOS device and, as such, should be handled carefully. CMOS devices can be easily damaged by static electricity. Some recommended precautions for handling CMOS devices include storing the chip in conductive foam when not in a circuit, wearing an antistatic wrist strap, turning off the power when inserting or removing the chip, and connecting all unused IC pins to either ground or Vcc when used in a circuit.

Designing the logic circuit with a PLD consists of developing the necessary Boolean equations that are then entered into a (computer) source file using a text editor (or a word processor program). A logic assembler or logic compiler (such as LC9000 from Programmable Logic Technologies, CUPL from Logical Devices, or ABEL from Data I/O) is then used by the computer to transform the circuit equations into a standard JEDEC file. The JEDEC file is then downloaded to a PLD programmer (such as the Logic Lab or Little Lab from Programmable Logic Technologies) that is used to program your design into the PLD. The PLD is then ready to be used in your application. Design changes can be implemented simply by altering the logic equations in the source file with the text editor, re-assembling the source file, and then reprogramming the PLD. The old EEPLD configuration is erased automatically by the programmer hardware when it is reprogrammed.

PLD DESIGN PROCEDURES
USING LC9000 WITH THE LATTICE GAL16V8A

(1)   Design the logic circuit.
    (a)   Identify input/output signals.
    (b)   Simplify logic expressions.
    (c)   Select pin numbers for input & output.

(2)   Create the PLD source file using a text editor.
        (or word processor with ASCII output)
    (a)   Identify target device with DEVICE statement.
    (b)   Document design with TITLE statement.
    (c)   Identify circuit designer with NAME statement.
    (d)   Assign input and output pin names with the PIN statements.
    (e)   Give Boolean expressions for circuit design using the following
        LC9000 logic symbols.

Function	Symbol
NOT	!
AND	&
OR	|

(f)   All LC9000 statements begin with a "keyword" or "pin name" and end with a semi-colon.

(g)   Comments may be inserted anywhere and are preceeded with a /* and ended with an */.

(h)   **SAVE** the PLD source file on your diskette.

(3)   Run the LC9000 assembler by entering LC.

(a)   Select the NEW SOURCE command from the menu & press ENTER.
Enter the PLD source filename when prompted.
Give the drive name if different than the default drive (and path if necessary) and the file extension if different than the assumed .PLD extension.
During assembly, errors are written to a file on the disk with the same filename as the source but with the extension .ERR.
If errors are detected, the source file must be corrected (see the EDIT command).
The EDIT command utility allows modification of a file without leaving the LC9000 program.

(b)   Select the JEDEC command from the menu & press ENTER.
A JEDEC file can only be produced from a file which has been successfully assembled (no syntax errors).
Enter the output file name when prompted.
The default name is the source filename with the extension .JED.
The JEDEC file is stored on the disk and is downloaded to the programmer later.

(c)   Select the LIST command from the menu & press ENTER.
The LIST command produces a document file that includes an outline of the designed part with pin assignments and an output equation listing.
A LIST file can only be produced from a file which has been successfully assembled.
Enter the output file name when prompted.
The default name is the source filename with the extension .DOC.

(d)   Press ESC to exit the LC9000 program.

(4)   Program the PLD device for your circuit design.

(a)   Connect the Logic Lab programmer's serial cable to the computer's serial port & plug the Logic Lab into AC power.

(b)   Enter LL on the computer to establish communications with the programmer.

(c)   **Place the GAL device (16V8A) to be programmed into the left hand ZIF socket with pin 1 oriented to the upper left & lock the chip into the socket by pushing the lever down.**

(d)   On-line help is available for each of the Logic Lab operations by moving the cursor to the operation desired with the left or right arrow keys & pressing <F1>. Press ESC to remove the help window.

(e)   If the target device listed on the Logic Lab main window is not a 16V8, move the cursor to SELECT & press ENTER. Then use the up or down arrow keys to highlight 16V8 & press ENTER again. Press any key to return to the main Logic Lab window.

(f)   Download your JEDEC file to the programmer's device buffer memory by selecting DOWNLOAD from the main Logic Lab window & entering the name of your file (& drive, if not the default drive) when prompted. Press any key to return to the main Logic Lab window.

(g)   Program the device in the programmer with the JEDEC data in the programmer's device buffer by selecting PROGRAM from the main Logic Lab window. When the programming has been completed, the message "Programming done" & the number of times that the part has been programmed (cycle counter status) are displayed. Hit any key to return to the main Logic Lab window.

(h)   If there are no more parts to be programmed, hit ESC while in the main window.

PLD Design Example

Design a logic circuit that will detect various input conditions for a 4-bit input value (DCBA). One output (GT9) will be low if the input value is greater than 9. Another output (LT4) will be low if the input value is less than 4. The output signal RNG will be high if the input is greater than 10 or less than 7. And the output signal TEN will be low if the input is equal to 10.

The first step is to define the problem in a truth table as shown in Table 8-1 and then determine appropriate logic expressions.

D	C	B	A	GT9	LT4	RNG	TEN
0	0	0	0	1	0	1	1
0	0	0	1	1	0	1	1
0	0	1	0	1	0	1	1
0	0	1	1	1	0	1	1
0	1	0	0	1	1	1	1
0	1	0	1	1	1	1	1
0	1	1	0	1	1	1	1
0	1	1	1	1	1	0	1
1	0	0	0	1	1	0	1
1	0	0	1	1	1	0	1
1	0	1	0	0	1	0	0
1	0	1	1	0	1	1	1
1	1	0	0	0	1	1	1
1	1	0	1	0	1	1	1
1	1	1	0	0	1	1	1
1	1	1	1	0	1	1	1

$$GT9 = \overline{D} + \overline{C}\,\overline{B}$$

$$LT4 = D + C$$

$$RNG = \overline{D}\,\overline{C} + C\,\overline{B} + C\,\overline{A} + D\,B\,A$$

$$\overline{TEN = D\,\overline{C}\,B\,\overline{A}}$$

Table 8-1   Truth table and equations for PLD example

46

The following LC9000 source file has been created for this PLD design.

```
DEVICE 16V8;
TITLE LAB EXAMPLE 1;
NAME G. MOSS;

/*      filename LAB_EX1.PLD
        logic circuit detects various input values    */


/* input pins */

pin 1 = D;
pin 2 = C;
pin 3 = B;
pin 4 = A;


/* output pins */

pin 12 = GT9;      /*    GT9 low if DCBA >9          */
pin 13 = LT4;      /*    LT4 low if DCBA <4          */
pin 14 = RNG;      /*    RNG high if DCBA >10 or <7  */
pin 15 = TEN;      /*    TEN low if DCBA = 10        */


/*   power & ground pins -- optional listing   */

pin 10 = GND;
pin 20 = VCC;


/* equations */

GT9  =  !D  |   !C & !B;

LT4  =  D  |  C;

RNG  =  !D & !C  |  C & !B  |  C & !A  |  D & B & A;

!TEN  =  D & !C & B & !A;
```

The following document file was created by the LIST command in LC9000.

```
LAB EXAMPLE 1
G. MOSS
                            16V8
                    ┌──────┐ ┌──────┐
            D       │  01  └─┘  20  │   VCC
            C       │  02       19  │   unused
            B       │  03       18  │   unused
            A       │  04       17  │   unused
       unused       │  05       16  │   unused
       unused       │  06       15  │   TEN
       unused       │  07       14  │   RNG
       unused       │  08       13  │   LT4
       unused       │  09       12  │   GT9
          GND       │  10       11  │   unused
                    └──────────────┘
```

```
LAB EXAMPLE 1
G. MOSS

Equations translated to Sum of Products form

  GT9
    = !D

    | !C & !B;

  LT4
    =  D

    |  C;

RNG
    = !D & !C

    | C & !B

    | C & !A

    | D & B & A;

!TEN
    = D & !C & B & !A;
```

48

Design PLD logic circuits for the following applications. Test your circuit designs in the lab.

PLD Design Procedure Summary

(1)   Define the problem with a truth table
(2)   Write a simplified logic expression for each output
(3)   Create the source file with a text editor
(4)   Compile (or assemble) the source file into a JEDEC file
(5)   Download the JEDEC file to the programmer
(6)   Insert PLD into programmer and program the `device`

8.1   Pattern generator
Design a logic circuit that will output the pattern illustrated by the following timing diagram. The inputs are DCBA and the outputs are WXYZ.

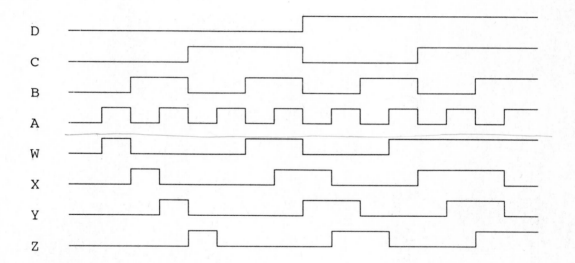

8.2   1's/2's complementer
Design a logic circuit that will output (WXYZ) either the one's or the two's complement of a 4-bit input (DCBA). The output function is controlled by the input F as indicated in the following function table.

F	WXYZ output
0	1's complement of DCBA
1	2's complement of DCBA

8.3   5-bit multiplier
Design a logic circuit that will output the product of a 3-bit number multiplied by a 2-bit number.

8.4 Programmable logic unit
Design a programmable logic circuit that will perform the following logic operations on the two 4-bit inputs.

M	N	Operation	inputs:
0	0	$F = A + B$	$A = (A3\ A2\ A1\ A0)$
0	1	$F = A \cdot B$	$B = (B3\ B2\ B1\ B0)$
1	0	$F = A \oplus B$	output:
1	1	$F = \overline{A}$	$F = (F3\ F2\ F1\ F0)$

UNIT 9

LOGIC SIMULATION OF FLIP-FLOPS AND LATCHES

Objectives ══

(1)   To be able to use logic simulation for analysis of flip-flops and latches implemented with simple logic gates.

(2)   To be able to simulate propagation delays in logic circuits.

(3)   To be able to use macros to define functional logic blocks for logic simulation.

Tutorial ═══

Flip-flops and Latches

Combinational logic circuits have outputs which are dependent upon only the current inputs to the circuit. Sequential circuits, on the other hand, are dependent not only on the current inputs but also upon the prior circuit conditions. Sequential circuits contain memory elements which allow them to utilize the prior circuit conditions in determining the circuit output. These memory elements consist of flip-flops and latches. There are various categories of flip-flops and latches including SR, D, and JK types. Several flip-flops or latches can be connected together in special circuit configurations to construct various types of registers and counters.

Logic Simulation of Propagation Delays

Propagation delay is the time interval from when an input signal to a device or circuit is changed to when the resulting output makes its change. Previous logic simulation projects with P/C-SILOS were performed with the device rise and fall propagation delays set to zero. The resulting circuit analysis was, therefore, performed with "ideal" devices. Since all devices have a finite amount of propagation delay, a much more realistic analysis of circuit performance should include these delays. Logic simulation using P/C-SILOS can take into account the propagation delays of the various devices in the circuit.

Using Macros in Logic Simulation

P/C-SILOS also provides the capability to describe a logic functional block in a macro. The logic block can consist of any number of interconnected components. The macro's circuit definition is saved in a library file with other macros. The macro can then be conveniently called for use by any source file to describe a circuit that contains the defined logic block. The macro can also be used any number of times in a single circuit description file.

D Latch Macro Example

Use P/C-SILOS to analyze the operation of the D latch in Fig. 9-1 when the following waveform is applied.

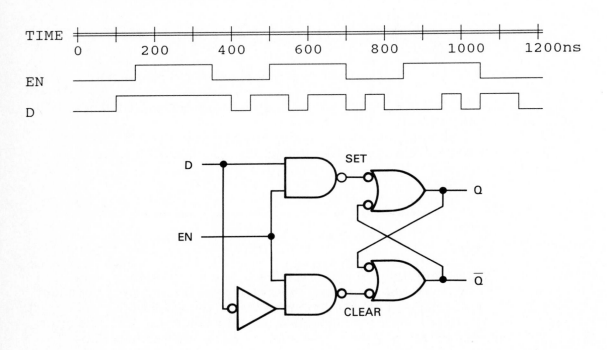

Fig. 9-1   D Latch and input conditions

The following macro can be used to describe the D Latch. Note the typical LS TTL delay values of 9ns (rise propagation delay) and 10ns (fall propagation delay) that has been included in the netlist description. This macro will be added to the file named MACRO.LIB.

```
$   D latch macro
$   the .MACRO statement below is the header for the
$      macro named D-LATCH
$   place holders for input & output signals follow
$      the macro name
$   the circuit's netlist defines the macro function
$   the instruction .EOM indicates the end of the
$      macro's netlist

.MACRO   DLATCH   EN D Q QBAR
SET    .NAND   9   10   D    EN
CLEAR  .NAND   9   10   NOTD   EN
NOTD   .INV    9   10   D
Q      .NAND   9   10   SET    QBAR
QBAR   .NAND   9   10   CLEAR   Q
.EOM
```

The following source file can then be used to analyze the circuit with the given inputs.

```
.TITLE   D-TYPE LATCH SIMULATION
$    Name:   G. Moss
.PATTERN   50     EN  D
                   0   0
                   0   0
                   0   1
                   1   1
                   1   1
                   1   1
                   1   1
                   0   1
                   0   0
                   0   1
                   1   1
                   1   0
                   1   1
                   1   1
                   0   0
                   0   1
                   0   0
                   1   0
                   1   0
                   1   1
                   1   0
                   0   1
                   0   1
                   0   0
.EOP
(EXAMPLE   DLATCH EN D Q QBAR
.MONITOR   EN;; D;; Q;; QBAR
.GRAPH   EN D Q QBAR
!SIM 1200
!TYPE GRAPH
```

```
$   The statement line starting with ( is a macro
$       expansion statement labeled EXAMPLE which calls
$       the macro named DLATCH.
$   The macro expansion statement provides parameter
$       passing between the macro and the source file.
$   The input & output signal names follow the
$       macro's name & represent signals in the same
$       order as listed in the macro itself.
$   The signal names in the source file may be
$       different from those used to define the macro.
```

Simulating this source file will produce the screen display shown in Fig. 9-2. The circles in the output waveforms indicate that the output is initially indeterminate.

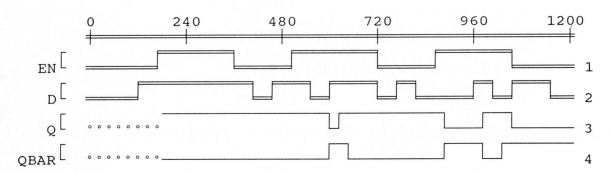

Fig. 9-2   D-type latch simulation results

Zooming in on the graph display will permit a closer inspection of the results due to the propagation delays such as is shown in Fig. 9-3.

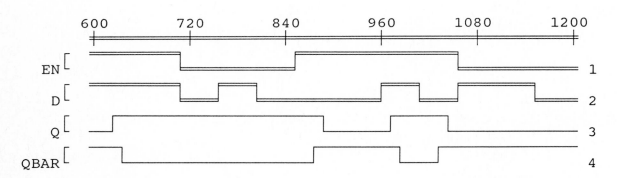

Fig. 9-3   D-latch simulation with expanded time scale

54

Another source file could be created to simulate a 4-bit transparent register that uses the same DLATCH macro. Note that when a macro is used several times in one source file, each expansion statement has a different label.

```
.TITLE   4-BIT TRANSPARENT REGISTER
$  Name:   G. Moss
.PATTERN   200 CLK D1 D2 D3 D4
                 0   0   0   0   0
                 0   0   0   1   1
                 1   0   0   1   1
                 1   0   0   1   1
                 0   0   0   1   1
                 0   1   1   0   0
                 1   1   1   0   0
                 1   1   1   0   0
                 0   1   1   1   1
                 0   1   0   1   0
                 1   1   0   1   0
                 1   0   1   0   1
                 0   1   0   1   0
                 0   0   0   0   0
                 1   0   0   0   0
                 1   0   1   1   0
                 0   0   1   1   0
                 0   1   0   0   1
                 1   1   0   0   1
                 1   0   0   0   0
.EOP
(FF1   DLATCH   CLK   D1   Q1   Q1BAR
(FF2   DLATCH   CLK   D2   Q2   Q2BAR
(FF3   DLATCH   CLK   D3   Q3   Q3BAR
(FF4   DLATCH   CLK   D4   Q4   Q4BAR
$  Note that each time the macro is used in a source
$     file, a different macro expansion label must be
$     used.
.MONITOR   CLK;; D1; D2; D3; D4;; Q1; Q2; Q3; Q4
.GRAPH     CLK D1 Q1 D2 Q2 D3 Q3 D4 Q4
!SIM 4000
!TYPE GRAPH
```

Simulation of the example source file for the transparent register produces the timing diagram in Fig. 9-4.

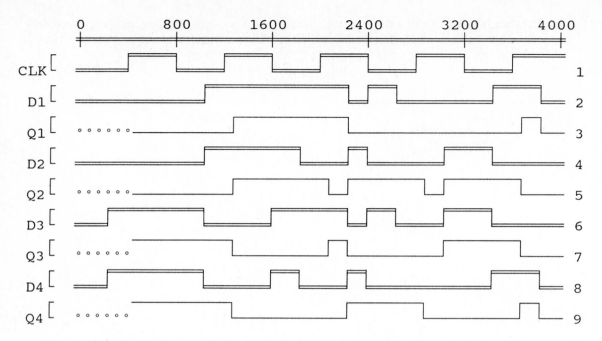

Fig. 9-4   4-bit transparent register simulation

Laboratory Projects

9.1   Clocked & unclocked SR latch simulation
Use logic simulation to compare the operation of the SR latch circuits shown in Fig. 9-5 when the given input waveforms are applied. Use typical LS TTL propagation delay times for the simulations.

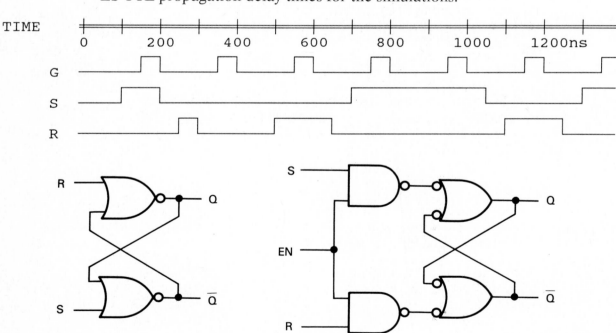

Fig. 9-5   Clocked & unclocked SR latch circuits

56

9.2 Master-Slave JK flip-flop simulation

Use logic simulation to analyze the Master-Slave JK flip-flop in Fig. 9-6 for the given input conditions. Assume the clock is a 10MHz square wave. Use typical LS TTL propagation delay times for the simulations. The simulation software will require that the initial output conditions be determined before it can analyze the circuit. This can be done by including the following P/C-SILOS statement in the source file to initialize both the master and the slave to a low output.

```
.INIT    QM=D0    QS=D0
```

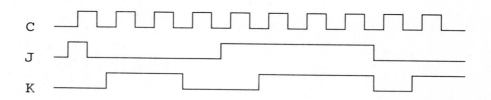

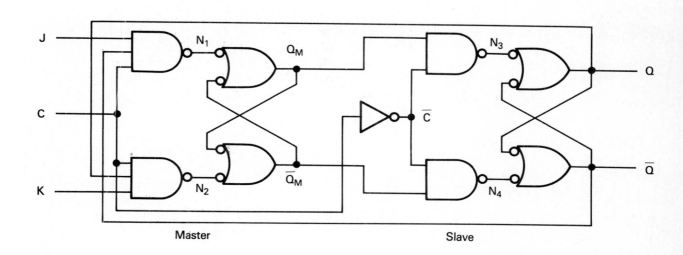

Fig. 9-6 M-S JK flip-flop gate circuit

9.3 Parallel data shifting simulation

Simulate the operation of the two parallel shift registers connected as shown in Fig. 9-7 for the given input waveform conditions. Use a macro to define the D-type latches.

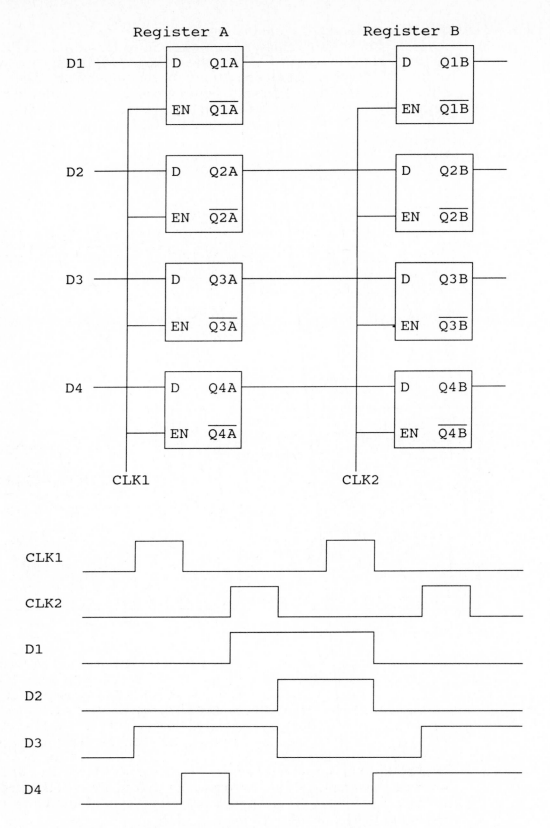

Fig. 9-7   Parallel data shift register circuit
and applied waveforms

58

UNIT 10

SCHMITT TRIGGERS, ASTABLES, AND ONE-SHOTS

Objectives ==

(1) To be able to convert analog signals into logic-compatible signals using Schmitt Trigger devices.
(2) To be able to design and construct astable multivibrators that produce specified square waveforms.
(3) To be able to design and construct monostable multivibrators that produce specified time delay patterns.

Tutorial ==

Schmitt Triggers

If a slow changing signal is applied to the input of a logic device, the device will often produce an output signal which oscillates as the input slowly transitions between high and low logic levels. A Schmitt trigger is a waveshaping device that is used to convert signals in which the voltage is slowly changing (and, therefore, incompatible with logic devices) to a signal of the same frequency but which is compatible with the signal transition times of logic devices. Schmitt trigger devices have an input hysteresis since they have a specific positive-going threshold voltage and a specific negative-going threshold voltage that triggers the Schmitt trigger's output between the two possible logic levels. The 74LS14 IC is a hex inverter chip with Schmitt trigger inputs.

One-shots (Monostable Multivibrators)

A one-shot is a timing device in which the output is triggered into a quasi-stable state for a time period and then returns to its stable state. The length of the time period is usually controlled by an external resistor and capacitor. One-shots are typically used to produce delays in control signals for digital systems. There are two types of one-shots, retriggerable and nonretriggerable. The 74LS221 IC contains two independent nonretriggerable one-shots.

Astable Multivibrators

An astable or free-running multivibrator has an output which continually switches back and forth between the two states. This type of signal is often used as a clock signal to control (or trigger) synchronous circuits. The 555 IC timer is a device that can be used to produce a clock signal whose frequency and duty cycle are dependent upon external timing resistors and capacitors. The 555 can also be configured as a one-shot.

Laboratory Projects

10.1 Schmitt trigger waveshaper
Use an oscilloscope to compare the output waveforms produced by a NOT gate in a 74LS04 and a 74LS14 (Schmitt trigger NOT) when either a triangle or sine waveform from a signal or function generator is applied to the inputs of the gates. Be sure to adjust the generator signal using the oscilloscope to $0 \leq V_i \leq +5v$ **before** applying it to the gate inputs.

10.2 Pulser (pushbutton switch debouncer)
Closing a mechanical switch causes a problem known as contact bounce. The random bouncing produces multiple voltage transitions at the switch's output which can cause erratic behavior in a logic circuit driven by the switch. There are various types of circuits that may be used to debounce a mechanical switch including latches, Schmitt triggers, and one-shots. Construct a pulser circuit (with switch debouncing) using a 74LS221 one-shot. Select appropriate components to make the pulse width approximately 0.5sec.

10.3 Variable frequency clock
Design and construct a clock generator circuit using a 555 timer. The duty cycle of the clock waveform should be approximately 50%. The clock output frequency should be variable in steps (by changing the 555 timing capacitor value). The 3 clock frequency values should be approximately 1 Hz, 1 KHz, and 10 KHz.

10.4   Waveform generator
Design and construct a waveform generator that will produce the waveforms given in Fig. 10.1. Use the 555 timer to generate one of the waveforms and then use that waveform to trigger the 2 one-shots in the 74LS221 to produce the other two waveforms.

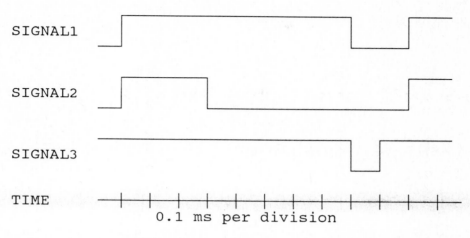

Fig. 10-1   Timing diagram for waveform generator

UNIT 11

ARITHMETIC CIRCUITS

Objectives ==

   (1)   To be able to design and implement logic circuits for basic adders using logic gates.

   (2)   To be able to design and implement arithmetic circuits using parallel adder chips.

Tutorial ==

Adder Circuits and Applications

The primary building blocks in adder circuits are half adders and full adders. The basic difference between half and full adders is that a full adder has an additional input that allows a carry input to be handled. Both half and full adders generate a sum and a carry output. These building blocks can be implemented a number of ways using various logic gates.

Due to their versatility and usefulness, parallel adders made up of several full adder stages are available as integrated circuit devices. The 74LS83A (or 74LS283), for example, is a 4-bit parallel binary adder chip. Parallel binary adders can be used in many arithmetic applications besides just simple addition.

Design logic circuits to implement each of the following arithmetic circuits. Test and verify your circuit designs.

11.1   Two-bit adder
Design a 2-bit binary adder with the 74LS83A. A 2-bit adder adds two 2-bit numbers together and produces a 3-bit sum. **Note that the unused inputs should be connected to some appropriate logic level and not left floating. There are several valid ways to connect this chip for this application. Compare this design with one that only uses logic gates.**

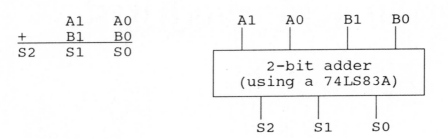

```
        A1  A0
    +   B1  B0
    ─────────────
    S2  S1  S0
```

11.2   Selected arithmetic function generator
Design a logic circuit using the 74LS83A and any additional necessary gates that will perform the following fixed arithmetic operations on a 4-bit input number (I3 I2 I1 I0). M and N are control inputs to the circuit that determine which of the 4 arithmetic operations is to be performed. The 4-bit output is F3 F2 F1 F0. Test a representative sampling of data for this circuit.

M	N	Operation
0	0	F = I + 1
0	1	F = I - 1
1	0	F = I + 4
1	1	F = I - 2

I = (I3 I2 I1 I0)
F = (F3 F2 F1 F0)

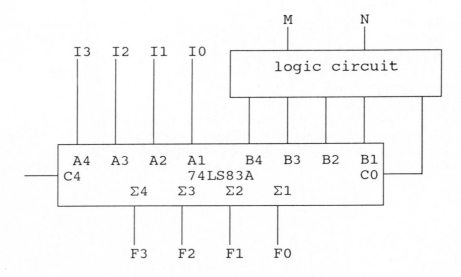

11.3   Four-bit adder/subtractor

Design a 4-bit adder/subtractor using the 74LS83A and any additional necessary logic gates (or a PLD). The circuit should handle signed numbers (using 2's complement arithmetic techniques). F is a control input to the circuit that determines if the circuit will add (A+B) or subtract (A-B) the 4-bit data inputs. Also provide an overflow detector circuit for the adder/subtractor. Hints: Perform subtraction by forming the 1's complement of the B input (the subtrahend) and adding 1 (with the carry input) plus the A input (the minuend). Remember that the B input should not be complemented for addition (F=0). To design the overflow circuit, define in a truth table when an overflow exists by monitoring each of the 3 sign bits (2 operands & answer).

F	Function
0	A+B
1	A-B

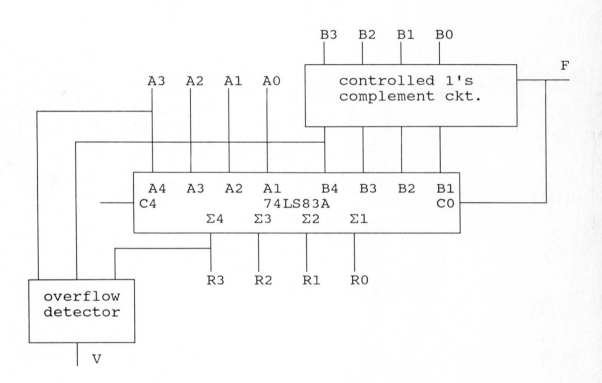

11.4 Binary multiplier

Design an unsigned binary multiplier using the 74LS83A, a GAL16V8A, and any additional necessary gates. The multiplier circuit should handle 3-bit multiplicands and 3-bit multipliers to produce 6-bit products. Use P/C-SILOS to simulate your circuit design. Hint: use the AND function to multiply <u>each pair</u> of bits.

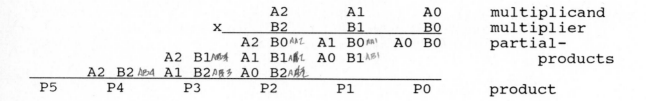

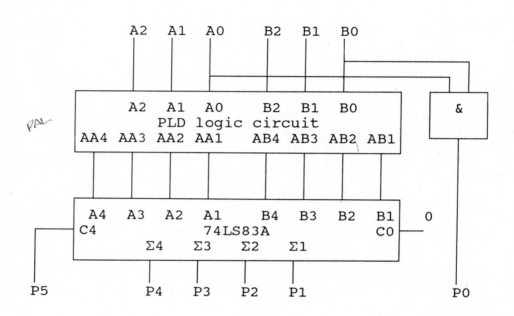

UNIT 12

ASYNCHRONOUS COUNTERS

Objectives
==

(1)   To be able to analyze asynchronous counter circuits and predict their theoretical operation.
(2)   To be able to construct and test asynchronous counter circuit designs.

Tutorial
==

Asynchronous Counter Analysis

Asynchronous or ripple counters are triggered by separate clocking signals on each flip-flop. Flip-flop output signals are used to provide the appropriate triggering signals for other flip-flops. Because of this clocking arrangement, the individual flip-flops do not change states at the same time. To determine the count sequence of an asynchronous counter requires that each flip-flop be individually analyzed starting with the one triggered by the system clock. If a flip-flop receives the appropriate triggering signal, its resultant output will depend upon the control signals present on the flip-flop's synchronous inputs. The count sequence may be an up- or down-count depending upon the circuit's configuration and the triggering signals used. Additionally, the flip-flop asynchronous control inputs, preset and clear, may be used to modify the count sequence. The mod number of a counter is the number of states present in the count sequence.

12.1   Asynchronous counter analysis & testing
Analyze each of the following asynchronous counters. Determine the
modulus and sketch the timing diagram for each counter. Construct and
test each of the counter circuits. Use an oscilloscope to compare the output
waveforms for each counter with your theoretical prediction. Sketch the
counter output and clock input waveforms for each counter circuit.

Circuit 1:

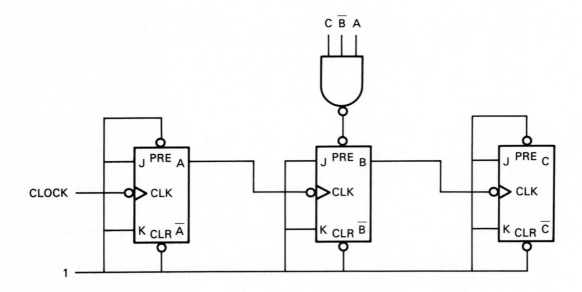

Circuit 2:

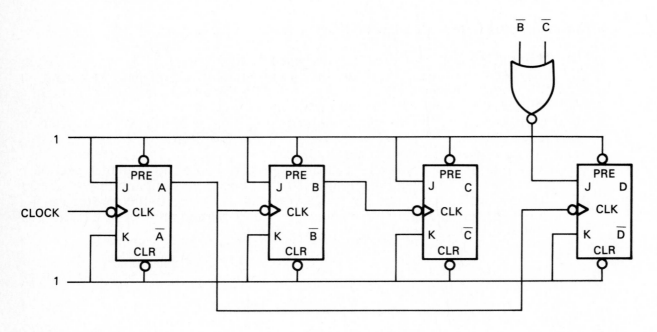

Circuit 3:

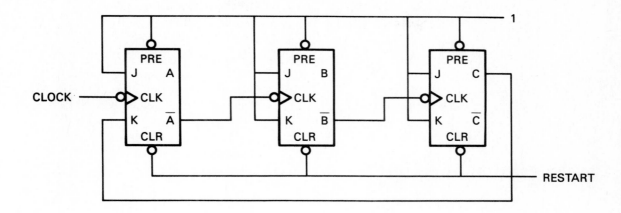

12.2   Self-stopping, asynchronous counter analysis & testing
Analyze the following asynchronous counter. Determine the counter's modulus and sketch the timing diagram after an active-low RESTART pulse has been applied to the counter. Construct and test the counter circuit and compare the output sequence of the counter with your theoretical prediction.

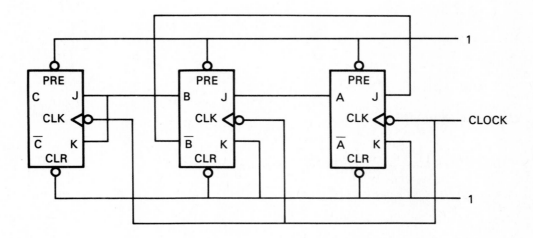

UNIT 13

SYNCHRONOUS COUNTERS

Objectives

(1) To be able to analyze synchronous counter circuits and predict their theoretical operation.
(2) To be able to construct and test synchronous counter circuit designs.

Tutorial

Synchronous Counter Analysis

Synchronous or parallel counters are triggered by a common clocking signal applied to each flip-flop. Because of this clocking arrangement, all flip-flops react to their individual synchronous control inputs at the same time. The count sequence depends upon the control signals input to each flip-flop. Additionally, the flip-flop asynchronous control inputs, preset and clear, may be used to modify the count sequence.

Laboratory Projects

13.1 Synchronous counter analysis & testing
Analyze each of the following synchronous counters. Determine the modulus and sketch the timing diagram for each counter. Construct and test each of the counter circuits. Use an oscilloscope to compare the output waveforms for each counter with your theoretical prediction. Sketch the counter output and clock input waveforms for each counter circuit.

71

Circuit 1:

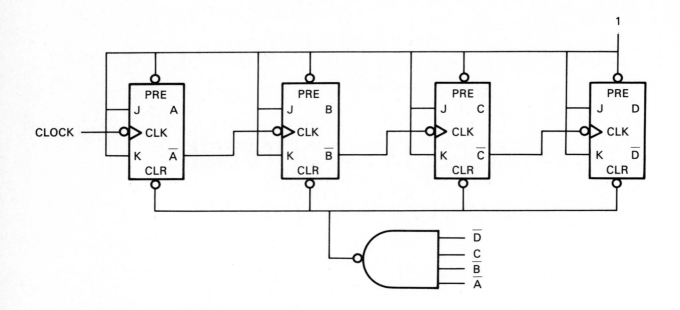

Circuit 2:

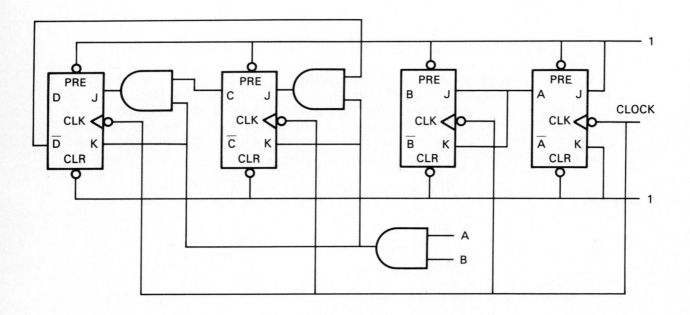

72

Circuit 3:

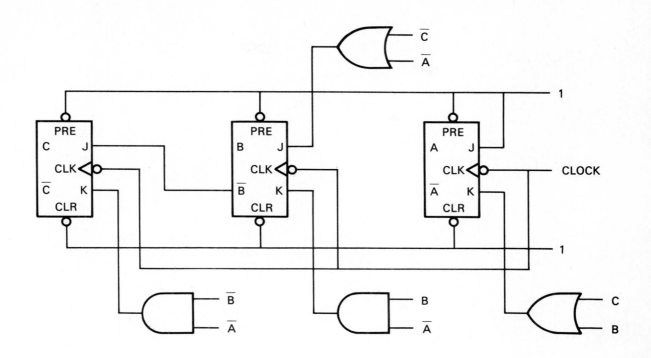

Circuit 4:

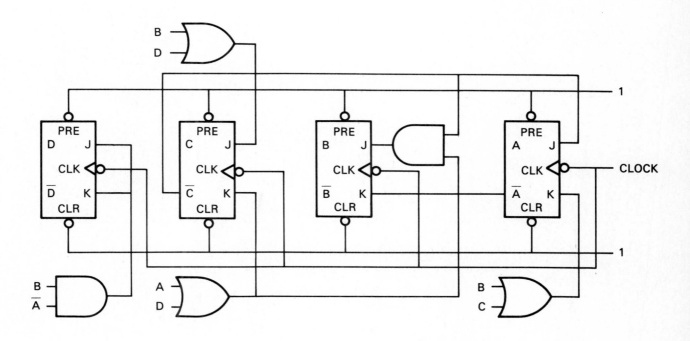

UNIT 14

LOGIC SIMULATION OF SEQUENTIAL CIRCUITS

Objectives ═══════════════════════════════════════

    (1)   To be able to use logic simulation software to analyze asynchronous counter designs.

    (2)   To be able to use logic simulation software to analyze synchronous counter designs.

Tutorial ═══════════════════════════════════════

Simulating Sequential Circuits

Logic simulation software can also be used to analyze sequential logic circuits. P/C-SILOS has the capability to define applied repetitive signals such as circuit clocking signals. Multiple signals can be defined in this fashion. This function can also be used to define non-repetitive signals by identifying specific signal transition times. The logic simulation software also has various pre-defined flip-flop models including JK, SR, D, and T flip-flop types for use in a circuit netlist. The flip-flops may be either negative-edge or positive-edge triggered and the asynchronous preset and clear controls are available in the models. The following additional source file keywords can be used in sequential circuit netlists.

75

P/C-SILOS SOURCE FILE KEYWORDS
FOR SEQUENTIAL CIRCUITS

```
.CLK         used to define repetitive clock signals

.JKNEFF      indicates a negative-edge triggered JK flip-flop
.JKPEFF      indicates a positive-edge triggered JK flip-flop
.SRNEFF      indicates a negative-edge triggered SR flip-flop
.SRPEFF      indicates a positive-edge triggered SR flip-flop
.DNEFF       indicates a negative-edge triggered D flip-flop
.DPEFF       indicates a positive-edge triggered D flip-flop
.TNEFF       indicates a negative-edge triggered T flip-flop
.TPEFF       indicates a positive-edge triggered T flip-flop

.INIT        used to specify the initial state of any node in
             the network
```

EXAMPLE USAGE OF P/C-SILOS KEYWORDS

```
CLOCK    .CLK    0  0    300  1    500  0    .REP  0
```

The signal named CLOCK is defined to be a low at time = 0, change to a high at time = 300, and then change back to a low at time = 500. The signal will then repeat this pattern continuously starting again at time = 0.

```
FF1 .JKNEFF 15 15 CLK1 SIGA SIGB SIGC SIGD / QA QABAR
```

The negative-edge triggered JK flip-flop named FF1 has rise and fall propagation delays of 15 time units each (representing perhaps the typical TTL LS delays of 15ns). The JK is clocked by a signal called CLK1. The following control signals are applied to FF1:

SIGA	J input
SIGB	K input
SIGC	Preset input
SIGD	Clear input

The Q output is called QA and the complementary output is called QABAR.

```
U1A .DPEFF 13 25 TRIG1 DIN .VCC .VCC  /  DATA DATABAR
```

The positive-edge triggered D flip-flop named U1A has a rise propagation delay of 13 time units and a fall propagation delay of 25 time units. The D is clocked by a signal called TRIG1. The following control signals are applied to U1A:

DIN	D input
.VCC	Preset input disabled
.VCC	Clear input disabled

The Q output is called DATA and the complementary output is called DATABAR.

Sequential Circuit Logic Simulation Example

Use P/C-SILOS to analyze the sequential logic circuit in Fig. 14-1. Assume that a 2MHz square wave signal is used for the CLOCK signal.

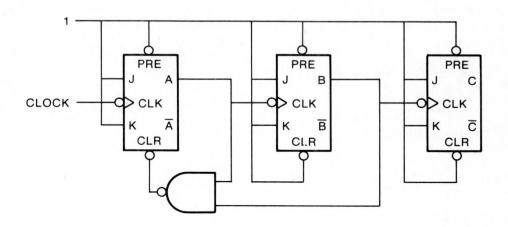

Fig. 14-1   Circuit Schematic for Simulation Example

The following P/C-SILOS source file can be used to simulate the given circuit.

```
.TITLE EXAMPLE ASYNCHRONOUS COUNTER
$    Name:  G. Moss
CLOCK .CLK    0 0    250 1    500 0    .REP 0
$  CLOCK is low for 250 ns, high for another 250 ns, &
$     then the cycle repeats

RESET .NAND      9  10    QB  QA
FF1   .JKNEFF   15 15    CLOCK .VCC .VCC .VCC RESET   / QA
FF2   .JKNEFF   15 15    QA    .VCC .VCC .VCC .VCC    / QB
FF3   .JKNEFF   15 15    QB    .VCC .VCC .VCC .VCC    / QC
$  Typical TTL LS propagation delays have been assumed
$     for the NAND gate & JK flip-flops

.INIT  QA=D0 QB=D0 QC=D0
$  Simulation is initialized to QA QB QC = 0 0 0

.MONITOR  CLOCK;; RESET; QC; QB; QA
.TABLE   QC; QB; QA
.GRAPH   CLOCK RESET QC QB QA

!SIMULATE 3000
$  Run simulation for 3000 ns

!TYPE GRAPH
$  Display timing diagram on screen
```

77

The screen display of the timing diagram is shown in Fig. 14-2.

* P/C-SILOS 3C.8 *   EXAMPLE ASYNCHRONOUS COUNTER

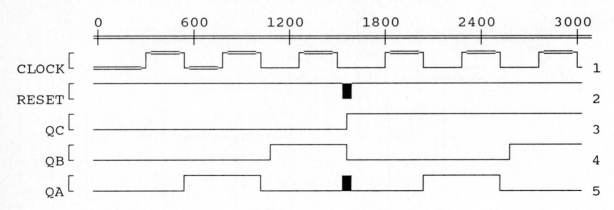

Fig. 14-2   Timing diagram for simulation example

The time scale on the waveforms can be expanded by zooming in on the graph display to better view the indicated signal glitches as seen in Fig. 14-3.

* P/C-SILOS 3C.8 *   EXAMPLE ASYNCHRONOUS COUNTER

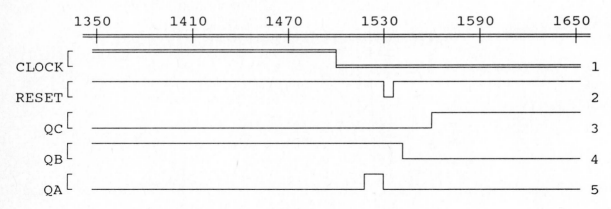

Fig. 14-3   Expanded time scale for simulation example

14.1 Computer simulation of asynchronous counters
Analyze each of the following asynchronous counters using P/C-SILOS.

Circuit 1:

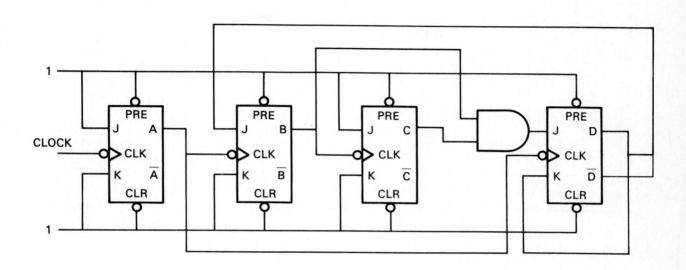

Circuit 2:

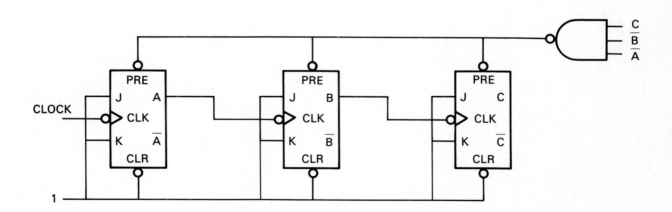

14.2 Computer simulation of synchronous counters
Analyze each of the following synchronous counters using P/C-SILOS.

Circuit 1:

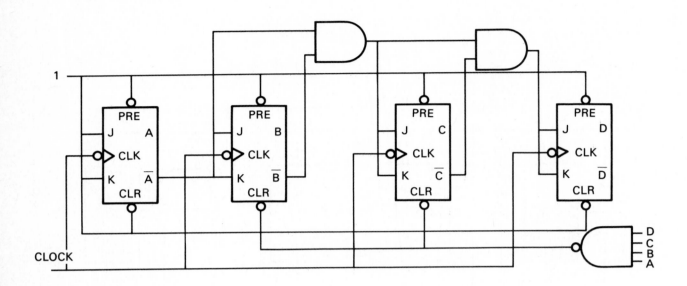

Circuit 2:

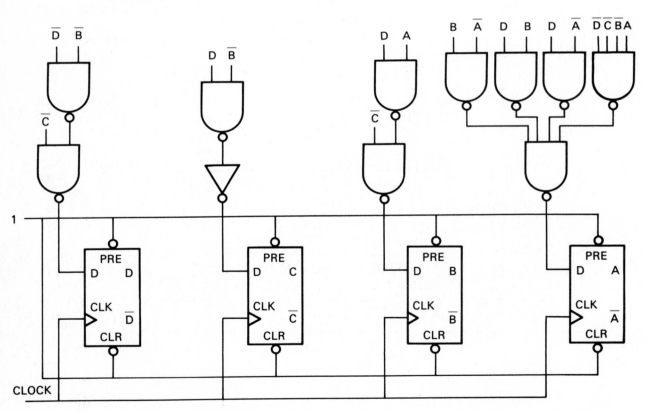

UNIT 15

IC COUNTERS

================================

(1)   To be able to design specified counter circuits by programming the count
        sequence of IC counter chips.
(2)   To be able to design counters for specified applications by cascading
        counter chips together.

Tutorial ================================

IC Counters

Various asynchronous and synchronous counter designs have been integrated into
chips to make circuit applications more convenient for the logic designer. Some
variations include the number of flip-flops contained in the chip, the counter
modulus, synchronous or asynchronous flip-flop triggering, synchronous or
asynchronous counter resetting, synchronous or asynchronous counter loading,
up/down count control, and various counter cascading implementations. Different
feature combinations are found in different part numbers. Mod-16 and mod-10 IC
counters are commonly available. A mod-10 counter is also referred to as a
decade or BCD counter. One common application for counters is in frequency
division in which the input signal (clock input) is divided by a specified factor to
produce the resultant output frequency of the scaler.

15.1 Mod-7 counter designs using IC counters
Design the mod-7 count sequences specified in the following state diagrams using the indicated IC counter chips. Construct and test each counter circuit.

Use the 74LS190 to produce the following sequences:

Circuit 1:

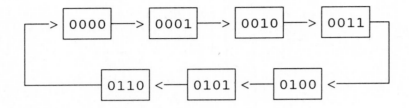

Circuit 2:

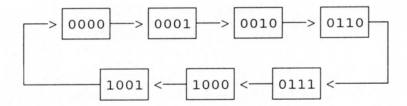

Circuit 3:

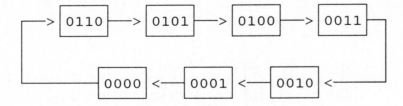

Use the 74LS160A to produce the following sequences:

Circuit 4:

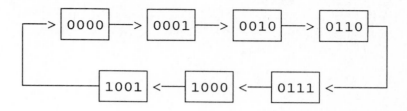

Circuit 5:

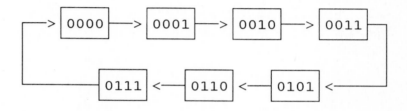

15.2 Mod-100 BCD counter and display
Design a mod-100 counter by cascading the 74LS190 and 74LS160A decade counters together. Display the count sequence on a 2-digit decimal display using 2 common-anode 7-segment displays and 74LS47 BCD-to-7-segment decoder drivers. Construct and test the counter circuit.

15.3 Frequency scaler circuits
Design and test 6 different frequency scaler circuits using a 74LS90 decade counter. Obtain the following frequency divisions: ÷ 2, ÷ 5, ÷ 10 (20% duty cycle), ÷ 10 (40% duty cycle), ÷ 10 (50% duty cycle), and ÷ 9. Use an oscilloscope to monitor the input and output signals of each scaler circuit. Sketch the input and output waveforms.

15.4 Divide-by-60 frequency scaler
Design 3 different logic circuits using a 74LS393 dual 4-bit binary counter chip that will divide the frequency of an input square wave signal by a factor of 60. Use a frequency counter to verify proper operation of your circuit designs. Construct and test each counter circuit.

UNIT 16

SYNCHRONOUS COUNTER DESIGN

Objectives
===

(1) To be able to design synchronous counter circuits that produce a specified sequence.
(2) To be able to use logic simulation software to verify synchronous counter designs.

Tutorial
===

Synchronous Counter Design

Synchronous sequential circuits may be designed by developing a transition table from the desired state sequence indicated in a next-state table. A next-state table lists each possible state for the sequential circuit and the corresponding next state that should occur after clocking. A transition table is used to identify the synchronous inputs that must be applied to each flip-flop in order to produce the specified count sequence. The Boolean expression for each flip-flop input can be derived by Karnaugh mapping the transition table information.

Synchronous Counter Design Example

Design a synchronous, mod-7 counter using JK flip-flops that produces the sequence given in the state diagram in Fig. 16-1.

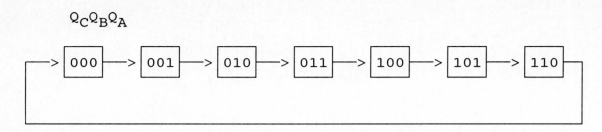

$Q_C Q_B Q_A$

Fig. 16-1   Mod-7 counter state diagram

First complete a next-state table as illustrated in Table 16-1 from the given state diagram.

Present State			Next State		
Q_C	Q_B	Q_A	Q_C	Q_B	Q_A
0	0	0	0	0	1
0	0	1	0	1	0
0	1	0	0	1	1
0	1	1	1	0	0
1	0	0	1	0	1
1	0	1	1	1	0
1	1	0	0	0	0
1	1	1	X	X	X

Table 16-1   Next-state table

Then determine the necessary flip-flop inputs to produce the indicated sequence and list the information in a transition table (see Table 16-2).

Present States			State Transitions			Flip-flop Inputs					
Q_C	Q_B	Q_A	Q_C	Q_B	Q_A	J_C	K_C	J_B	K_B	J_A	K_A
0	0	0	0 -> 0	0 -> 0	0 -> 1	0	X	0	X	1	X
0	0	1	0 -> 0	0 -> 1	1 -> 0	0	X	1	X	X	1
0	1	0	0 -> 0	1 -> 1	0 -> 1	0	X	X	0	1	X
0	1	1	0 -> 1	1 -> 0	1 -> 0	1	X	X	1	X	1
1	0	0	1 -> 1	0 -> 0	0 -> 1	X	0	0	X	1	X
1	0	1	1 -> 1	0 -> 1	1 -> 0	X	0	1	X	X	1
1	1	0	1 -> 0	1 -> 0	0 -> 0	X	1	X	1	0	X
1	1	1	1 -> X	1 -> X	1 -> X	X	X	X	X	X	X

Table 16-2   Transition table

86

Record the information for each flip-flop input in a separate K-map and determine the appropriate simplified Boolean expressions. Note that "don't care" output conditions (X's in the K-maps) may be defined as either zeros or ones and may be used to simplify the expressions as much as possible.

Q_C \ Q_BQ_A	00	01	11	10
0	0	0	1	0
1	X	X	X	X

$$J_C = Q_B\ Q_A$$

Q_C \ Q_BQ_A	00	01	11	10
0	X	X	X	X
1	0	0	X	1

$$K_C = Q_B$$

Q_C \ Q_BQ_A	00	01	11	10
0	0	1	X	X
1	0	1	X	X

$$J_B = Q_A$$

Q_C \ Q_BQ_A	00	01	11	10
0	X	X	1	0
1	X	X	X	1

$$K_B = Q_A + Q_C$$

Q_C \ Q_BQ_A	00	01	11	10
0	1	X	X	1
1	1	X	X	0

$$J_A = \overline{Q}_B + \overline{Q}_C$$

Q_C \ Q_BQ_A	00	01	11	10
0	X	1	1	X
1	X	1	X	X

$$K_A = 1$$

The schematic for the synchronous circuit design shown in Fig. 16-2 can now be drawn from the J and K flip-flop inputs determined with K-mapping.

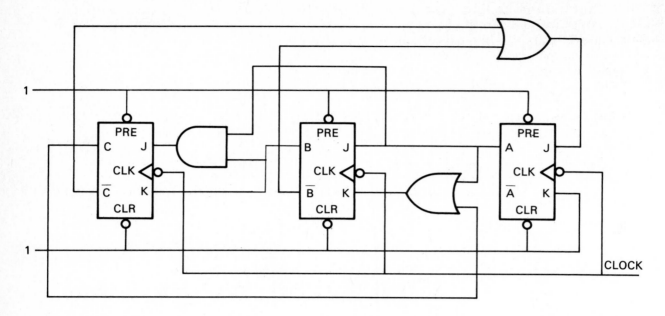

Fig. 16-2 Schematic for synchronous circuit design example

The circuit design should then be analyzed to verify proper circuit operation and to determine if the circuit design is self-correcting. Analyzing this circuit design gives the state diagram shown in Fig. 16-3 and verifies correct circuit operation. Note that the circuit is self-correcting since the state 111 returns to the proper sequence loop.

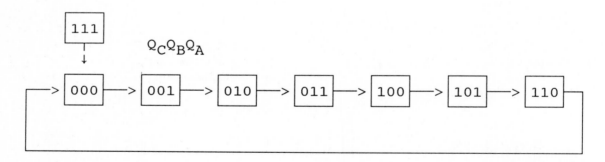

Fig. 16-3 State diagram to verify circuit design

Laboratory Projects

16.1 Synchronous counter design
Design synchronous counters using JK flip-flops for each of the given state diagrams. Do not use the asynchronous flip-flop inputs for the circuit designs. Verify that each circuit design should produce the required sequence and determine if each circuit is self-correcting by analyzing the

circuit designs. Construct and test each circuit design. Use an oscilloscope to display the timing diagram for each counter.

Mod-6 circuit:

$Q_C Q_B Q_A$

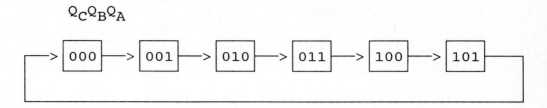

Mod-5 circuit:

$Q_3 Q_2 Q_1$

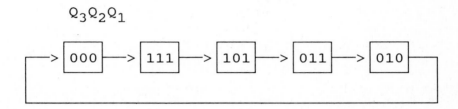

16.2   Synchronous BCD counter design
Design synchronous, decade counters using JK flip-flops for each of the given BCD (5421 and 8421) sequences. Do not use the asynchronous flip-flop inputs for the circuit designs. Verify that each circuit design should produce the required sequence and determine if each circuit is self-correcting by analyzing the circuit designs. Construct and test each circuit design. Connect the 8421 BCD counter to a 7-segment display using a 74LS47 decoder/driver.

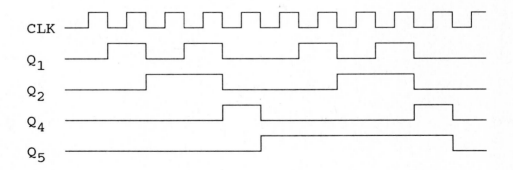

Timing diagram for a recycling 5421 BCD counter

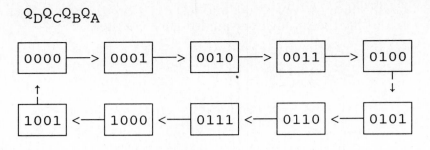

$Q_D Q_C Q_B Q_A$

State diagram for an 8421 BCD counter

16.3 Design verification using logic simulation
Use P/C-SILOS to simulate each of the synchronous counter designs and verify correct operation.

UNIT 17

SHIFT REGISTERS

(1)   To be able to design various serial and parallel digital data transfer circuits using shift registers.
(2)   To be able to design various types of shift register counter circuits.
(3)   To be able to use logic simulation software to verify shift register counter designs.

Tutorial

Shift Registers

Registers consist of a set of flip-flops used to store and transfer binary data in a digital system. Registers can be classified according to the types of input and output data movement. With the two basic forms of data transfer, serial and parallel, there are the following categories of registers:

1.   Parallel-in/Parallel-out (PIPO)
2.   Serial-in/Serial-out (SISO)
3.   Parallel-in/Serial-out (PISO)
4.   Serial-in/Parallel-out (SIPO)

By using feedback, counters can also be implemented with shift registers. The most common types of shift register counters are ring counters and Johnson counters.

17.1 Waveform pattern generator
Design a waveform pattern generator using a parallel-in, serial-out shift register. Wire the shift register to produce the repetitive, 8-bit waveform pattern given below. Use an IC counter chip to control the parallel loading/serial shifting sequence. Construct and test the logic circuit and compare the output sequence with the one specified. Observe the data pattern produced by the circuit with an oscilloscope.

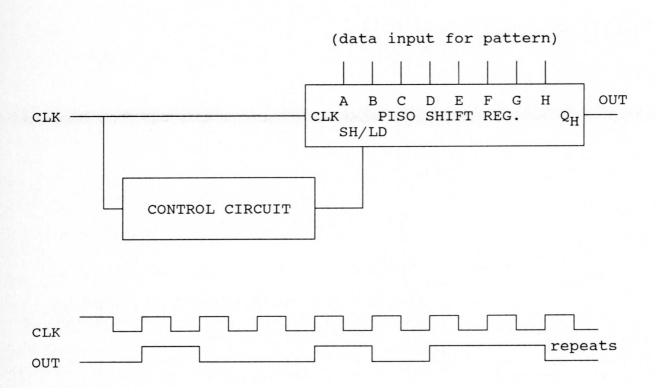

17.2 Serial data buffer
Design a serial data buffer using a serial-in, parallel-out shift register and a D-type latch. The circuit will accept 8 bits of serial data and then automatically transfer (in parallel) the data to a register. The register's output will be updated with new data after every 8 clock cycles. Use an IC counter chip to control the serial shifting/parallel transfer sequence. Construct and test the logic circuit.

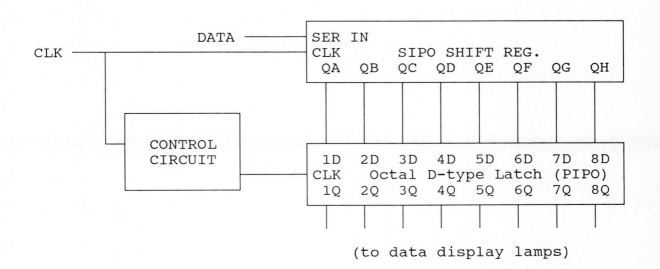

(to data display lamps)

17.3 Ring counter
Design a self-starting (and self-correcting), mod-6 ring counter using the 74LS164 IC. Construct and test the counter circuit and compare the output sequence of the counter with your theoretical prediction.

17.4 Johnson counter
Design a mod-13 Johnson (twisted ring) counter using the 74LS164 IC. Construct and test the counter circuit and compare the output sequence of the counter with your theoretical prediction.

17.5 Design verification using logic simulation
Use P/C-SILOS to simulate each of the two shift register counter designs.

UNIT 18

SEQUENTIAL CIRCUIT DESIGN USING PROGRAMMABLE LOGIC DEVICES

Objectives

(1)   To be able to design and implement sequential circuits using programmable logic devices.

Tutorial

Sequential Circuits Using PLDs

Many programmable logic devices contain flip-flops, and therefore, can be used to implement sequential circuits. The GAL16V8A can optionally be programmed to provide registered outputs on any of the 8 possible output pins. The sequential circuit design and implementation procedures for the GAL16V8A using LC9000 is essentially the same as for combinatorial circuits. A registered output pin is defined by using the pin modifier ".D" with the output pin name in the Boolean expression. In the registered mode of operation, pin 1 is the clock pin and pin 11 is the output enable pin for all registered outputs. Neither pin can be used as an input to an equation when the PLD is configured for a registered output.

PLD Design Example

Design a counter which produces the irregular, recycling sequence given in the timing diagram of Fig. 18-1.

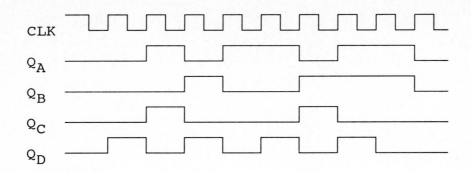

Fig. 18-1   Timing diagram for design example

First complete a next-state table shown in Table 18-1 from the given timing diagram.

Present State				Next State			
Q_D	Q_C	Q_B	Q_A	Q_D	Q_C	Q_B	Q_A
0	0	0	0	1	0	0	0
0	0	0	1	1	0	0	1
0	0	1	0	X	X	X	X
0	0	1	1	0	0	0	0
0	1	0	0	X	X	X	X
0	1	0	1	1	0	1	0
0	1	1	0	1	0	1	1
0	1	1	1	X	X	X	X
1	0	0	0	0	1	0	1
1	0	0	1	0	1	1	0
1	0	1	0	0	0	0	1
1	0	1	1	0	0	1	1
1	1	0	0	X	X	X	X
1	1	0	1	X	X	X	X
1	1	1	0	X	X	X	X
1	1	1	1	X	X	X	X

Table 18-1   Next-state table

Only D-type flip-flops are used in the GAL16V8A, and therefore, the "Next State" information from Table 18-1 represents the necessary flip-flop inputs to produce the indicated sequence. Record the input information for each flip-flop in a separate K-map and determine the appropriate simplified Boolean expressions (see Fig. 18-2).

$Q_D Q_C$ \ $Q_B Q_A$	00	01	11	10
00	1	1	0	X
01	X	1	X	1
11	X	X	X	X
10	0	0	0	0

$$D_D = Q_C + \overline{Q}_D \, \overline{Q}_B$$

$Q_D Q_C$ \ $Q_B Q_A$	00	01	11	10
00	0	0	0	X
01	X	0	X	0
11	X	X	X	X
10	1	1	0	0

$$D_C = Q_D \, \overline{Q}_B$$

$Q_D Q_C$ \ $Q_B Q_A$	00	01	11	10
00	0	0	0	X
01	X	1	X	1
11	X	X	X	X
10	0	1	1	0

$$D_B = Q_C + Q_D \, Q_A$$

$Q_D Q_C$ \ $Q_B Q_A$	00	01	11	10
00	0	1	0	X
01	X	0	X	1
11	X	X	X	X
10	1	0	1	1

$$D_A = Q_B \, \overline{Q}_A + Q_D \, Q_B$$
$$+ \, Q_D \, \overline{Q}_A + \overline{Q}_D \, \overline{Q}_C \, \overline{Q}_B \, Q_A$$

Fig. 18-2 K-maps for design example

The following LC9000 source file has been created for this PLD design.

```
DEVICE 16V8;
TITLE   SEQUENTIAL CIRCUIT EXAMPLE 1;
NAME    G. MOSS;

/*  filename:  SEQCKT1.PLD  */

/*  description:
     Synchronous counter with the hex sequence:
     0 -> 8 -> 5 -> A -> 1 -> 9 -> 6 -> B -> 3 -> 0
*/


/*  input pins  */

PIN 1 = CLK  ;
PIN 11 = OE  ;


/*  output pins  */

PIN 14 = QA  ;
PIN 15 = QB  ;
PIN 16 = QC  ;
PIN 17 = QD  ;


/*  equations  */

QD.D = QC    |    !QD & !QB  ;


QC.D = QD & !QB  ;


QB.D = QC    |    QD & QA  ;


QA.D = QB & !QA    |    QD & QB    |    QD & !QA

    |    !QD & !QC & !QB & QA  ;
```

The LIST command in LC9000 produced the following document file.

```
SEQUENTIAL CIRCUIT EXAMPLE
G. MOSS
```

```
                                    16V8
                          _____\  /_____
                  CLK  | 01              20 |  unused
               unused  | 02              19 |  unused
               unused  | 03              18 |  unused
               unused  | 04              17 |  QD
               unused  | 05              16 |  QC
               unused  | 06              15 |  QB
               unused  | 07              14 |  QA
               unused  | 08              13 |  unused
               unused  | 09              12 |  unused
               unused  | 10              11 |  OE
                       |_____|
```

```
SEQUENTIAL CIRCUIT EXAMPLE
G. MOSS

Equations translated to Sum of Products form

 QD.D
   =  QC

   | !QB & !QD;

 QC.D
   = !QB &  QD;

 QB.D
   =  QC

   |  QA &  QD;

 QA.D
   = !QA &  QB

   |  QB &  QD

   | !QA &  QD

   |  QA & !QB & !QC & !QD;
```

99

Note that additional counter features may be easily incorporated into the basic counter sequence design. For example, active-high count enable and counter clear controls may be added by modifying the source file as shown below.

```
DEVICE 16V8;
TITLE   SEQUENTIAL CIRCUIT EXAMPLE 2;
NAME    G. MOSS;

/*  filename:  SEQCKT2.PLD  */
/*  description:
      Synchronous counter with the hex sequence:
      0 -> 8 -> 5 -> A -> 1 -> 9 -> 6 -> B -> 3 -> 0
      & the following synchronous control signals:
   CLR   CTEN    function
    0     0      DISABLE COUNTER (hold same value)
    0     1      COUNT ENABLE
    1     0      CLEAR COUNTER (QD QC QB QA = 0 0 0 0) */


/*  input pins  */
PIN 1 = CLK   ;
PIN 2 = CLR   ;
PIN 3 = CTEN  ;
PIN 11 = OE   ;


/*  output pins  */
PIN 14 = QA   ;
PIN 15 = QB   ;
PIN 16 = QC   ;
PIN 17 = QD   ;


/*  equations  */

QD.D = (CTEN & (QC | !QD & !QB)      /* COUNT ENABLED */
       | !CTEN & QD)                 /* COUNT DISABLED  */
       & !CLR ;                      /* IF NOT CLEARING */


QC.D = (CTEN & (QD & !QB) | !CTEN & QC) & !CLR ;


QB.D = (CTEN & (QC | QD & QA) | !CTEN & QB) & !CLR ;


QA.D = (CTEN & (QB & !QA | QD & QB | QD & !QA
       | !QD & !QC & !QB & QA) | !CTEN & QA) & !CLR ;
```

The new document file would appear as shown on the next page.

100

SEQUENTIAL CIRCUIT EXAMPLE 2
G. MOSS

16V8

```
                    ┌──────┐
        CLK  │ 01      20 │  unused
        CLR  │ 02      19 │  unused
       CTEN  │ 03      18 │  unused
     unused  │ 04      17 │  QD
     unused  │ 05      16 │  QC
     unused  │ 06      15 │  QB
     unused  │ 07      14 │  QA
     unused  │ 08      13 │  unused
     unused  │ 09      12 │  unused
     unused  │ 10      11 │  OE
             └──────┘
```

SEQUENTIAL CIRCUIT EXAMPLE 2
G. MOSS

Equations translated to Sum of Products form

```
QD.D
   = !CLR &  CTEN &  QC

   | !CLR &  CTEN & !QB & !QD

   | !CLR & !CTEN &  QD;

QC.D
   = !CLR &  CTEN & !QB &  QD

   | !CLR & !CTEN &  QC;

QB.D
   = !CLR &  CTEN &  QC

   | !CLR &  CTEN &  QA &  QD

   | !CLR & !CTEN &  QB;

QA.D
   = !CLR &  CTEN & !QA &  QB

   | !CLR &  CTEN &  QB &  QD

   | !CLR &  CTEN & !QA &  QD

   | !CLR &  CTEN &  QA & !QB & !QC & !QD

   | !CLR & !CTEN &  QA;
```

18.1   Custom sequential circuit
Design a custom sequential circuit using a GAL16V8A that will produce
the sequence given in the following state diagram.

$Q_D Q_C Q_B Q_A$

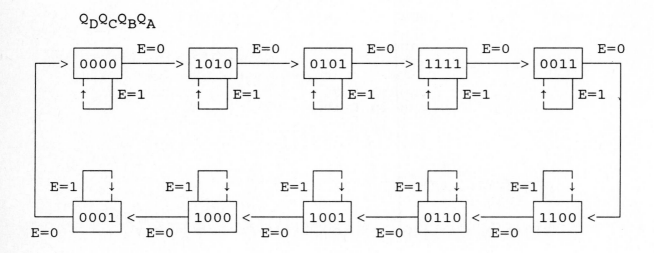

18.2   Gray code counter
Design a 4-bit, up/down, Gray code counter using a GAL16V8A. The
count direction is controlled by the signal called F as indicated in the
following function table. Label counter outputs $Q_D\ Q_C\ Q_B\ Q_A$.

F	Direction
0	Count Up
1	Count Down

18.3 Special purpose data register
Design an 8-bit data register using a GAL16V8A which operates according to the following function table. The register function is selected with the controls S1 and S0. The 4-bit data input is labeled I3 I2 I1 I0 and the register output is labeled Q7 Q6 Q5 Q4 Q3 Q2 Q1 Q0.

S1	S0	° Operation	Register outputs after clock							
			Q7	Q6	Q5	Q4	Q3	Q2	Q1	Q0
0	0	Load L.S. nibble	$Q7_n$	$Q6_n$	$Q5_n$	$Q4_n$	$I3_n$	$I2_n$	$I1_n$	$I0_n$
0	1	Load M.S. nibble	$I3_n$	$I2_n$	$I1_n$	$I0_n$	$Q3_n$	$Q2_n$	$Q1_n$	$Q0_n$
1	0	Swap nibbles	$Q3_n$	$Q2_n$	$Q1_n$	$Q0_n$	$Q7_n$	$Q6_n$	$Q5_n$	$Q4_n$
1	1	Rotate data right	$Q0_n$	$Q7_n$	$Q6_n$	$Q5_n$	$Q4_n$	$Q3_n$	$Q2_n$	$Q1_n$

Note: L.S. = Least Significant
M.S. = Most Significant

18.4 Multifunction data register
Design a 6-bit data register using a GAL16V8A which is capable of performing the operations given in the following function table. The register function is selected with the controls S2 S1 S0. The 6-bit data input is labeled D5 D4 D3 D2 D1 D0 and the register output is labeled Q5 Q4 Q3 Q2 Q1 Q0.

S2	S1	S0	Function
0	0	0	Clear register
0	0	1	Load (parallel) register
0	1	X	Hold data in register
1	0	0	AND data in register with D inputs
1	0	1	OR data in register with D inputs
1	1	0	XOR data in register with D inputs
1	1	1	NOT (1's complement) data in register

103

UNIT 19

MEASURING DEVICE PARAMETERS

Objectives ═══════════════════════════════════

    (1)   To be able to measure the power requirements for logic chips.
    (2)   To be able to measure propagation delays of logic gates.
    (3)   To be able to measure the output current capabilities of a logic gate.
    (4)   To be able to measure the logic level input voltage thresholds for logic gates.
    (5)   To be able to measure the transfer characteristic of logic gates.

Tutorial ═══════════════════════════════════

Device Parameters

For proper operation, digital chips must meet standardized parametric specifications. Parametric testing of various digital device voltage, current, and time delay characteristics may be performed to ensure that a device meets these specifications.

Chip Power Supply Current Requirements

The power requirements for a logic chip are determined by measuring the amount of current drawn by the chip from its power supply. Since an individual gate's current needs may vary depending on its output logic level, the average current is often specified. The supply current for SSI chips is measured with all gate outputs at a high logic level (I_{CCH} or I_{DDH}) and again with the outputs at a low logic level (I_{CCL} or I_{DDL}). An average current is then computed. The simplest technique would be to use a DMM to measure the supply currents for the two output conditions for the device under test (DUT). Tie the gate inputs to the appropriate logic levels to produce the two specified static gate output conditions. The supply current level for CMOS chips (I_{DD}) is dependent upon the frequency of the input signals. This may be tested by applying a compatible square wave signal to the gate inputs and measuring I_{DD}. The current reading will automatically be averaged with the 50% duty cycle square wave input.

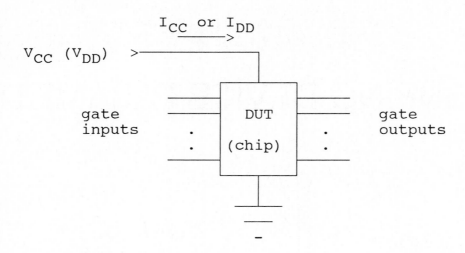

Fig. 19-1 Measuring supply current

Propagation Delays

Propagation delay times are measured from the 50% transition point on the input waveform to the 50% transition point on the resulting output waveform. The two propagation delay times specified for a gate output are called t_{PLH} and t_{PHL} and are referenced, respectively, to the low-to-high and high-to-low transitions of the output waveform. Propagation delay times are difficult to measure since they are typically only a few nanoseconds and it is best to use a high bandwidth scope (>100MHz) for more precise measurements. However, it is possible to cascade several gates together to measure an overall propagation delay and then calculate an average delay per gate. The input signal should be a voltage-compatible square wave of around 1MHz.

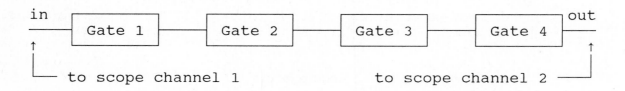

Fig. 19-2 Measuring average propagation delays

Output Current Sinking and Sourcing

The output current drive capability of a logic gate limits the number of gate inputs that can be connected to a single output. This loading capacity is referred to as the fan-out of a logic gate. The current-sinking (I_{OL}) and current-sourcing (I_{OH}) ability of a logic gate can be measured as shown in Fig. 19-3. Apply the appropriate input signals to produce the desired high or low output level from the gate (DUT) while the variable resistor (use approximately 1K ohms for TTL gates and 50K ohms for CMOS gates) is at its maximum resistance. Then adjust the variable resistor to increase the output current until the measured output voltage reaches the specified V_{OLmax} or V_{OHmin}. Measure the maximum output current levels.

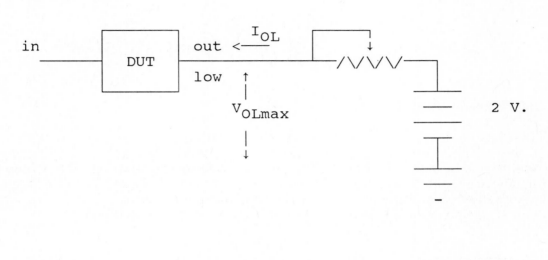

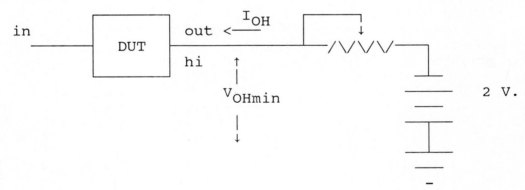

Fig. 19-3   Measuring output current drive

Input Voltage Levels

Logic level voltages for gates are defined by the triggering threshold values which cause the gate outputs to change states. Gate triggering thresholds can be measured by varying the input voltage from 0 volts to the chip's supply voltage value and monitoring the gate output voltage for the specified V_{OLmax} and

107

V_{OHmin}. Use a DMM to measure V_I and V_O. Gate outputs will often oscillate when the input voltage is between V_{ILmax} and V_{IHmin}.

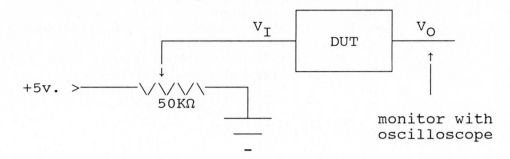

Fig. 19-4   Measuring input threshold voltages

Gate Transfer Characteristics

The transfer characteristic for a device is the relationship between its input and output signals. The transfer characteristic can be obtained graphically using an oscilloscope in the X-Y mode. A triangle (or sine) wave signal is used to sweep the device's input between the two extremes (ground and V_{CC}). The DUT input voltage signal is monitored on the X (horizontal) input and the DUT output voltage signal is monitored on the Y (vertical) input of the oscilloscope.

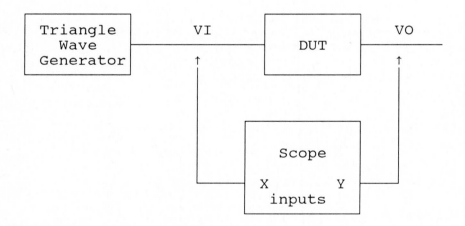

Fig. 19-5   Measuring device's transfer characteristic

108

19.1 Logic chip power requirements
Use a DMM to measure the average supply current for a typical TTL logic chip (such as a 74LS00) and a functionally equivalent CMOS chip (such as a 74HC00). Measure the supply current for the following gate input conditions: static inputs, 1KHz, and 1MHz square wave (TTL compatible) input signals.

19.2 Gate propagation delay times
Use an oscilloscope to measure the propagation delays for a typical TTL logic chip (such as a 74LS00) and a functionally equivalent CMOS chip (such as a 74HC00).

19.3 Gate output current capabilities
Use a DMM to measure the output current sourcing and sinking ability (I_{OH} and I_{OL}) for a typical TTL logic chip (such as a 74LS00) and a functionally equivalent CMOS chip (such as a 74HC00).

19.4 Gate input voltage levels
Use a DMM to measure the input voltage levels V_{IHmin} and V_{ILmax} for a typical TTL logic chip (such as a 74LS00) and a functionally equivalent CMOS chip (such as a 74HC00).

19.5 Schmitt trigger transfer characteristic
Use an oscilloscope (in X-Y mode) to obtain the transfer characteristic of one of the Schmitt trigger inverters in a 74LS14. Be sure to adjust the triangle or sine wave generator signal using the oscilloscope to $0 \leq V_i \leq +5v$ **before** applying it to the gate's input.

UNIT 20

DECODERS AND ENCODERS

Objectives

(1) To be able to design and implement circuits for various decoder applications.
(2) To be able to design and implement circuits for various encoder applications.

Tutorial

Decoder and Encoder Circuits

A decoder is used to detect a specific combination of bits applied to the input of the circuit and to display that information in a specified fashion. Logic gates can be used to design any type of decoder circuit. Some decoders are available as IC chips. Decoder/drivers can be used with various kinds of display devices such as 7-segment displays.

An encoder has several input lines, only one of which can be activated at a time (except for a priority type of encoder), and is used to convert that input into a representative binary coded output.

A 7-segment display device is commonly used to display the decimal characters 0-9. The display segments are often constructed using light emitting diodes in which the appropriate LED segments are forward-biased (and therefore emitting light) for the desired symbol shape. Decoder/driver circuits are used to control the LED biasing for the display of the appropriate characters. Series current limiting resistors are employed to protect the individual LED segments from damage caused by too much forward-biased diode current. The pin-out configuration for a common 7-segment display is illustrated in Fig. 20-1.

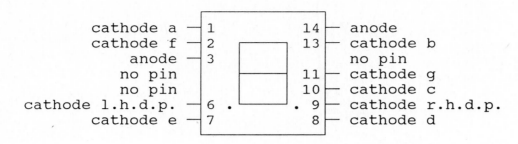

Fig. 20-1   MAN 72 (or equivalent) 7-segment common-anode display pin assignments (top view)

Standard BCD-to-7-segment decoder/driver chips are available to provide the necessary biasing signals for a 7-segment LED display device to produce the decimal characters of 0 through 9.   Since common-anode and common-cathode 7-segment devices are available, an appropriate decoder/driver chip must be selected to match the display type. The 74LS47 shown in Fig. 20-2 is designed to be used with a common-anode type device. Note that a series is needed for each segment of the display to limit the amount of LED current to a safe level.

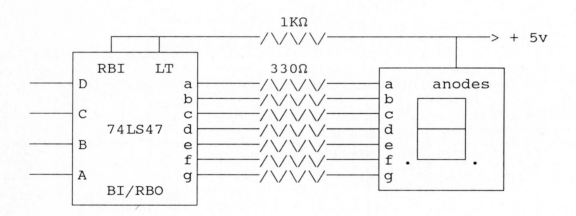

Fig. 20-2   Standard Decoder/Driver & Display Circuit

Laboratory Projects

Design decoder and encoder circuits for the following applications, test, and verify your designs.

20.1   Seven-segment character decoder
Design a decoder circuit using a GAL16V8A that can be used to produce the following display patterns on a 7-segment common-anode LED display. The inputs for the decoder and display circuit are ECBA. Remember to

112

UNIT 21

MULTIPLEXERS & DEMULTIPLEXERS

Objectives

(1) To be able to design circuits for the application of multiplexing data.
(2) To be able to design circuits for the application of demultiplexing data.

Tutorial

Multiplexers and Demultiplexers

A multiplexer (or data selector) is a logic circuit that accepts several data inputs, but allows only one of the data inputs to appear on the output. Select inputs are used to control which data input value will be routed to the output. Multiplexers may also be used to synthesize combinational logic functions.

A demultiplexer has several data output lines but only one data input line. The data is sent to a single output line determined by the specific select code applied to the demultiplexer. A decoder circuit can also function as a demultiplexer if the input lines (of the decoder) are used as select lines and if an enable (for the decoder) is used as the data input to the demultiplexer.

Implement and test the following circuit applications.

21.1   Multiplexed BCD display
Design a single-digit, 7-segment display multiplexer using a GAL16V8A
and a 74LS47 decoder/driver chip. Use logic switches for one BCD input
and the 74LS393 counter for the other BCD input to the MUX. Only one
of the two BCD (8421) numbers input to the multiplexer will be displayed
on the 7-segment display as indicated by the following function table. The
gating control G will produce an invalid BCD output from the MUX when
it is disabled. Hints: you will need to design a quad 2-line-to-1-line MUX
& the counter can be cleared (reset) on the state 1010 with a decoding gate
to produce a BCD output sequence from the counter.

```
G   S  |      MUX Output
1   0  |  SW3  SW2  SW1  SW0
1   1  |  QD   QC   QB   QA
0   X  |  1    1    1    1
```

21.2   Dual waveform pattern generator
Design a logic circuit using a 74LS151 one-of-eight multiplexer which will
output either of two possible recycling waveform patterns selected by F.
Use a 3-bit binary counter (74LS393) to sequence the multiplexer. View
the CLOCK and OUT waveforms with a dual trace oscilloscope. Hint: use
the 3-bit counter to select the appropriate data value to be output in the
sequence.

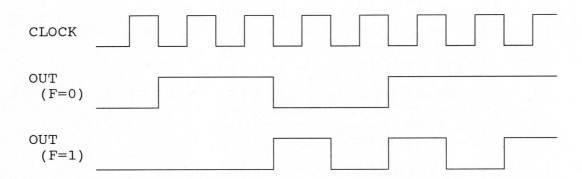

21.3   Variable frequency divider
Design a circuit that will select (multiplex) a specified frequency to be output. A 200 KHz clock signal will be divided into a number of different frequencies by a 74LS393 counter chip. The desired frequency will be selected by a 74LS151 one-of-eight multiplexer as indicated in the following function table. The frequency selection is determined by the state of S_2 S_1 S_0. The various frequencies are produced by the 74LS393 connected as shown in Fig. 21-1. Use a frequency counter to measure the signal frequency output by the multiplexer.

S_2 S_1 S_0	output frequency (Hz)
0 0 0	0
0 0 1	1.25K
0 1 0	2.5K
0 1 1	5.0K
1 0 0	10.0K
1 0 1	20.0K
1 1 0	100K
1 1 1	200K

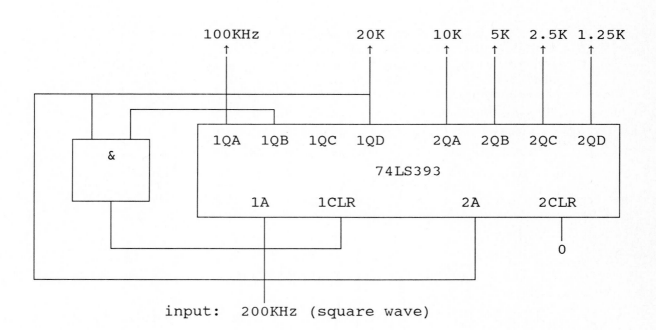

Fig. 21-1 Frequency division using a counter chip

21.4   Prime number detector using a MUX
Implement a logic function generator using the 74150 multiplexer chip that will detect 5-bit prime numbers. The output should be high only if a prime number (1, 2, 3, 5, 7, 11, 13, 17, 19, 23, 29, or 31) is input to the detector. Hint: with 5 input bits to the detector and only 4 select lines on the MUX, some of the data inputs to the MUX can be variable instead of fixed and dependent upon the fifth bit.

21.5   Output line selection using a DMUX
Use the 74LS138 as a demultiplexer to drive any one of 4 possible lamps by a 1 Hz (approximate) clock signal. The specific lamp to receive the clock input will be selected by the control signals M and N. The selected output should be high when the clock input is high. Use the 74LS393 counter to automatically sequence the DMUX circuit by driving M with QD and N with QC. How many times does each lamp flash in turn with the counter controlling the sequence?

M	N	Lamp 1	Lamp 2	Lamp 3	Lamp 4
0	0	flashing	off	off	off
0	1	off	flashing	off	off
1	0	off	off	flashing	off
1	1	off	off	off	flashing

21.6   4-bit demultiplexer
Design and construct a 4-bit demultiplexer using a PLD so that the 4-bit input data (I3 I2 I1 I0) can be sent to one of 2 sets of lights controlled by the select input S. Also include a gating control G on the demultiplexer circuit as indicated in the following function table.

G	S	A3	A2	A1	A0	B3	B2	B1	B0
0	0	I3	I2	I1	I0	0	0	0	0
0	1	0	0	0	0	I3	I2	I1	I0
1	X	0	0	0	0	0	0	0	0

/////// LIGHTS \\\\\\\\

UNIT 22

COMPARATOR CIRCUITS

Objectives ==

    (1)   To be able to design and implement comparator circuits using logic gates.
    (2)   To be able to design and implement various circuit applications using comparator chips.

Tutorial ==

Comparators

Magnitude comparators are used to determine the magnitude relationships between two quantities. A typical comparator will indicate whether two input values are equivalent or, if not, which of the values is larger. Logic gates can be used to implement various types of comparator circuits or 4-bit comparator chips such as the 74LS85 can be easily used in a variety of magnitude comparator applications.

**Laboratory
Projects** ==

Design logic circuits to implement each of the following comparator applications. Test and verify your designs.

    22.1   Equal to or less than 9 comparator
            Design a comparator circuit in which the single output will be high if the 4-bit data input value produced by a 74LS393 binary counter (QD QC QB

QA) is equal to or less than 9. Use the 74LS85 comparator chip and any additional necessary gates. Display the counter and comparator outputs on lamps.

22.2　Data biasing circuit
Design a logic circuit to bias a 4-bit input value (I3 I2 I1 I0) to produce the 4-bit output (R3 R2 R1 R0) according to the following relationship. Use the 74LS85 and 74LS83 chips.

IF	THEN		WHERE
I < 9	R = I + 1		I = I3 I2 I1 I0
I = 9	R = I		R = R3 R2 R1 R0
I > 9	R = I - 1		

22.3　Programmable comparator
Design a comparator circuit that can compare a 4-bit data input value (I3 I2 I1 I0) with any one of 4 possible constants as indicated by the following table. R and S are control signals that determine which constant is selected for the B input to the comparator. Your circuit should provide the 4 output signals listed below. Use the 74LS85 comparator and any additional necessary gates.

controls		constants			
R	S	B3	B2	B1	B0
0	0	0	1	1	1
0	1	1	0	0	1
1	0	1	0	1	0
1	1	1	1	0	0

output signals needed:
```
EQ = equal
NE = not equal
GE = greater than or equal
LE = less than or equal
```

22.4　Adjustable window comparator (range detector)
Design a logic circuit using a GAL16V8A that will compare a 4-bit input value to one of two specified 4-bit input ranges selected by the control R. The comparator should have three outputs to indicate that the input value is either less than (LTR) or greater than (GTR) the range of values in the current window or within the range (RNG) of window values.

R	Selected range of window values:
0	5 thru 7
1	8 thru 10

22.5   Number selector
Design a logic circuit which will output a specified larger or smaller value
from two 4-bit inputs. Use a 74LS85 comparator chip to determine which
4-bit input is larger (or smaller) and a GAL16V8A to select the specified
value. The PLD will function as a multiplexer with a more complex select
control. A signal (F) will control the selection of the larger or smaller value
as indicated in the following function table.

F	Selector output
0	smaller value of A or B
1	larger value of A or B

note: when A=B, select either A or B
        A = A3 A2 A1 A0
        B = B3 B2 B1 B0

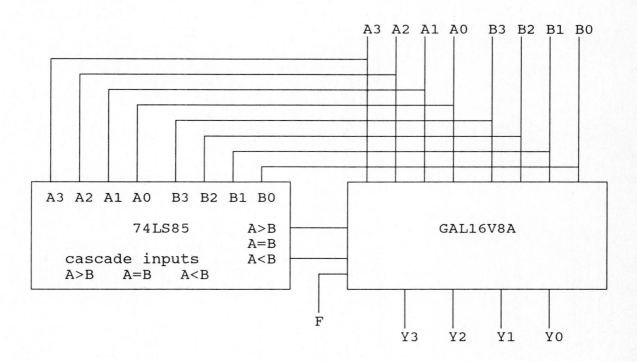

Hint:

F	A>B	A<B	Y	
0	0	0	X	(A=B, select either)
0	0	1	A	(select A input)
0	1	0	B	(select B input)
0	1	1	X	(impossible)
1	0	0	X	(A=B, select either)
1	0	1	B	(select B input)
1	1	0	A	(select A input)
1	1	1	X	(impossible)

X means we "don't care" which value (A or B) is output

121

UNIT 23

CODE CONVERTERS

Objective ══════════════════════════════════════

(1) To be able to design and implement a general interface circuit that must convert from one code (the output code) to another (the necessary input code for another circuit).

Tutorial ══════════════════════════════════════

General Interface Design and Code Conversion Circuits

Two systems which represent information with different coding techniques can be connected together by designing the necessary interface circuit between them. Common MSI functional blocks can sometimes be used to interconnect the systems and provide the necessary code conversion between them. Additionally, special purpose logic chips have been designed to perform some of the more common code conversion tasks. Many interfacing tasks require custom designed logic circuits to perform the necessary code conversions. In designing interface circuits for some applications, there may be input combinations that are not defined. If so, a simpler circuit design may be realized by using "don't care" mapping techniques.

Design the following interface circuits. Test and verify your designs.

23.1 Excess-3/8421 BCD code converter
Design a code converter circuit using a 74LS83 and any additional necessary logic gates that will either convert an excess-3 coded input value to an equivalent 8421 BCD coded output or an 8421 BCD coded input value to an equivalent excess-3 coded output. The conversion function will be controlled by F. The circuit should also have an enable control E as shown in the following function table.

```
E   F  | Function
0   0  | 8421 to X-3
0   1  | X-3 to 8421
1   X  | disabled (data outputs are all high)
```

23.2 4-bit binary-to-BCD converter
Design a binary-to-BCD (8421) converter using the 74LS83 4-bit adder, a 74LS47 decoder/driver and 7-segment display, and any additional necessary logic devices. The circuit should accept a 4-bit binary input from the 74LS393 counter (representing decimal 0 through 15) and output the 2 digits (usually called 1 1/2 digits since the tens digit can only be either a 0 or a 1) of information on the display. Use the 7-segment display for the ones digit and a single LED for the tens digit (representing either a 0 or a 1 in the tens position). Hint: the circuit needs to identify inputs that are over 9 and then correct those inputs by adding 6.

23.3 BCD-to-binary converter
Implement a 6-bit BCD-to-binary converter using the 74184 converter chip. Note that the 74184 is an **open-collector** device, and therefore, you will need to use **pull-up resistors** on the outputs that are used. You only need to test selected BCD inputs to the converter to represent each of the 4 possible decade inputs.

23.4 2421-to-5421 BCD code converter
Design and construct a 2421-BCD-to-5421-BCD code converter using a GAL16V8A. Hint: use "don't care" states in the Karnaugh mapping to simplify your design as much as possible.

2	4	2	1	5	4	2	1
D	C	B	A	W	X	Y	Z
0	0	0	0	0	0	0	0
0	0	0	1	0	0	0	1
0	0	1	0	0	0	1	0
0	0	1	1	0	0	1	1
0	1	0	0	0	1	0	0
1	0	1	1	1	0	0	0
1	1	0	0	1	0	0	1
1	1	0	1	1	0	1	0
1	1	1	0	1	0	1	1
1	1	1	1	1	1	0	0

23.5 5-bit binary-to-BCD converter
Design and construct a PLD circuit that will convert a 5-bit binary number input into the equivalent Binary Coded Decimal representation. Display the BCD output on a 7-segment display using a 74LS47 (ones digit) and 2 LEDs (tens digit).

23.6 Binary-to-BCD converter simulation
Use P/C-SILOS to simulate the PLD circuit design for the 5-bit binary-to-BCD converter in Project 23.5.

UNIT 24

DIGITAL/ANALOG AND ANALOG/ DIGITAL CONVERSION

Objectives

(1) To be able to construct a digital-to-analog conversion circuit using a commercial DAC IC chip.
(2) To be able to construct an analog-to-digital conversion circuit using a commercial ADC IC chip.

Tutorial

Digital to Analog Conversion

Digital system outputs often must be interfaced to analog devices. One type of interfacing involves converting a digital data word into a representative analog signal (either a current or a voltage). Various digital to analog converter chips are available to perform this type of conversion. An example of a complete D/A converter in a single IC chip is the AD557 manufactured by Analog Devices. This 8-bit D/A converter is powered by a single 5 volt power supply and has a full-scale output of 2.55 volts. The resolution or incremental analog step size of the DAC is dependent upon the number of digital input bits. The output voltage step size for this device is 10 mv. Fig. 24-1 shows how to use the AD557 to produce an analog output from 0 to 2.55 volts.

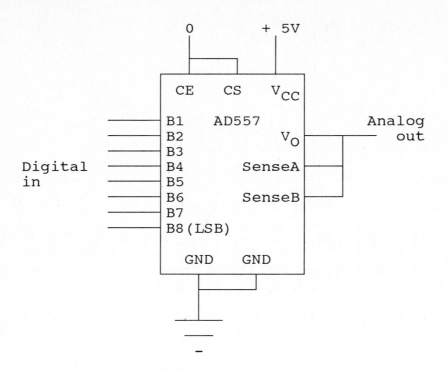

Fig. 24-1 Digital to analog conversion IC

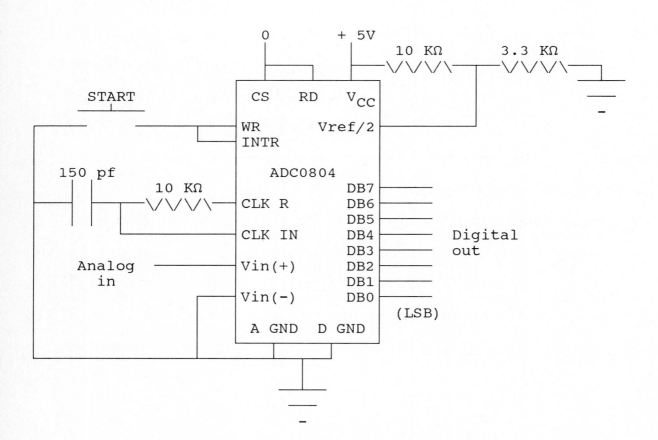

Fig. 24-2 Analog to digital conversion IC

Analog to Digital Conversion

For a digital system to be able to process analog information, the analog signal must first be digitized or converted from analog to digital. The analog input signal is then represented by a digital value in the digital system. There are various analog to digital converter chips available to perform this type of conversion. The ADC0804 manufactured by National Semiconductor is an example of an 8-bit successive approximation converter contained in a single IC chip. This device will handle an analog input range from 0 to 5 volts and is powered by a single 5 volt power supply. The quantization error of an ADC is dependent upon the number of digital output bits. With a resolution of 8 bits, the ADC0804 will have a quantization error of approximately 20 mv. Fig. 24-2 shows how to connect the ADC0804 in a self-clocking, free-running mode.

Laboratory Projects

24.1 Digital to analog converter
Construct and test a D/A converter using an Analog Devices AD557 IC chip.

24.2 Analog to digital converter
Construct and test an A/D converter using a National ADC0804 IC chip.

24.3 Reconstructing a digitized signal
Use the A/D converter to digitize a sine wave input signal and then reconvert the representative digital signal into an analog signal. Connect the D/A converter to the output of the A/D converter as shown in the diagram below. Adjust the input sine wave to 5 V_{p-p} with a DC offset of 2.5 volts. Use an oscilloscope to compare the analog input and output waveforms. Change the input signal frequency to a very low value and note the resultant output signal. Increase the input signal frequency and note the effect on the resultant output signal.

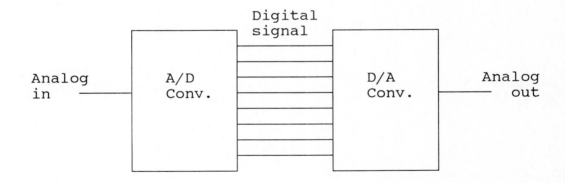

UNIT 25

MEMORY SYSTEMS

Objectives ================================

(1) To be able to connect a semiconductor RAM chip for reading and writing data.
(2) To be able to combine RAM chips to expand word size and/or memory capacity.

Tutorial ================================

Memory Devices and Systems

Memory devices are used in digital systems to store digital information. A specific storage location in memory is identified with a unique binary value called an address. Accessing data stored at a specified address is referred to as a read operation. Storing new data at a specified address is referred to as a write operation.

Random Access Memory (RAM) is the term used frequently for memory which can be read from or written into with equal ease. Ordinary semiconductor RAM devices are said to be volatile because the information stored in the device is lost if the electrical power for the memory is removed. Semiconductor RAM may be either static, which does not need the stored data to be periodically refreshed, or dynamic which does require the data to be periodically rewritten into the memory cells. Static RAM memory chips have the following types of pins: address pins that are used to select a specific memory location, data pins that are used to input the data into or output the data from the addressed memory location, a chip select pin to enable a specific chip (or set of chips) in a memory system, and a

131

Read/Write pin to control the chip's read or write function (read = 1 and write = 0). The block diagram for a static RAM chip containing 1024 4-bit words is shown in Fig. 25-1.

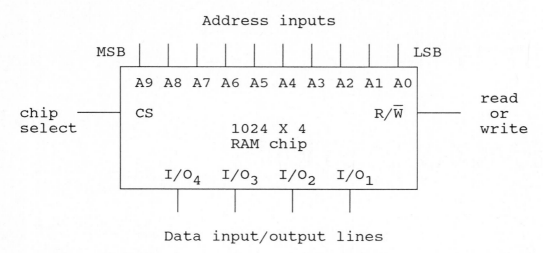

Fig. 25-1 Block diagram for a typical static RAM chip

Read Only Memory (ROM) often refers to a broad category of memory devices that normally have their data permanently stored in them while they are used in a digital system. There are various subtypes of ROM devices, some of which can have the stored data erased and replaced with new information.

Various memory devices (part numbers) are available which differ in word size and memory capacity. The memory chip's word size is the number of bits which are accessed simultaneously in the chip with a given address. The memory capacity for a chip is the total number of words (2^n where n = number of address bits) which can be addressed on the chip. Several memory chips can be interconnected to expand the total system memory. This expansion can be in word size (see Fig. 25-2), total number of addressable words (see Fig. 25-3), or both.

Tri-State Bus Drivers

In addition to high and low output levels, a tri-state output device also has a high impedance output condition. This type of output structure is normally used to connect several possible sources of digital information to a common bus such as a data bus in a memory system. Only one source of information will be enabled at a time and allowed to place data on the bus. Most memory chips today have built-in tri-state buffers for the data pins which are enabled when the chip is selected and a read operation is performed. The source of data for a write operation must also be tri-stated from the data bus when a write operation is not being performed. Separate tri-state buffer or bus driver chips are available to accomplish this task.

132

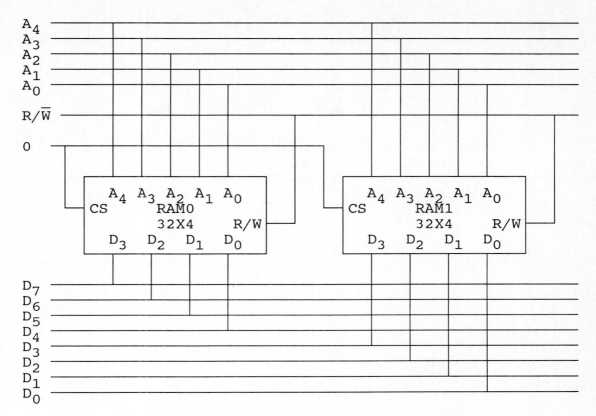

Fig. 25-2 Expanding memory word size to 8-bits

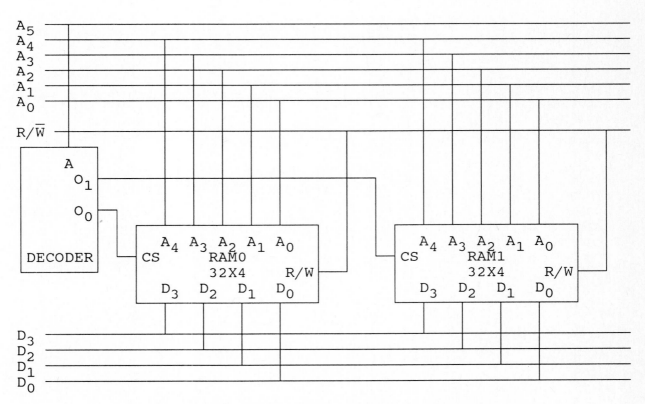

Fig. 25-3 Expanding memory capacity to 64 words

133

25.1 RAM memory chip
Test a 2114 (1024X4) memory chip by writing 4-bit data words to some selected memory locations and then verifying the data storage by reading the same selected addresses. Use a 74LS244 as the data bus buffer (enabled only during a write operation) for a set of 4 logic switches that provide the data to be stored. Use a manually clocked 74LS393 counter (with the two 4-bit counters cascaded together) connected to A_0 through A_7 to provide the address bus information. Connect the remaining two address pins (A8 and A9) to ground so that only one-fourth of the 2114 is being used. Monitor the data and address buses with LEDs.

25.2 Memory word-size expansion
Use two 2114 chips to design a 1024X8 memory system. Construct and test your design.

25.3 Memory capacity expansion
Use two 2114 chips to design a 2048X4 memory system. Construct and test your design.

APPENDIX A

LOGIC CIRCUIT TESTER

An inexpensive digital testing system having many of the capabilities of a commercially available system can be constructed with parts listed in the equipment list. The basic logic circuit tester described here may be either temporarily breadboarded as needed or mounted more permanently on some type of circuit board.

Lamp Monitor

A Light Emitting Diode (LED) can be easily used as a lamp monitor for digital signals. A driver circuit (see Fig. A-1) using an inverter from a 74LS04 can be used to turn on the LED without loading down the monitored gate's output.

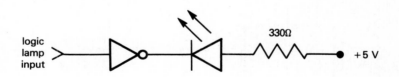

Fig. A-1   LED lamp monitor circuit

Logic Switches

A SPST toggle switch can be conveniently used for logic inputs in digital circuit testing. Fig. A-2 shows how to wire a simple logic switch.

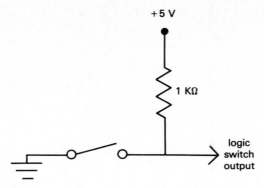

Fig. A-2   Logic switch circuit

Pushbutton

A pushbutton can be easily debounced, thereby making it suitable for use in digital circuits, using a simple NAND latch as shown in Fig. A-3.

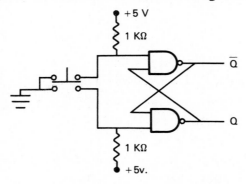

Fig. A-3   Debounced pushbutton circuit

Clock

A 555 timer chip can be conveniently used to produce a TTL compatible square wave for clocking digital circuits. The frequency may be varied by changing the timing components R_A, R_B, and C. Fig. A-4 shows the clock circuit schematic and equations for determining the output frequency.

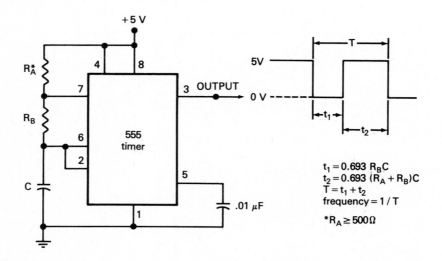

$t_1 = 0.693\ R_B C$
$t_2 = 0.693\ (R_A + R_B)C$
$T = t_1 + t_2$
frequency $= 1 / T$

$^*R_A \geq 500\ \Omega$

Fig. A-4   Clock circuit using a 555 timer

136

APPENDIX B

MANUFACTURERS' DATA SHEETS

- Package Options Include Plastic ''Small Outline'' Packages, Ceramic Chip Carriers and Flat Packages, and Plastic and Ceramic DIPs

- Dependable Texas Instruments Quality and Reliability

description

These devices contain four independent 2-input-NAND gates.

The SN5400, SN54LS00, and SN54S00 are characterized for operation over the full military temperature range of −55 °C to 125 °C. The SN7400, SN74LS00, and SN74S00 are characterized for operation from 0 °C to 70 °C.

FUNCTION TABLE (each gate)

INPUTS		OUTPUT
A	B	Y
H	H	L
L	X	H
X	L	H

logic symbol†

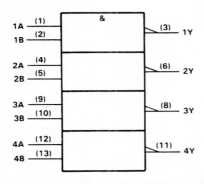

†This symbol is in accordance with ANSI/IEEE Std. 91-1984 and IEC Publication 617-12.
Pin numbers shown are for D, J, and N packages.

SN5400 . . . J PACKAGE
SN54LS00, SN54S00 . . . J OR W PACKAGE
SN7400 . . . N PACKAGE
SN74LS00, SN74S00 . . . D OR N PACKAGE
(TOP VIEW)

```
1A  [1    14]  Vcc
1B  [2    13]  4B
1Y  [3    12]  4A
2A  [4    11]  4Y
2B  [5    10]  3B
2Y  [6     9]  3A
GND [7     8]  3Y
```

SN5400 . . . W PACKAGE
(TOP VIEW)

```
1A  [1    14]  4Y
1B  [2    13]  4B
1Y  [3    12]  4A
Vcc [4    11]  GND
2Y  [5    10]  3B
2A  [6     9]  3A
2B  [7     8]  3Y
```

SN54LS00, SN54S00 . . . FK PACKAGE
(TOP VIEW)

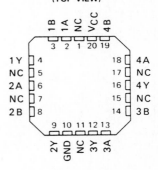

NC - No internal connection

logic diagram (positive logic)

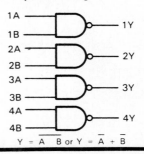

TEXAS
INSTRUMENTS

POST OFFICE BOX 655012 • DALLAS, TEXAS 75265

2

TTL Devices

2-3

SN5400, SN54LS00, SN54S00,
SN7400, SN74LS00, SN74S00
QUADRUPLE 2-INPUT POSITIVE-NAND GATES

schematics (each gate)

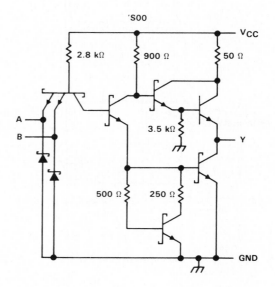

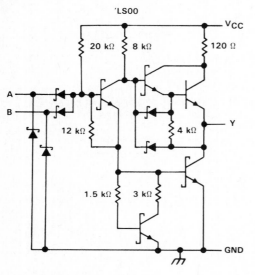

Resistor values shown are nominal.

absolute maximum ratings over operating free-air temperature range (unless otherwise noted)

Supply voltage, V_{CC} (see Note 1) . . . . 7 V
Input voltage: '00, 'S00 . . . . 5.5 V
               'LS00 . . . . 7 V
Operating free-air temperature range: SN54' . . . . −55°C to 125°C
                                  SN74' . . . . 0°C to 70°C
Storage temperature range . . . . −65°C to 150°C

NOTE 1: Voltage values are with respect to network ground terminal.

TEXAS
INSTRUMENTS

POST OFFICE BOX 655012 • DALLAS, TEXAS 75265

recommended operating conditions

		SN5400			SN7400			UNIT
		MIN	NOM	MAX	MIN	NOM	MAX	
V_{CC}	Supply voltage	4.5	5	5.5	4.75	5	5.25	V
V_{IH}	High-level input voltage	2			2			V
V_{IL}	Low-level input voltage			0.8			0.8	V
I_{OH}	High-level output current			−0.4			−0.4	mA
I_{OL}	Low-level output current			16			16	mA
T_A	Operating free-air temperature	−55		125	0		70	°C

electrical characteristics over recommended operating free-air temperature range (unless otherwise noted)

PARAMETER	TEST CONDITIONS†			SN5400			SN7400			UNIT
			MIN	TYP‡	MAX	MIN	TYP‡	MAX		
V_{IK}	V_{CC} = MIN,	I_I = −12 mA			−1.5			−1.5		V
V_{OH}	V_{CC} = MIN,	V_{IL} = 0.8 V, I_{OH} = −0.4 mA	2.4	3.4		2.4	3.4			V
V_{OL}	V_{CC} = MIN,	V_{IH} = 2 V, I_{OL} = 16 mA		0.2	0.4		0.2	0.4		V
I_I	V_{CC} = MAX,	V_I = 5.5 V			1			1		mA
I_{IH}	V_{CC} = MAX,	V_I = 2.4 V			40			40		µA
I_{IL}	V_{CC} = MAX,	V_I = 0.4 V			−1.6			−1.6		mA
I_{OS}§	V_{CC} = MAX		−20		−55	−18		−55		mA
I_{CCH}	V_{CC} = MAX,	V_I = 0 V		4	8		4	8		mA
I_{CCL}	V_{CC} = MAX,	V_I = 4.5 V		12	22		12	22		mA

† For conditions shown as MIN or MAX, use the appropriate value specified under recommended operating conditions.
‡ All typical values are at V_{CC} = 5 V, T_A = 25°C.
§ Not more than one output should be shorted at a time.

switching characteristics, V_{CC} = 5 V, T_A = 25°C (see note 2)

PARAMETER	FROM (INPUT)	TO (OUTPUT)	TEST CONDITIONS	MIN	TYP	MAX	UNIT
t_{PLH}	A or B	Y	R_L = 400 Ω, C_L = 15 pF		11	22	ns
t_{PHL}					7	15	ns

NOTE 2: Load circuits and voltage waveforms are shown in Section 1.

recommended operating conditions

		SN54LS00			SN74LS00			UNIT
		MIN	NOM	MAX	MIN	NOM	MAX	
V_{CC}	Supply voltage	4.5	5	5.5	4.75	5	5.25	V
V_{IH}	High-level input voltage	2			2			V
V_{IL}	Low-level input voltage			0.7			0.8	V
I_{OH}	High-level output current			−0.4			−0.4	mA
I_{OL}	Low-level output current			4			8	mA
T_A	Operating free-air temperature	−55		125	0		70	°C

electrical characteristics over recommended operating free-air temperature range (unless otherwise noted)

PARAMETER	TEST CONDITIONS †			SN54LS00			SN74LS00			UNIT
			MIN	TYP‡	MAX	MIN	TYP‡	MAX		
V_{IK}	V_{CC} = MIN,	I_I = −18 mA			−1.5			−1.5		V
V_{OH}	V_{CC} = MIN,	V_{IL} = MAX, I_{OH} = −0.4 mA	2.5	3.4		2.7	3.4			V
V_{OL}	V_{CC} = MIN,	V_{IH} = 2 V, I_{OL} = 4 mA		0.25	0.4		0.25	0.4		V
	V_{CC} = MIN,	V_{IH} = 2 V, I_{OL} = 8 mA					0.35	0.5		
I_I	V_{CC} = MAX,	V_I = 7 V			0.1			0.1		mA
I_{IH}	V_{CC} = MAX,	V_I = 2.7 V			20			20		µA
I_{IL}	V_{CC} = MAX,	V_I = 0.4 V			−0.4			−0.4		mA
I_{OS} §	V_{CC} = MAX,		−20		−100	−20		−100		mA
I_{CCH}	V_{CC} = MAX,	V_I = 0 V		0.8	1.6		0.8	1.6		mA
I_{CCL}	V_{CC} = MAX,	V_I = 4.5 V		2.4	4.4		2.4	4.4		mA

† For conditions shown as MIN or MAX, use the appropriate value specified under recommended operating conditions.
‡ All typical values are at V_{CC} = 5 V, T_A = 25°C
§ Not more than one output should be shorted at a time, and the duration of the short-circuit should not exceed one second.

switching characteristics, V_{CC} = 5 V, T_A = 25°C (see note 2)

PARAMETER	FROM (INPUT)	TO (OUTPUT)	TEST CONDITIONS		MIN	TYP	MAX	UNIT
t_{PLH}	A or B	Y	R_L = 2 kΩ,	C_L = 15 pF		9	15	ns
t_{PHL}						10	15	ns

NOTE 2: Load circuits and voltage waveforms are shown in Section 1.

TEXAS
INSTRUMENTS
POST OFFICE BOX 655012 • DALLAS, TEXAS 75265

SN54HC00, SN74HC00
QUADRUPLE 2-INPUT POSITIVE-NAND GATES

D2684, DECEMBER 1982 – REVISED MARCH 1984

- **Package Options Include Plastic ''Small Outline'' Packages, Ceramic Chip Carriers, and Standard Plastic and Ceramic 300-mil DIPs**

- **Dependable Texas Instruments Quality and Reliability**

2

HCMOS Devices

description

These devices contain four independent 2-input NAND gates. They perform the Boolean functions $Y = \overline{A \cdot B}$ or $Y = \overline{A} + \overline{B}$ in positive logic.

The SN54HC00 is characterized for operation over the full military temperature range of $-55\,°C$ to $125\,°C$. The SN74HC00 is characterized for operation from $-40\,°C$ to $85\,°C$.

FUNCTION TABLE (each gate)

INPUTS		OUTPUT
A	**B**	**Y**
H	H	L
L	X	H
X	L	H

SN54HC00 . . . J PACKAGE
SN74HC00 . . . D OR N PACKAGE
(TOP VIEW)

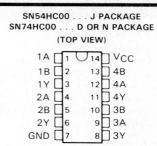

SN54HC00 . . . FK PACKAGE
(TOP VIEW)

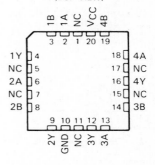

NC – No internal connection

logic symbol†

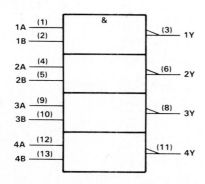

† This symbol is in accordance with ANSI/IEEE Std 91-1984 and IEC Publication 617-12.
Pin numbers shown are for D, J, or N packages.

logic diagram (each gate)

TEXAS INSTRUMENTS

POST OFFICE BOX 655012 • DALLAS, TEXAS 75265

SN54HC00, SN74HC00
QUADRUPLE 2-INPUT POSITIVE-NAND GATES

absolute maximum ratings over operating free-air temperature range[†]

Supply voltage, V_{CC}	−0.5 V to 7 V
Input clamp current, I_{IK} (V_I < 0 or V_I > V_{CC})	±20 mA
Output clamp current, I_{OK} (V_O < 0 or V_O > V_{CC})	±20 mA
Continuous output current, I_O (V_O = 0 to V_{CC})	±25 mA
Continuous current through V_{CC} or GND pins	±50 mA
Lead temperature 1,6 mm (1/16 in) from case for 60 s: FK or J package	300 °C
Lead temperature 1,6 mm (1/16 in) from case for 10 s: D or N package	260 °C
Storage temperature range	−65 °C to 150 °C

[†] Stresses beyond those listed under "absolute maximum ratings" may cause permanent damage to the device. These are stress ratings only, and functional operation of the device at these or any other conditions beyond those indicated under "recommended operating conditions" is not implied. Exposure to absolute-maximum-rated conditions for extended periods may affect device reliability.

recommended operating conditions

			SN54HC00			SN74HC00			UNIT
			MIN	NOM	MAX	MIN	NOM	MAX	
V_{CC}	Supply voltage		2	5	6	2	5	6	V
V_{IH}	High-level input voltage	V_{CC} = 2 V	1.5			1.5			V
		V_{CC} = 4.5 V	3.15			3.15			
		V_{CC} = 6 V	4.2			4.2			
V_{IL}	Low-level input voltage	V_{CC} = 2 V	0		0.3	0		0.3	V
		V_{CC} = 4.5 V	0		0.9	0		0.9	
		V_{CC} = 6 V	0		1.2	0		1.2	
V_I	Input voltage		0		V_{CC}	0		V_{CC}	V
V_O	Output voltage		0		V_{CC}	0		V_{CC}	V
t_t	Input transition (rise and fall) times	V_{CC} = 2 V	0		1000	0		1000	ns
		V_{CC} = 4.5 V	0		500	0		500	
		V_{CC} = 6 V	0		400	0		400	
T_A	Operating free-air temperature		−55		125	−40		85	°C

electrical characteristics over recommended operating free-air temperature range (unless otherwise noted)

PARAMETER	TEST CONDITIONS	V_{CC}	T_A = 25°C			SN54HC00		SN74HC00		UNIT
			MIN	TYP	MAX	MIN	MAX	MIN	MAX	
V_{OH}	V_I = V_{IH} or V_{IL}, I_{OH} = −20 μA	2 V	1.9	1.998		1.9		1.9		V
		4.5 V	4.4	4.499		4.4		4.4		
		6 V	5.9	5.999		5.9		5.9		
	V_I = V_{IH} or V_{IL}, I_{OH} = −4 mA	4.5 V	3.98	4.30		3.7		3.84		
	V_I = V_{IH} or V_{IL}, I_{OH} = −5.2 mA	6 V	5.48	5.80		5.2		5.34		
V_{OL}	V_I = V_{IH} or V_{IL}, I_{OL} = 20 μA	2 V		0.002	0.1		0.1		0.1	V
		4.5 V		0.001	0.1		0.1		0.1	
		6 V		0.001	0.1		0.1		0.1	
	V_I = V_{IH} or V_{IL}, I_{OL} = 4 mA	4.5 V		0.17	0.26		0.4		0.33	
	V_I = V_{IH} or V_{IL}, I_{OL} = 5.2 mA	6 V		0.15	0.26		0.4		0.33	
I_I	V_I = V_{CC} or 0	6 V		±0.1	±100		±1000		±1000	nA
I_{CC}	V_I = V_{CC} or 0, I_O = 0	6 V			2		40		20	μA
C_i		2 to 6 V		3	10		10		10	pF

switching characteristics over recommended operating free-air temperature range (unless otherwise noted), C_L = 50 pF (see Note 1)

PARAMETER	FROM (INPUT)	TO (OUTPUT)	V_{CC}	T_A = 25°C			SN54HC00		SN74HC00		UNIT
				MIN	TYP	MAX	MIN	MAX	MIN	MAX	
t_{pd}	A or B	Y	2 V		45	90		135		115	ns
			4.5 V		9	18		27		23	
			6 V		8	15		23		20	
t_t		Y	2 V		38	75		110		95	ns
			4.5 V		8	15		22		19	
			6 V		6	13		19		16	

C_{pd}	Power dissipation capacitance per gate	No load, T_A = 25°C	20 pF typ

NOTE 1: Load circuit and voltage waveforms are shown in Section 1.

2

HCMOS Devices

SN5402, SN54LS02, SN54S02, SN7402, SN74LS02, SN74S02
QUADRUPLE 2-INPUT POSITIVE-NOR GATES

DECEMBER 1983—REVISED MARCH 1988

- ● Package Options Include Plastic ''Small Outline'' Packages, Ceramic Chip Carriers and Flat Packages, and Plastic and Ceramic DIPs

- ● Dependable Texas Instruments Quality and Reliability

description

These devices contain four independent 2-input-NOR gates.

The SN5402, SN54LS02, and SN54S02 are characterized for operation over the full military temperature range of −55°C to 125°C. The SN7402, SN74LS02, and SN74S02 are characterized for operation from 0°C to 70°C.

FUNCTION TABLE (each gate)

INPUTS		OUTPUT
A	B	Y
H	X	L
X	H	L
L	L	H

logic symbol[†]

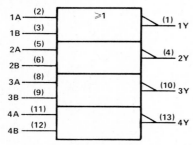

[†]This symbol is in accordance with ANSI/IEEE Std. 91-1984 and IEC Publication 617-12.
Pin numbers shown are for D, J, and N packages.

logic diagram (positive logic)

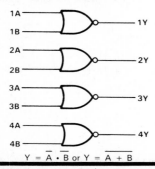

$$Y = \overline{A} \cdot \overline{B} \text{ or } Y = \overline{A + B}$$

SN5402 . . . J PACKAGE
SN54LS02, SN54S02 . . . J OR W PACKAGE
SN7402 . . . N PACKAGE
SN74LS02, SN74S02 . . . D OR N PACKAGE
(TOP VIEW)

```
      ___ ___
1Y  [1    14] V_CC
1A  [2    13] 4Y
1B  [3    12] 4B
2Y  [4    11] 4A
2A  [5    10] 3Y
2B  [6     9] 3B
GND [7     8] 3A
```

SN5402 . . . W PACKAGE
(TOP VIEW)

```
      ___ ___
1A  [1    14] 4Y
1B  [2    13] 4B
1Y  [3    12] 4A
V_CC[4    11] GND
2Y  [5    10] 3B
2A  [6     9] 3A
2B  [7     8] 3Y
```

SN54LS02, SN54S02 . . . FK PACKAGE
(TOP VIEW)

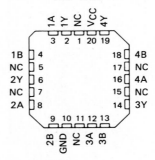

NC – No internal connection

TEXAS
INSTRUMENTS

POST OFFICE BOX 655012 • DALLAS, TEXAS 75265

2

TTL Devices

SN5402, SN54LS02, SN54S02, SN7402, SN74LS02, SN74S02
QUADRUPLE 2-INPUT POSITIVE-NOR GATES

schematics (each gate)

'02

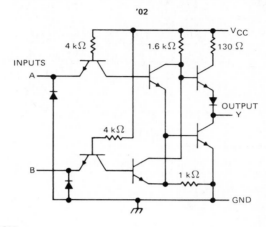

'LS02

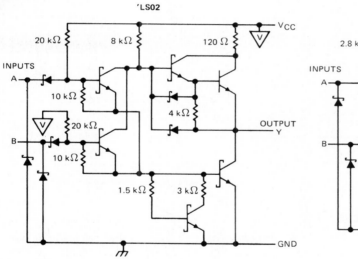

'S02

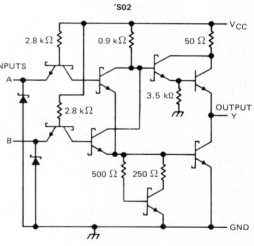

Resistor values shown are nominal.

absolute maximum ratings over operating free-air temperature range (unless otherwise noted)

Supply voltage, V_{CC} (see Note 1) . . . . 7 V
Input voltage: '02, 'S02 . . . . 5.5 V
               'LS02 . . . . 7 V
Off-state output voltage . . . . 7 V
Operating free-air temperature range: SN54' . . . . −55°C to 125°C
                             SN74' . . . . 0°C to 70°C
Storage temperature range . . . . −65°C to 150°C

NOTE 1. Voltage values are with respect to network ground terminal.

2

TTL Devices

TEXAS INSTRUMENTS
POST OFFICE BOX 655012 • DALLAS, TEXAS 75265

recommended operating conditions

		SN54LS02			SN74LS02			UNIT
		MIN	NOM	MAX	MIN	NOM	MAX	
V_{CC}	Supply voltage	4.5	5	5.5	4.75	5	5.25	V
V_{IH}	High-level input voltage	2			2			V
V_{IL}	Low-level input voltage			0.7			0.8	V
I_{OH}	High-level output current			−0.4			−0.4	mA
I_{OL}	Low-level output current			4			8	mA
T_A	Operating free-air temperature	−55		125	0		70	°C

electrical characteristics over recommended operating free-air temperature range (unless otherwise noted)

PARAMETER	TEST CONDITIONS †		SN54LS02			SN74LS02			UNIT
			MIN	TYP‡	MAX	MIN	TYP‡	MAX	
V_{IK}	V_{CC} = MIN,	I_I = −18 mA			−1.5			−1.5	V
V_{OH}	V_{CC} = MIN,	V_{IL} = MAX, I_{OH} = −0.4 mA	2.5	3.4		2.7	3.4		V
V_{OL}	V_{CC} = MIN,	V_{IH} = 2 V, I_{OL} = 4 mA		0.25	0.4		0.25	0.4	V
	V_{CC} = MIN,	V_{IH} = 2 V, I_{OL} = 8 mA					0.35	0.5	
I_I	V_{CC} = MAX,	V_I = 7 V			0.1			0.1	mA
I_{IH}	V_{CC} = MAX,	V_I = 2.7 V			20			20	µA
I_{IL}	V_{CC} = MAX,	V_I = 0.4 V			−0.4			−0.4	mA
I_{OS}§	V_{CC} = MAX		−20		−100	−20		−100	mA
I_{CCH}	V_{CC} = MAX,	V_I = 0 V		1.6	3.2		1.6	3.2	mA
I_{CCL}	V_{CC} = MAX,	See Note 2		2.8	5.4		2.8	5.4	mA

† For conditions shown as MIN or MAX, use the appropriate value specified under recommended operating conditions.
‡ All typical values are at V_{CC} = 5 V, T_A = 25°C
§ Not more than one output should be shorted at a time, and the duration of the short-circuit should not exceed one second.
NOTE 2: One input at 4.5 V, all others at GND.

switching characteristics, V_{CC} = 5 V, T_A = 25°C (see note 3)

PARAMETER	FROM (INPUT)	TO (OUTPUT)	TEST CONDITIONS		MIN	TYP	MAX	UNIT
t_{PLH}	A or B	Y	R_L = 2 kΩ,	C_L = 15 pF		10	15	ns
t_{PHL}						10	15	ns

NOTE 3: Load circuits and voltage waveforms are shown in Section 1.

TEXAS
INSTRUMENTS
POST OFFICE BOX 655012 • DALLAS, TEXAS 75265

SN5404, SN54LS04, SN54S04, SN7404, SN74LS04, SN74S04
HEX INVERTERS

DECEMBER 1983 – REVISED MARCH 1988

- **Package Options Include Plastic ''Small Outline'' Packages, Ceramic Chip Carriers and Flat Packages, and Plastic and Ceramic DIPs**

- **Dependable Texas Instruments Quality and Reliability**

description

These devices contain six independent inverters.

The SN5404, SN54LS04, and SN54S04 are characterized for operation over the full military temperature range of −55°C to 125°C. The SN7404, SN74LS04, and SN74S04 are characterized for operation from 0°C to 70°C.

FUNCTION TABLE (each inverter)

INPUTS A	OUTPUT Y
H	L
L	H

logic symbol[†]

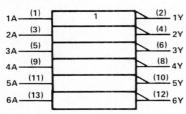

1A (1) 1 (2) 1Y
2A (3) (4) 2Y
3A (5) (6) 3Y
4A (9) (8) 4Y
5A (11) (10) 5Y
6A (13) (12) 6Y

[†]This symbol is in accordance with ANSI/IEEE Std. 91-1984 and IEC Publication 617-12.
Pin numbers shown are for D, J, and N packages.

logic diagram (positive logic)

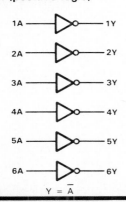

1A —▷o— 1Y

2A —▷o— 2Y

3A —▷o— 3Y

4A —▷o— 4Y

5A —▷o— 5Y

6A —▷o— 6Y

$$Y = \overline{A}$$

SN5404 . . . J PACKAGE
SN54LS04, SN54S04 . . . J OR W PACKAGE
SN7404 . . . N PACKAGE
SN74LS04, SN74S04 . . . D OR N PACKAGE
(TOP VIEW)

```
1A  [1      14] VCC
1Y  [2      13] 6A
2A  [3      12] 6Y
2Y  [4      11] 5A
3A  [5      10] 5Y
3Y  [6       9] 4A
GND [7       8] 4Y
```

SN5404 . . . W PACKAGE
(TOP VIEW)

```
1A  [1      14] 1Y
2Y  [2      13] 6A
2A  [3      12] 6Y
VCC [4      11] GND
3A  [5      10] 5Y
3Y  [6       9] 5A
4A  [7       8] 4Y
```

SN54LS04, SN54S04 . . . FK PACKAGE
(TOP VIEW)

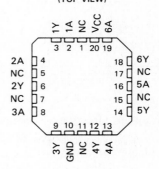

```
        1Y  1A  NC  VCC 6A
         3   2   1  20  19
2A [4                    18] 6Y
NC [5                    17] NC
2Y [6                    16] 5A
NC [7                    15] NC
3A [8                    14] 5Y
         9  10  11  12  13
        3Y GND NC  4Y  4A
```

NC - No internal connection

TEXAS INSTRUMENTS

POST OFFICE BOX 655012 • DALLAS, TEXAS 75265

2

TTL Devices

SN5404, SN54LS04, SN54S04, SN7404, SN74LS04, SN74S04 HEX INVERTERS

schematics (each gate)

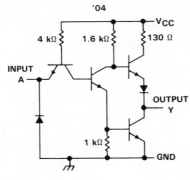

'04

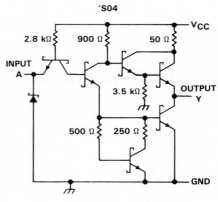

'LS04

'S04

Resistor values shown are nominal.

absolute maximum ratings over operating free-air temperature range (unless otherwise noted)

Supply voltage, V_{CC} (see Note 1) . . . . 7 V
Input voltage: '04, 'S04 . . . . 5.5 V
              'LS04 . . . . 7 V
Operating free-air temperature range: SN54' . . . . −55°C to 125°C
                                    SN74' . . . . 0°C to 70°C
Storage temperature range . . . . −65°C to 150°C

NOTE 1: Voltage values are with respect to network ground terminal.

TEXAS
INSTRUMENTS
POST OFFICE BOX 655012 • DALLAS, TEXAS 75265

SN54LS04, SN74LS04
HEX INVERTERS

recommended operating conditions

		SN54LS04			SN74LS04			UNIT
		MIN	NOM	MAX	MIN	NOM	MAX	
V_{CC}	Supply voltage	4.5	5	5.5	4.75	5	5.25	V
V_{IH}	High-level input voltage	2			2			V
V_{IL}	Low-level input voltage			0.7			0.8	V
I_{OH}	High-level output current			−0.4			−0.4	mA
I_{OL}	Low-level output current			4			8	mA
T_A	Operating free-air temperature	−55		125	0		70	°C

electrical characteristics over recommended operating free-air temperature range (unless otherwise noted)

PARAMETER	TEST CONDITIONS †			SN54LS04			SN74LS04			UNIT
				MIN	TYP‡	MAX	MIN	TYP‡	MAX	
V_{IK}	V_{CC} = MIN,	I_I = −18 mA				−1.5			−1.5	V
V_{OH}	V_{CC} = MIN,	V_{IL} = MAX,	I_{OH} = −0.4 mA	2.5	3.4		2.7	3.4		V
V_{OL}	V_{CC} = MIN,	V_{IH} = 2 V,	I_{OL} = 4 mA		0.25	0.4			0.4	V
	V_{CC} = MIN,	V_{IH} = 2 V,	I_{OL} = 8 mA					0.25	0.5	
I_I	V_{CC} = MAX,	V_I = 7 V				0.1			0.1	mA
I_{IH}	V_{CC} = MAX,	V_I = 2.7 V				20			20	μA
I_{IL}	V_{CC} = MAX,	V_I = 0.4 V				−0.4			−0.4	mA
I_{OS} §	V_{CC} = MAX			−20		−100	−20		−100	mA
I_{CCH}	V_{CC} = MAX,	V_I = 0 V			1.2	2.4		1.2	2.4	mA
I_{CCL}	V_{CC} = MAX,	V_I = 4.5 V			3.6	6.6		3.6	6.6	mA

† For conditions shown as MIN or MAX, use the appropriate value specified under recommended operating conditions.
‡ All typical values are at V_{CC} = 5 V, T_A = 25°C.
§ Not more than one output should be shorted at a time, and the duration of the short-circuit should not exceed one second.

switching characteristics, V_{CC} = 5 V, T_A = 25°C (see note 2)

PARAMETER	FROM (INPUT)	TO (OUTPUT)	TEST CONDITIONS		MIN	TYP	MAX	UNIT
t_{PLH}	A	Y	R_L = 2 kΩ,	C_L = 15 pF		9	15	ns
t_{PHL}						10	15	ns

NOTE 2: Load circuits and voltage waveforms are shown in Section 1.

TEXAS
INSTRUMENTS
POST OFFICE BOX 655012 • DALLAS, TEXAS 75265

2

TTL Devices

- **Package Options Include Plastic ''Small Outline'' Packages, Ceramic Chip Carriers and Flat Packages, and Plastic and Ceramic DIPs**

- **Dependable Texas Instruments Quality and Reliability**

description

These devices contain four independent 2-input AND gates.

The SN5408, SN54LS08, and SN54S08 are characterized for operation over the full military temperature range of −55°C to 125°C. The SN7408, SN74LS08 and SN74S08 are characterized for operation from 0° to 70°C.

FUNCTION TABLE (each gate)

INPUTS		OUTPUT
A	B	Y
H	H	H
L	X	L
X	L	L

logic symbol[†]

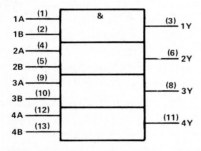

[†] This symbol is in accordance with ANSI/IEEE Std 91-1984 and IEC Publication 617-12.
Pin numbers shown are for D, J, N, and W packages.

SN5408, SN54LS08, SN54S08 . . . J OR W PACKAGE
SN7408 . . . J OR N PACKAGE
SN74LS08, SN74S08 . . . D, J OR N PACKAGE
(TOP VIEW)

```
1A  [1    14] VCC
1B  [2    13] 4B
1Y  [3    12] 4A
2A  [4    11] 4Y
2B  [5    10] 3B
2Y  [6     9] 3A
GND [7     8] 3Y
```

SN54LS08, SN54S08 . . . FK PACKAGE
(TOP VIEW)

```
       1B 1A NC VCC 4B
        3  2  1 20 19
1Y [4              18] 4A
NC [5              17] NC
2A [6              16] 4Y
NC [7              15] NC
2B [8              14] 3B
        9 10 11 12 13
       2Y GND NC 3Y 3A
```

NC—No internal connection

logic diagram (positive logic)

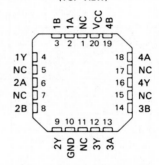
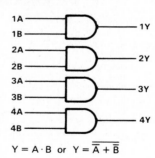

$$Y = A \cdot B \quad \text{or} \quad Y = \overline{\overline{A} + \overline{B}}$$

2

TTL Devices

TEXAS INSTRUMENTS
POST OFFICE BOX 655012 • DALLAS, TEXAS 75265

SN5408, SN54LS08, SN54S08, SN7408, SN74LS08, SN74S08
QUADRUPLE 2-INPUT POSITIVE-AND GATES

schematics (each gate)

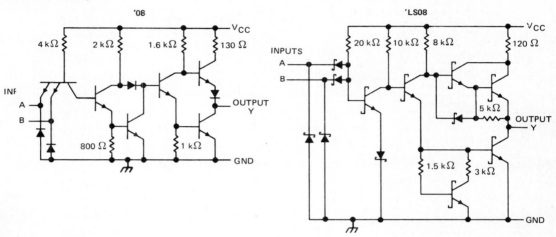

Resistor values are nominal.

absolute maximum ratings over operating free-air temperature range (unless otherwise noted)

Supply voltage, V_{CC} (see Note 1) .... 7 V
Input voltage: '08, 'S08 .... 5.5 V
             'LS08 .... 7 V
Operating free-air temperature range: SN54' .... -55°C to 125°C
                     SN74' .... 0°C to 70°C
Storage temperature range .... -65°C to 150°C

NOTE 1: Voltage values are with respect to network ground terminal.

TEXAS
INSTRUMENTS

POST OFFICE BOX 655012 • DALLAS, TEXAS 75265

recommended operating conditions

		SN54LS08 MIN	NOM	MAX	SN74LS08 MIN	NOM	MAX	UNIT
V_{CC}	Supply voltage	4.5	5	5.5	4.75	5	5.25	V
V_{IH}	High-level input voltage	2			2			V
V_{IL}	Low-level input voltage			0.7			0.8	V
I_{OH}	High-level output current			−0.4			−0.4	mA
I_{OL}	Low-level output current			4			8	mA
T_A	Operating free-air temperature	−55		125	0		70	°C

electrical characteristics over recommended operating free-air temperature range (unless otherwise noted)

PARAMETER	TEST CONDITIONS †	SN54LS08 MIN	TYP‡	MAX	SN74LS08 MIN	TYP‡	MAX	UNIT
V_{IK}	V_{CC} = MIN, I_I = −18 mA			−1.5			−1.5	V
V_{OH}	V_{CC} = MIN, V_{IH} = 2 V, I_{OH} = −0.4 mA	2.5	3.4		2.7	3.4		V
V_{OL}	V_{CC} = MIN, V_{IL} = MAX, I_{OL} = 4 mA		0.25	0.4		0.25	0.4	V
	V_{CC} = MIN, V_{IL} = MAX, I_{OL} = 8 mA					0.35	0.5	
I_I	V_{CC} = MAX, V_I = 7 V			0.1			0.1	mA
I_{IH}	V_{CC} = MAX, V_I = 2.7 V			20			20	µA
I_{IL}	V_{CC} = MAX, V_I = 0.4 V			−0.4			−0.4	mA
I_{OS} §	V_{CC} = MAX	−20		−100	−20		−100	mA
I_{CCH}	V_{CC} = MAX, V_I = 4.5 V		2.4	4.8		2.4	4.8	mA
I_{CCL}	V_{CC} = MAX, V_I = 0 V		4.4	8.8		4.4	8.8	mA

† For conditions shown as MIN or MAX, use the appropriate value specified under recommended operating conditions.
‡ All typical values are at V_{CC} = 5 V, T_A = 25°C.
§ Not more than one output should be shorted at a time, and the duration of the short-circuit should not exceed one second.

switching characteristics, V_{CC} = 5 V, T_A = 25°C (see note 2)

PARAMETER	FROM (INPUT)	TO (OUTPUT)	TEST CONDITIONS	MIN	TYP	MAX	UNIT
t_{PLH}	A or B	Y	R_L = 2 kΩ, C_L = 15 pF		8	15	ns
t_{PHL}					10	20	ns

NOTE 2: Load circuits and voltage waveforms are shown in Section 1.

TEXAS
INSTRUMENTS
POST OFFICE BOX 655012 • DALLAS, TEXAS 75265

- Package Options Include Plastic ''Small Outline'' Packages, Ceramic Chip Carriers and Flat Packages, and Plastic and Ceramic DIPs

- Dependable Texas Instruments Quality and Reliability

description

These devices contain three independent 3-input NAND gates.

The SN5410, SN54LS10, and SN54S10 are characterized for operation over the full military temperature range of −55°C to 125°C. The SN7410, SN74LS10, and SN74S10 are characterized for operation from 0°C to 70°C.

FUNCTION TABLE (each gate)

INPUTS			OUTPUT
A	B	C	Y
H	H	H	L
L	X	X	H
X	L	X	H
X	X	L	H

logic symbol[†]

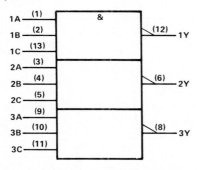

[†]This symbol is in accordance with ANSI/IEEE Std. 91-1984 and IEC Publication 617-12.
Pin numbers shown are for D, J, and N packages.

positive logic

$$Y = \overline{A \cdot B \cdot C} \quad \text{or} \quad Y = \overline{A} + \overline{B} + \overline{C}$$

SN5410 . . . J PACKAGE
SN54LS10, SN54S10 . . . J OR W PACKAGE
SN7410 . . . N PACKAGE
SN74LS10, SN74S10 . . . D OR N PACKAGE
(TOP VIEW)

```
1A  [1    14] VCC
1B  [2    13] 1C
2A  [3    12] 1Y
2B  [4    11] 3C
2C  [5    10] 3B
2Y  [6     9] 3A
GND [7     8] 3Y
```

SN5410 . . . W PACKAGE
(TOP VIEW)

```
1A  [1    14] 1C
1B  [2    13] 3Y
1Y  [3    12] 3C
VCC [4    11] GND
2Y  [5    10] 3B
2A  [6     9] 3A
2B  [7     8] 2C
```

SN54LS10, SN54S10 . . . FK PACKAGE
(TOP VIEW)

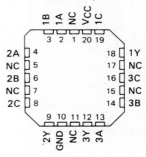

NC - No internal connection

logic diagram (positive logic)

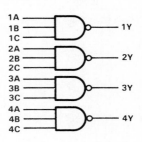

TEXAS
INSTRUMENTS

POST OFFICE BOX 655012 • DALLAS, TEXAS 75265

2
TTL Devices

- **Operation from Very Slow Edges**
- **Improved Line-Receiving Characteristics**
- **High Noise Immunity**

description

Each circuit functions as an inverter, but because of the Schmitt action, it has different input threshold levels for positive (V_{T+}) and for negative going (V_{T-}) signals.

These circuits are temperature-compensated and can be triggered from the slowest of input ramps and still give clean, jitter-free output signals.

The SN5414 and SN54LS14 are characterized for operation over the full military temperature range of –55°C to 125°C. The SN7414 and the SN74LS14 are characterized for operation from 0°C to 70°C.

logic symbol[†]

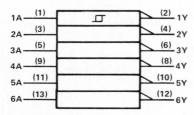

[†] This symbol is in accordance with ANSI/IEEE Std 91-1984 and IEC Publication 617-12.
Pin numbers shown are for D, J, N, and W packages.

logic diagram (positive logic)

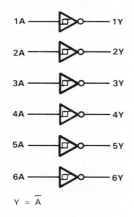

$$Y = \overline{A}$$

SN5414, SN54LS14 . . . J OR W PACKAGE
SN7414 . . . N PACKAGE
SN74LS14 . . . D OR N PACKAGE
(TOP VIEW)

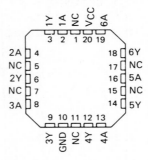

```
1A   [1   U  14]  VCC
1Y   [2      13]  6A
2A   [3      12]  6Y
2Y   [4      11]  5A
3A   [5      10]  5Y
3Y   [6       9]  4A
GND  [7       8]  4Y
```

SN54LS14 . . . FK PACKAGE
(TOP VIEW)

```
           1Y 1A NC VCC 6A
            3  2  1  20 19
    2A [4              18] 6Y
    NC [5              17] NC
    2Y [6              16] 5A
    NC [7              15] NC
    3A [8              14] 5Y
            9 10 11 12 13
           3Y GND NC 4Y 4A
```

NC—No internal connection

TTL Devices

2

![TI] **TEXAS INSTRUMENTS**
POST OFFICE BOX 655012 • DALLAS, TEXAS 75265

SN5414, SN54LS14, SN7414, SN74LS14
HEX SCHMITT-TRIGGER INVERTERS

schematics

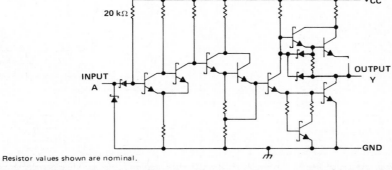

Resistor values shown are nominal.

absolute maximum ratings over operating free-air temperature range (unless otherwise noted)

Supply voltage, V_{CC} (see Note 1)	7 V
Input voltage: '14	5.5 V
'LS14	7 V
Operating free-air temperature: SN54'	−55°C to 125°C
SN74'	0°C to 70°C
Storage temperature range	−65°C to 150°C

NOTE 1: Voltage values are with respect to network ground terminal.

TEXAS
INSTRUMENTS

POST OFFICE BOX 655012 • DALLAS, TEXAS 75265

SN54LS14, SN74LS14
HEX SCHMITT-TRIGGER INVERTERS

recommended operating conditions

		SN54LS14			SN74LS14			UNIT
		MIN	NOM	MAX	MIN	NOM	MAX	
V_{CC}	Supply voltage	4.5	5	5.5	4.75	5	5.25	V
I_{OH}	High-level output current			− 0.4			− 0.4	mA
I_{OL}	Low-level output current			4			8	mA
T_A	Operating free-air temperature	− 55		125	0		70	°C

electrical characteristics over recommended operating free-air temperature range (unless otherwise noted)

PARAMETER	TEST CONDITIONS†			SN54LS14			SN74LS14			UNIT
				MIN	TYP‡	MAX	MIN	TYP‡	MAX	
V_{T+}	$V_{CC} = 5$ V			1.4	1.6	1.9	1.4	1.6	1.9	V
$V_{T−}$	$V_{CC} = 5$ V			0.5	0.8	1	0.5	0.8	1	V
Hysteresis $(V_{T+} - V_{T−})$	$V_{CC} = 5$ V			0.4	0.8		0.4	0.8		V
V_{IK}	$V_{CC} = $ MIN,	$I_I = − 18$ mA				− 1.5			− 1.5	V
V_{OH}	$V_{CC} = $ MIN,	$V_I = 0.5$ V,	$I_{OH} = − 0.4$ mA	2.5	3.4		2.7	3.4		V
V_{OL}	$V_{CC} = $ MIN,	$V_I = 1.9$ V	$I_{OL} = 4$ mA		0.25	0.4		0.25	0.4	V
			$I_{OL} = 8$ mA					0.35	0.5	
I_{T+}	$V_{CC} = 5$ V,	$V_I = V_{T+}$			− 0.14			− 0.14		mA
$I_{T−}$	$V_{CC} = 5$ V,	$V_I = V_{T−}$			− 0.18			− 0.18		mA
I_I	$V_{CC} = $ MAX,	$V_I = 7$ V				0.1			0.1	mA
I_{IH}	$V_{CC} = $ MAX,	$V_{IH} = 2.7$ V				20			20	μA
I_{IL}	$V_{CC} = $ MAX,	$V_{IL} = 0.4$ V				− 0.4			− 0.4	mA
I_{OS}§	$V_{CC} = $ MAX			− 20		− 100	− 20		− 100	mA
I_{CCH}	$V_{CC} = $ MAX				8.6	16		8.6	16	mA
I_{CCL}	$V_{CC} = $ MAX				12	21		12	21	mA

† For conditions shown as MIN or MAX, use the appropriate value specified under recommended operating conditions.
‡ All typical values are at $V_{CC} = 5$ V, $T_A = 25$°C.
§ Not more than one output should be shorted at a time, and duration of the short-circuit should not exceed one second.

switching characteristics, $V_{CC} = 5$ V, $T_A = 25$°C

PARAMETER	FROM (INPUT)	TO (OUTPUT)	TEST CONDITIONS		MIN	TYP	MAX	UNIT
t_{PLH}	A	Y	$R_L = 2$ kΩ,	$C_L = 15$ pF		15	22	ns
t_{PHL}						15	22	ns

TEXAS
INSTRUMENTS
POST OFFICE BOX 655012 • DALLAS, TEXAS 75265

TYPICAL CHARACTERISTICS OF 'LS14 CIRCUITS

POSITIVE-GOING THRESHOLD VOLTAGE
vs
FREE-AIR TEMPERATURE

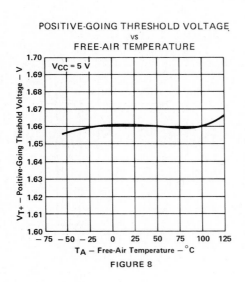

FIGURE 8

NEGATIVE-GOING THRESHOLD VOLTAGE
vs
FREE-AIR TEMPERATURE

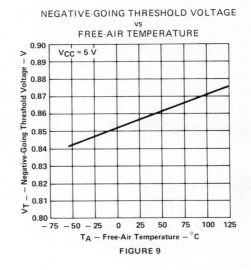

FIGURE 9

HYSTERESIS
vs
FREE-AIR TEMPERATURE

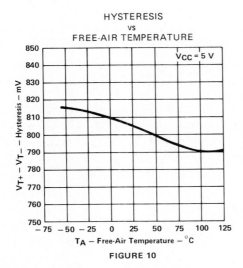

FIGURE 10

DISTRIBUTION OF UNITS
FOR HYSTERESIS

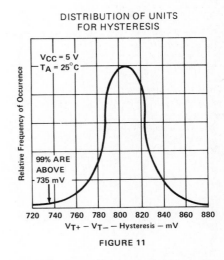

FIGURE 11

Data for temperatures below 0°C and above 70°C and supply voltages below 4.75 V and above 5.25 V are applicable for SN54LS14 only.

2

TTL Devices

TEXAS INSTRUMENTS
POST OFFICE BOX 655012 • DALLAS, TEXAS 75265

SN54LS14, SN74LS14
HEX SCHMITT-TRIGGER INVERTERS

TYPICAL CHARACTERISTICS OF 'LS14 CIRCUITS

THRESHOLD VOLTAGES AND HYSTERESIS
vs
SUPPLY VOLTAGE

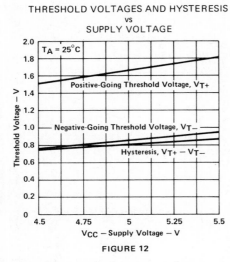

FIGURE 12

OUTPUT VOLTAGE
vs
INPUT VOLTAGE

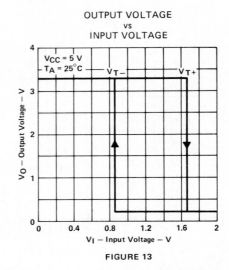

FIGURE 13

Data for temperatures below 0°C and above 70°C and supply voltages below 4.75 V and above 5.25 V are applicable for SN54LS14 only.

Texas
INSTRUMENTS

POST OFFICE BOX 655012 • DALLAS, TEXAS 75265

TYPICAL APPLICATION DATA

2

TTL Devices

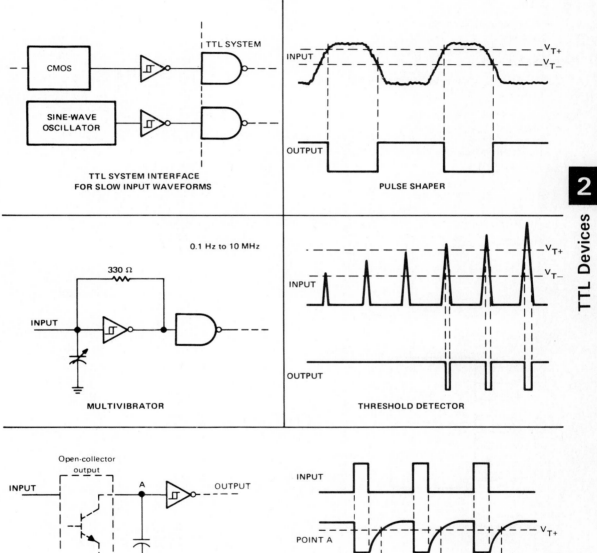

TTL SYSTEM INTERFACE
FOR SLOW INPUT WAVEFORMS

PULSE SHAPER

0.1 Hz to 10 MHz

330 Ω

INPUT

MULTIVIBRATOR

THRESHOLD DETECTOR

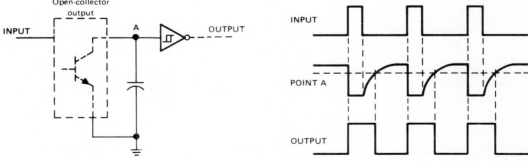

PULSE STRETCHER

- Package Options Include Plastic ''Small Outline'' Packages, Ceramic Chip Carriers and Flat Packages, and Plastic and Ceramic DIPs

- Dependable Texas Instruments Quality and Reliability

description

These devices contain two independent 4-input NAND gates.

The SN5420, SN54LS20, and SN54S20 are characterized for operation over the full military range of −55°C to 125°C. The SN7420, SN74LS20, and SN74S20 are characterized for opertion from 0°C to 70°C.

FUNCTION TABLE (each gate)

INPUTS				OUTPUT
A	B	C	D	Y
H	H	H	H	L
L	X	X	X	H
X	L	X	X	H
X	X	L	X	H
X	X	X	L	H

logic symbol[†]

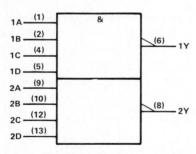

[†]This symbol is in accordance with ANSI/IEEE Std. 91-1984 and IEC Publication 617-12.
Pin numbers shown are for D, J, N, and W packages.

SN5420 . . . J PACKAGE
SN54LS20, SN54S20 . . . J OR W PACKAGE
SN7420 . . . N PACKAGE
SN74LS20, SN74S20 . . . D OR N PACKAGE
(TOP VIEW)

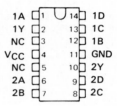

SN5420 . . . W PACKAGE
(TOP VIEW)

SN54LS20, SN54S20 . . . FK PACKAGE
(TOP VIEW)

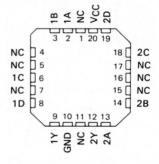

NC - No internal connection

logic diagram

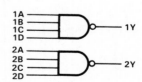

positive logic $Y = \overline{A \cdot B \cdot C \cdot D}$ or $Y = \overline{A} + \overline{B} + \overline{C} + \overline{D}$

2

TTL Devices

TEXAS
INSTRUMENTS
POST OFFICE BOX 655012 • DALLAS, TEXAS 75265

SN5427, SN54LS27, SN7427, SN74LS27
TRIPLE 3-INPUT POSITIVE-NOR GATES

DECEMBER 1983 – REVISED MARCH 1988

- **Package Options Include Plastic "Small Outline" Packages, Ceramic Chip Carriers and Flat Packages, and Plastic and Ceramic DIPs**

- **Dependable Texas Instruments Quality and Reliability**

description

These devices contain three independent 3-input NOR gates.

The SN5427 and SN54LS27 are characterized for operation over the full military temperature range of −55°C to 125°C. The SN7427 and SN74LS27 are characterized for operation from 0°C to 70°C.

FUNCTION TABLE (each gate)

INPUTS			OUTPUT
A	B	C	Y
H	X	X	L
X	H	X	L
X	X	H	L
L	L	L	H

logic symbol†

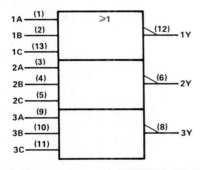

† This symbol is in accordance with ANSI/IEEE Std 91-1984 and IEC Publication 617-12.
Pin numbers shown are for D, J, N, and W packages.

SN5427, SN54LS27 . . . J OR W PACKAGE
SN7427 . . . N PACKAGE
SN74LS27 . . . D OR N PACKAGE
(TOP VIEW)

1A	1	14 V_CC
1B	2	13 1C
2A	3	12 1Y
2B	4	11 3C
2C	5	10 3B
2Y	6	9 3A
GND	7	8 3Y

SN54LS27 . . . FK PACKAGE
(TOP VIEW)

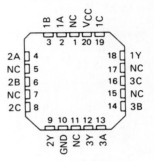

NC – No internal connection

logic diagram

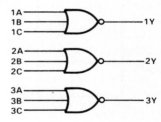

positive logic

$$Y = \overline{A + B + C} \text{ or } Y = \overline{A} \cdot \overline{B} \cdot \overline{C}$$

PRODUCTION DATA documents contain information current as of publication date. Products conform to specifications per the terms of Texas Instruments standard warranty. Production processing does not necessarily include testing of all parameters.

TEXAS INSTRUMENTS
POST OFFICE BOX 225012 • DALLAS, TEXAS 75265

2

TTL Devices

● Package Options Include Plastic ''Small Outline'' Packages, Ceramic Chip Carriers and Flat Packages, and Plastic and Ceramic DIPs

● Dependable Texas Instruments Quality and Reliability

description

These devices contain four independent 2-input OR gates.

The SN5432, SN54LS32 and SN54S32 are characterized for operation over the full military range of −55°C to 125°C. The SN7432, SN74LS32 and SN74S32 are characterized for operation from 0°C to 70°C.

SN5432, SN54LS32, SN54S32 . . . J OR W PACKAGE
SN7432 . . . N PACKAGE
SN74LS32, SN74S32 . . . D OR N PACKAGE
(TOP VIEW)

```
      ┌───┬─U─┬───┐
1A  [ 1        14 ]  VCC
1B  [ 2        13 ]  4B
1Y  [ 3        12 ]  4A
2A  [ 4        11 ]  4Y
2B  [ 5        10 ]  3B
2Y  [ 6         9 ]  3A
GND [ 7         8 ]  3Y
      └────────────┘
```

SN54LS32, SN54S32 . . . FK PACKAGE
(TOP VIEW)

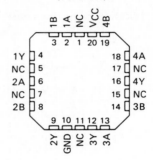

NC - No internal connection

FUNCTION TABLE (each gate)

INPUTS		OUTPUT
A	**B**	**Y**
H	X	H
X	H	H
L	L	L

logic symbol[†]

```
1A ──(1)──┐ ≥1
           │        ┌──(3)── 1Y
1B ──(2)──┘
2A ──(4)──┐
           │        ┌──(6)── 2Y
2B ──(5)──┘
3A ──(9)──┐
           │        ┌──(8)── 3Y
3B ──(10)─┘
4A ──(12)─┐
           │        ┌──(11)── 4Y
4B ──(13)─┘
```

[†] This symbol is in accordance with ANSI IEEE Std 91 1984 and IEC Publication 617 12.
Pin numbers shown are for D, J, N, or W packages.

logic diagram

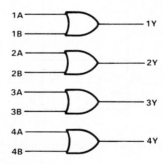

positive logic

$$Y = A + B \text{ or } Y = \overline{\overline{A} \cdot \overline{B}}$$

TEXAS INSTRUMENTS
POST OFFICE BOX 655012 • DALLAS, TEXAS 75265

2

TTL Devices

'46A, '47A, 'LS47 feature	'48, 'LS48 features	'LS49 feature
• **Open-Collector Outputs Drive Indicators Directly**	• **Internal Pull-Ups Eliminate Need for External Resistors**	• **Open-Collector Outputs**
• **Lamp-Test Provision**	• **Lamp-Test Provision**	• **Blanking Input**
• **Leading/Trailing Zero Suppression**	• **Leading/Trailing Zero Suppression**	

SN5446A, SN5447A, SN54LS47, SN5448,
SN54LS48 . . . J PACKAGE
SN7446A, SN7447A,
SN7448 . . . N PACKAGE
SN74LS47, SN74LS48 . . . D OR N PACKAGE
(TOP VIEW)

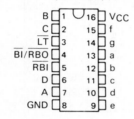

SN54LS47, SN54LS48 . . . FK PACKAGE
(TOP VIEW)

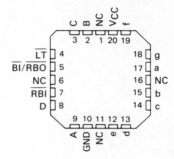

SN54LS49 . . . J OR W PACKAGE
SN74LS49 . . . D OR N PACKAGE
(TOP VIEW)

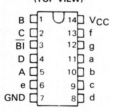

SN54LS49 . . . FK PACKAGE
(TOP VIEW)

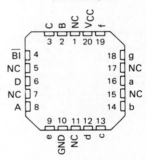

NC — No internal connection

TEXAS INSTRUMENTS
POST OFFICE BOX 655012 • DALLAS, TEXAS 75265

2

TTL Devices

- All Circuit Types Feature Lamp Intensity Modulation Capability

TYPE	DRIVER OUTPUTS				TYPICAL POWER DISSIPATION	PACKAGES
	ACTIVE LEVEL	OUTPUT CONFIGURATION	SINK CURRENT	MAX VOLTAGE		
SN5446A	low	open-collector	40 mA	30 V	320 mW	J, W
SN5447A	low	open-collector	40 mA	15 V	320 mW	J, W
SN5448	high	2-kΩ pull-up	6.4 mA	5.5 V	265 mW	J,W
SN54LS47	low	open-collector	12 mA	15 V	35 mW	J, W
SN54LS48	high	2-kΩ pull-up	2 mA	5.5 V	125 mW	J, W
SN54LS49	high	open-collector	4 mA	5.5 V	40 mW	J, W
SN7446A	low	open-collector	40 mA	30 V	320 mW	J, N
SN7447A	low	open-collector	40 mA	15 V	320 mW	J, N
SN7448	high	2-kΩ pull-up	6.4 mA	5.5 V	265 mW	J, N
SN74LS47	low	open-collector	24 mA	15 V	35 mW	J, N
SN74LS48	high	2-kΩ pull-up	6 mA	5.5 V	125 mW	J, N
SN74LS49	high	open-collector	8 mA	5.5 V	40 mW	J, N

logic symbols[†]

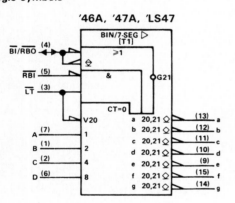

'46A, '47A, 'LS47

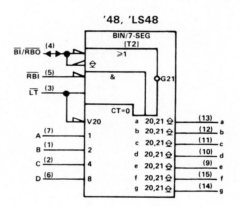

'48, 'LS48

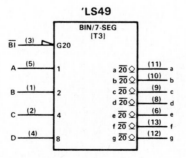

'LS49

[†]These symbols are in accordance with ANSI/IEEE Std 91-1984 and IEC Publication 617-12.
Pin numbers shown are for D, J, N, and W packages.

TEXAS
INSTRUMENTS
POST OFFICE BOX 655012 • DALLAS, TEXAS 75265

description

The '46A, '47A, and 'LS47 feature active-low outputs designed for driving common-anode LEDs or incandescent indicators directly. The '48, 'LS48, and 'LS49 feature active-high outputs for driving lamp buffers or common-cathode LEDs. All of the circuits except 'LS49 have full ripple-blanking input/output controls and a lamp test input. The 'LS49 circuit incorporates a direct blanking input. Segment identification and resultant displays are shown below. Display patterns for BCD input counts above 9 are unique symbols to authenticate input conditions.

The '46A, '47A, '48, 'LS47, and 'LS48 circuits incorporate automatic leading and/or trailing-edge zero-blanking control ($\overline{RBI}$ and $\overline{RBO}$). Lamp test ($\overline{LT}$) of these types may be performed at any time when the $\overline{BI}/\overline{RBO}$ node is at a high level. All types (including the '49 and 'LS49) contain an overriding blanking input ($\overline{BI}$), which can be used to control the lamp intensity by pulsing or to inhibit the outputs. Inputs and outputs are entirely compatible for use with TTL logic outputs.

The SN54246/SN74246 and '247 and the SN54LS247/SN74LS247 and 'LS248 compose the ⌐ and the ⌐ with tails and were designed to offer the designer a choice between two indicator fonts.

SEGMENT IDENTIFICATION

NUMERICAL DESIGNATIONS AND RESULTANT DISPLAYS

'46A, '47A, 'LS47 FUNCTION TABLE (T1)

DECIMAL OR FUNCTION	INPUTS						BI/RBO†	OUTPUTS							NOTE
	$\overline{LT}$	$\overline{RBI}$	D	C	B	A		a	b	c	d	e	f	g	
0	H	H	L	L	L	L	H	ON	ON	ON	ON	ON	ON	OFF	
1	H	X	L	L	L	H	H	OFF	ON	ON	OFF	OFF	OFF	OFF	
2	H	X	L	L	H	L	H	ON	ON	OFF	ON	ON	OFF	ON	
3	H	X	L	L	H	H	H	ON	ON	ON	ON	OFF	OFF	ON	
4	H	X	L	H	L	L	H	OFF	ON	ON	OFF	OFF	ON	ON	
5	H	X	L	H	L	H	H	ON	OFF	ON	ON	OFF	ON	ON	
6	H	X	L	H	H	L	H	OFF	OFF	ON	ON	ON	ON	ON	
7	H	X	L	H	H	H	H	ON	ON	ON	OFF	OFF	OFF	OFF	1
8	H	X	H	L	L	L	H	ON	ON	ON	ON	ON	ON	ON	
9	H	X	H	L	L	H	H	ON	ON	ON	OFF	OFF	ON	ON	
10	H	X	H	L	H	L	H	OFF	OFF	OFF	ON	ON	OFF	ON	
11	H	X	H	L	H	H	H	OFF	OFF	ON	ON	OFF	OFF	ON	
12	H	X	H	H	L	L	H	OFF	ON	OFF	OFF	OFF	ON	ON	
13	H	X	H	H	L	H	H	ON	OFF	OFF	ON	OFF	ON	ON	
14	H	X	H	H	H	L	H	OFF	OFF	OFF	ON	ON	ON	ON	
15	H	X	H	H	H	H	H	OFF	OFF	OFF	OFF	OFF	OFF	OFF	
BI	X	X	X	X	X	X	L	OFF	OFF	OFF	OFF	OFF	OFF	OFF	2
RBI	H	L	L	L	L	L	L	OFF	OFF	OFF	OFF	OFF	OFF	OFF	3
LT	L	X	X	X	X	X	H	ON	ON	ON	ON	ON	ON	ON	4

H = high level, L = low level, X = irrelevant

NOTES: 1. The blanking input ($\overline{BI}$) must be open or held at a high logic level when output functions 0 through 15 are desired. The ripple blanking input ($\overline{RBI}$) must be open or high if blanking of a decimal zero is not desired.
2. When a low logic level is applied directly to the blanking input ($\overline{BI}$), all segment outputs are off regardless of the level of any other input.
3. When ripple blanking input ($\overline{RBI}$) and inputs A, B, C, and D are at a low level with the lamp test input high, all segment outputs go off and the ripple blanking output ($\overline{RBO}$) goes to a low level (response condition).
4. When the blanking input/ripple blanking output ($\overline{BI}/\overline{RBO}$) is open or held high and a low is applied to the lamp test input, all segment outputs are on.

†$\overline{BI}/\overline{RBO}$ is wire AND logic serving as blanking input ($\overline{BI}$) and/or ripple blanking output ($\overline{RBO}$).

TEXAS INSTRUMENTS
POST OFFICE BOX 655012 • DALLAS, TEXAS 75265

2

TTL Devices

'48, 'LS48
FUNCTION TABLE (T2)

DECIMAL OR FUNCTION	INPUTS						$\overline{BI}/\overline{RBO}$†	OUTPUTS							NOTE
	$\overline{LT}$	$\overline{RBI}$	D	C	B	A		a	b	c	d	e	f	g	
0	H	H	L	L	L	L	H	H	H	H	H	H	H	L	
1	H	X	L	L	L	H	H	L	H	H	L	L	L	L	
2	H	X	L	L	H	L	H	H	H	L	H	H	L	H	
3	H	X	L	L	H	H	H	H	H	H	H	L	L	H	
4	H	X	L	H	L	L	H	L	H	H	L	L	H	H	
5	H	X	L	H	L	H	H	H	L	H	H	L	H	H	
6	H	X	L	H	H	L	H	L	L	H	H	H	H	H	
7	H	X	L	H	H	H	H	H	H	H	L	L	L	L	
8	H	X	H	L	L	L	H	H	H	H	H	H	H	H	1
9	H	X	H	L	L	H	H	H	H	H	L	L	H	H	
10	H	X	H	L	H	L	H	L	L	H	H	L	L	H	
11	H	X	H	L	H	H	H	L	L	H	H	L	L	H	
12	H	X	H	H	L	L	H	L	H	L	L	L	H	H	
13	H	X	H	H	L	H	H	H	L	L	H	L	H	H	
14	H	X	H	H	H	L	H	L	L	L	H	H	H	H	
15	H	X	H	H	H	H	H	L	L	L	L	L	L	L	
BI	X	X	X	X	X	X	L	L	L	L	L	L	L	L	2
RBI	H	L	L	L	L	L	L	L	L	L	L	L	L	L	3
LT	L	X	X	X	X	X	H	H	H	H	H	H	H	H	4

H = high level, L = low level, X = irrelevant

NOTES: 1. The blanking input ($\overline{BI}$) must be open or held at a high logic level when output functions 0 through 15 are desired. The ripple-blanking input ($\overline{RBI}$) must be open or high, if blanking of a decimal zero is not desired.
2. When a low logic level is applied directly to the blanking input ($\overline{BI}$), all segment outputs are low regardless of the level of any other input.
3. When ripple-blanking input ($\overline{RBI}$) and inputs A, B, C, and D are at a low level with the lamp-test input high, all segment outputs go low and the ripple-blanking output ($\overline{RBO}$) goes to a low level (response condition).
4. When the blanking input/ripple-blanking output ($\overline{BI}/\overline{RBO}$) is open or held high and a low is applied to the lamp-test input, all segment outputs are high.

†$\overline{BI}/\overline{RBO}$ is wire-AND logic serving as blanking input ($\overline{BI}$) and/or ripple-blanking output ($\overline{RBO}$).

'LS49
FUNCTION TABLE (T3)

DECIMAL OR FUNCTION	INPUTS					OUTPUTS							NOTE
	D	C	B	A	$\overline{BI}$	a	b	c	d	e	f	g	
0	L	L	L	L	H	H	H	H	H	H	H	L	
1	L	L	L	H	H	L	H	H	L	L	L	L	
2	L	L	H	L	H	H	H	L	H	H	L	H	
3	L	L	H	H	H	H	H	H	H	L	L	H	
4	L	H	L	L	H	L	H	H	L	L	H	H	
5	L	H	L	H	H	H	L	H	H	L	H	H	
6	L	H	H	L	H	L	L	H	H	H	H	H	
7	L	H	H	H	H	H	H	H	L	L	L	L	
8	H	L	L	L	H	H	H	H	H	H	H	H	1
9	H	L	L	H	H	H	H	H	L	L	H	H	
10	H	L	H	L	H	L	L	L	H	H	L	H	
11	H	L	H	H	H	L	L	H	H	L	L	H	
12	H	H	L	L	H	L	H	L	L	L	H	H	
13	H	H	L	H	H	H	L	L	H	L	H	H	
14	H	H	H	L	H	L	L	H	H	H	H	H	
15	H	H	H	H	H	L	L	L	L	L	L	L	
BI	X	X	X	X	L	L	L	L	L	L	L	L	2

H = high level, L = low level, X = irrelevant

NOTES: 1. The blanking input ($\overline{BI}$) must be open or held at a high logic level when output functions 0 through 15 are desired.
2. When a low logic level is applied directly to the blanking input ($\overline{BI}$), all segment outputs are low regardless of the level of any other input.

TEXAS
INSTRUMENTS

POST OFFICE BOX 655012 • DALLAS, TEXAS 75265

logic diagrams (positive logic)

'46A, '47A, 'LS47

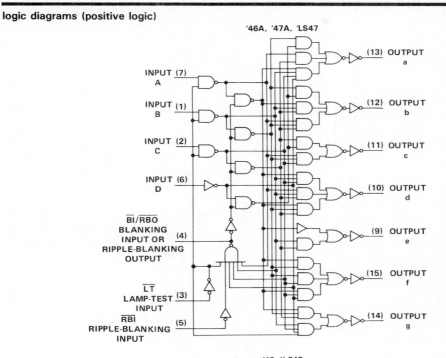

'48, 'LS48

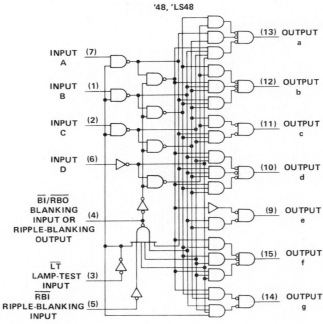

Pin numbers shown are for D, J, N, and W packages.

logic diagrams (continued)

'LS49

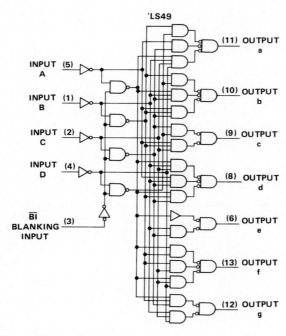

Pin numbers shown are for D, J, N, and W packages.

TEXAS
INSTRUMENTS
POST OFFICE BOX 655012 • DALLAS, TEXAS 75265

schematics of inputs and outputs

'LS47, 'LS48, 'LS49

EQUIVALENT OF EACH INPUT
EXCEPT $\overline{BI}/\overline{RBO}$

$\overline{LT}$ and $\overline{RBI}$ ('LS47, 'LS48): R_{eq} = 20 kΩ NOM
$\overline{BI}$ ('LS49): R_{eq} = 20 kΩ NOM
A, B, C, and D: R_{eq} = 25 kΩ NOM

'LS47, 'LS48, 'LS49

EQUIVALENT OF $\overline{BI}/\overline{RBO}$

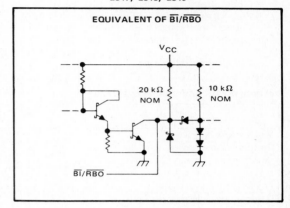

'LS47

TYPICAL OF OUTPUTS
a THRU g

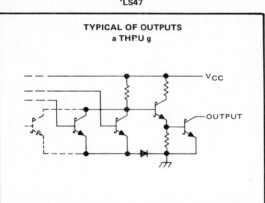

'LS48

TYPICAL OF OUTPUTS
a THRU g

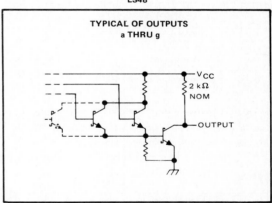

'LS49

TYPICAL OF OUTPUTS
a THRU g

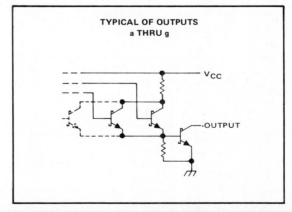

TEXAS
INSTRUMENTS
POST OFFICE BOX 655012 • DALLAS, TEXAS 75265

absolute maximum ratings over operating free-air temperature range (unless otherwise noted)

Supply voltage, V_{CC} (see Note 1) . . . . 7 V
Input voltage . . . . 7 V
Peak output current ($t_W \leqslant 1$ ms, duty cycle $\leqslant 10\%$) . . . . 200 mA
Current forced into any output in the off state . . . . 1 mA
Operating free-air temperature range: SN54LS47 . . . . -55°C to 125°C
                                       SN74LS47 . . . . 0°C to 70°C
Storage temperature range . . . . -65°C to 150°C

NOTE 1: Voltage values are with respect to network ground terminal.

recommended operating conditions

		SN54LS47 MIN	NOM	MAX	SN74LS47 MIN	NOM	MAX	UNIT
Supply voltage, V_{CC}		4.5	5	5.5	4.75	5	5.25	V
Off-state output voltage, $V_{O(off)}$	a thru g			15			15	V
On-state output current, $I_{O(on)}$	a thru g			12			24	mA
High-level output current, I_{OH}	$\overline{BI}/\overline{RBO}$			-50			-50	μA
Low-level output current, I_{OL}	$\overline{BI}/\overline{RBO}$			1.6			3.2	mA
Operating free-air temperature, T_A		-55		125	0		70	$^{\circ}$C

electrical characteristics over recommended operating free-air temperature range (unless otherwise noted)

	PARAMETER	TEST CONDITIONS[†]		SN54LS47 MIN	TYP[‡]	MAX	SN74LS47 MIN	TYP[‡]	MAX	UNIT
V_{IH}	High-level input voltage			2			2			V
V_{IL}	Low-level input voltage					0.7			0.8	V
V_{IK}	Input clamp voltage	V_{CC} = MIN,	I_I = -18 mA			-1.5			-1.5	V
V_{OH}	High-level output voltage $\overline{BI}/\overline{RBO}$	V_{CC} = MIN, V_{IH} = 2 V, V_{IL} = V_{IL} max, I_{OH} = -50 μA		2.4	4.2		2.4	4.2		V
V_{OL}	Low-level output voltage $\overline{BI}/\overline{RBO}$	V_{CC} = MIN, V_{IH} = 2 V, V_{IL} = V_{IL} max	I_{OL} = 1.6 mA		0.25	0.4		0.25	0.4	V
			I_{OL} = 3.2 mA					0.35	0.5	
$I_{O(off)}$	Off-state output current a thru g	V_{CC} = MAX, V_{IH} = 2 V, V_{IL} = V_{IL} max, $V_{O(off)}$ = 15 V				250			250	μA
$V_{O(on)}$	On-state output voltage a thru g	V_{CC} = MIN, V_{IH} = 2 V, V_{IL} = V_{IL} max	$I_{O(on)}$ = 12 mA		0.25	0.4		0.25	0.4	V
			$I_{O(on)}$ = 24 mA					0.35	0.5	
I_I	Input current at maximum input voltage	V_{CC} = MAX,	V_I = 7 V			0.1			0.1	mA
I_{IH}	High-level input current	V_{CC} = MAX,	V_I = 2.7 V			20			20	μA
I_{IL}	Low-level input current	Any input except $\overline{BI}/\overline{RBO}$ V_{CC} = MAX, V_I = 0.4 V				-0.4			-0.4	mA
		$\overline{BI}/\overline{RBO}$				-1.2			-1.2	
I_{OS}	Short-circuit output current $\overline{BI}/\overline{RBO}$	V_{CC} = MAX		-0.3		-2	-0.3		-2	mA
I_{CC}	Supply current	V_{CC} = MAX,	See Note 2		7	13		7	13	mA

[†]For conditions shown as MIN or MAX, use the appropriate value specified under recommended operating conditions.
[‡]All typical values are at V_{CC} = 5 V, T_A = 25°C.
NOTE 2: I_{CC} is measured with all outputs open and all inputs at 4.5 V.

switching characteristics, V_{CC} = 5 V, T_A = 25°C

	PARAMETER	TEST CONDITIONS	MIN	TYP	MAX	UNIT
t_{off}	Turn-off time from A input	C_L = 15 pF, R_L = 665 Ω, See Note 3			100	ns
t_{on}	Turn-on time from A input				100	
t_{off}	Turn-off time from $\overline{RBI}$ input, outputs (a-f) only				100	ns
t_{on}	Turn-on time from $\overline{RBI}$ input, outputs (a-f) only				100	

NOTE 3: Load circuits and voltage waveforms are shown in Section 1.

TEXAS INSTRUMENTS
POST OFFICE BOX 655012 • DALLAS, TEXAS 75265

2

TTL Devices

SN5483A, SN54LS83A, SN7483A, SN74LS83A
4-BIT BINARY FULL ADDDERS WITH FAST CARRY

MARCH 1974 – REVISED MARCH 1988

- **Full-Carry Look-Ahead across the Four Bits**
- **Systems Achieve Partial Look-Ahead Performance with the Economy of Ripple Carry**
- **SN54283/SN74283 and SN54LS283/SN74LS283 Are Recommended For New Designs as They Feature Supply Voltage and Ground on Corner Pins to Simplify Board Layout**

TYPE	TYPICAL ADD TIMES		TYPICAL POWER DISSIPATION PER 4-BIT ADDER
	TWO 8-BIT WORDS	TWO 16-BIT WORDS	
'83A	23 ns	43 ns	310 mW
'LS83A	25 ns	45 ns	95 mW

description

These improved full adders perform the addition of two 4-bit binary numbers. The sum (Σ) outputs are provided for each bit and the resultant carry (C4) is obtained from the fourth bit. These adders feature full internal look ahead across all four bits generating the carry term in ten nanoseconds typically. This provides the system designer with partial look-ahead performance at the economy and reduced package count of a ripple-carry implementation.

The adder logic, including the carry, is implemented in its true form meaning that the end-around carry can be accomplished without the need for logic or level inversion.

Designed for medium-speed applications, the circuits utilize transistor-transistor logic that is compatible with most other TTL families and other saturated low-level logic families.

Series 54 and 54LS circuits are characterized for operation over the full military temperature range of -55°C to 125°C, and Series 74 and 74LS circuits are characterized for operation from 0°C to 70°C.

logic symbol†

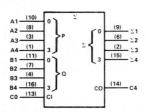

†This symbol is in accordance with ANSI/IEEE Std 91-1984 and IEC Publication 617-12.
Pin numbers are for D, J, N, and W packages.

SN5483A,SN54LS83A . . . J OR W PACKAGE
SN7483A . . . N PACKAGE
SN74LS83A . . . D OR N PACKAGE
(TOP VIEW)

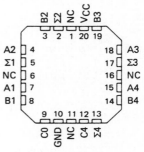

A4 [1	16] B4
Σ3 [2	15] Σ4
A3 [3	14] C4
B3 [4	13] C0
VCC [5	12] GND
Σ2 [6	11] B1
B2 [7	10] A1
A2 [8	9] Σ1

SN54LS83A . . . FK PACKAGE
(TOP VIEW)

NC - No internal connection

FUNCTION TABLE

A1 / A3	B1 / B3	A2 / A4	B2 / B4	WHEN C0 = L, WHEN C2 = L: Σ1 / Σ3	Σ2 / Σ4	C2 / C4	WHEN C0 = H, WHEN C2 = H: Σ1 / Σ3	Σ2 / Σ4	C2 / C4
L	L	L	L	L	L	L	H	L	L
H	L	L	L	H	L	L	L	H	L
L	H	L	L	H	L	L	L	H	L
H	H	L	L	L	H	L	H	L	L
L	L	H	L	L	H	L	L	H	L
H	L	H	L	H	H	L	H	L	H
L	H	H	L	H	H	L	H	L	H
H	H	H	L	L	L	H	L	H	H
L	L	L	H	L	H	L	L	H	L
H	L	L	H	H	H	L	H	L	H
L	H	L	H	H	H	L	H	L	H
H	H	L	H	L	L	H	L	H	H
L	L	H	H	L	L	H	L	H	H
H	L	H	H	H	L	H	H	H	H
L	H	H	H	H	L	H	H	H	H
H	H	H	H	L	H	H	H	H	H

H = high level, L = low level

NOTE: Input conditions at A1, B1, A2, B2, and C0 are used to determine outputs Σ1 and Σ2 and the value of the internal carry C2. The values at C2, A3, B3, A4, and B4 are then used to determine outputs Σ3, Σ4, and C4.

2

TTL Devices

TEXAS INSTRUMENTS
POST OFFICE BOX 655012 • DALLAS, TEXAS 75265

logic diagram (positive logic)

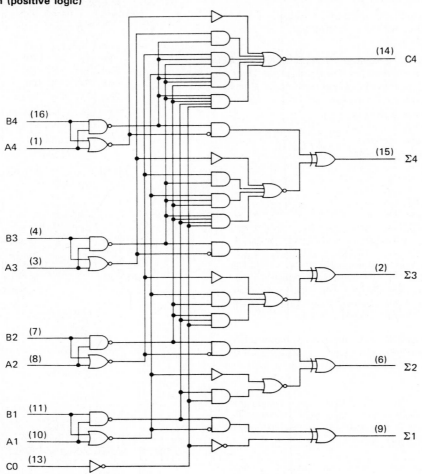

Pin numbers shown are for D, J, N, and W packages.

absolute maximum ratings over operating free-air temperature range (unless otherwise noted)

Supply voltage, V_{CC} (see Note 1)	7 V
Input voltage: '83A	5.5 V
'LS83A	7 V
Interemitter voltage (see Note 2)	5.5 V
Operating free-air temperature range: SN5483A, SN54LS83A	−55°C to 125°C
SN7483A, SN74LS83A	0°C to 70°C
Storage temperature range	−65°C to 150°C

NOTES: 1. Voltage values, except interemitter voltage, are with respect to network ground terminal.
2. This is the voltage between two emitters of a multiple-emitter transistor. This rating applies for the '83A only between the following pairs: A1 and B1, A2 and B2, A3 and B3, A4 and B4.

TEXAS
INSTRUMENTS
POST OFFICE BOX 655012 • DALLAS, TEXAS 75265

2

TTL Devices

TYPE	TYPICAL POWER DISSIPATION	TYPICAL DELAY (4-BIT WORDS)
'85	275 mW	23 ns
'LS85	52 mW	24 ns
'S85	365 mW	11 ns

description

These four-bit magnitude comparators perform comparison of straight binary and straight BCD (8-4-2-1) codes. Three fully decoded decisions about two 4-bit words (A, B) are made and are externally available at three outputs. These devices are fully expandable to any number of bits without external gates. Words of greater length may be compared by connecting comparators in cascade. The A > B, A < B, and A = B outputs of a stage handling less-significant bits are connected to the corresponding A > B, A < B, and A = B inputs of the next stage handling more-significant bits. The stage handling the least-significant bits must have a high-level voltage applied to the A = B input. The cascading paths of the '85, 'LS85, and 'S85 are implemented with only a two-gate-level delay to reduce overall comparison times for long words. An alternate method of cascading which further reduces the comparison time is shown in the typical application data.

SN5485, SN54LS85, SN54S85 . . . J OR W PACKAGE
SN7485 . . . N PACKAGE
SN74LS85, SN74S85 . . . D OR N PACKAGE
(TOP VIEW)

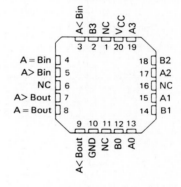

B3	1	16	V_CC
A< Bin	2	15	A3
A = Bin	3	14	B2
A> Bin	4	13	A2
A> Bout	5	12	A1
A = Bout	6	11	B1
A< Bout	7	10	A0
GND	8	9	B0

SN54LS85, SN54S85 . . . FK PACKAGE
(TOP VIEW)

NC - No internal connection

FUNCTION TABLE

COMPARING INPUTS				CASCADING INPUTS			OUTPUTS		
A3, B3	A2, B2	A1, B1	A0, B0	A > B	A < B	A = B	A > B	A < B	A = B
A3 > B3	X	X	X	X	X	X	H	L	L
A3 < B3	X	X	X	X	X	X	L	H	L
A3 = B3	A2 > B2	X	X	X	X	X	H	L	L
A3 = B3	A2 < B2	X	X	X	X	X	L	H	L
A3 = B2	A2 = B2	A1 > B1	X	X	X	X	H	L	L
A3 = B3	A2 = B2	A1 < B1	X	X	X	X	L	H	L
A2 = B2	A2 = B2	A1 = B1	A0 > B0	X	X	X	H	L	L
A3 = B3	A2 = B2	A1 = B1	A0 < B0	X	X	X	L	H	L
A3 = B3	A2 = B2	A1 = B1	A0 = B0	H	L	L	H	L	L
A3 = B3	A2 = B2	A1 = B1	A0 = B0	L	H	L	L	H	L
A3 = B3	A2 = B2	A1 = B1	A0 = B0	X	X	H	L	L	H
A3 = B3	A2 = B2	A1 = B1	A0 = B0	H	H	L	L	L	L
A3 = B3	A2 = B2	A1 = B1	A0 = B0	L	L	L	H	H	L

TEXAS
INSTRUMENTS

POST OFFICE BOX 655012 • DALLAS. TEXAS 75265

2

TTL Devices

SN5485, SN54LS85, SN54S85,
SN7485, SN74LS85, SN74S85
4-BIT MAGNITUDE COMPARATORS

logic diagrams (positive logic)

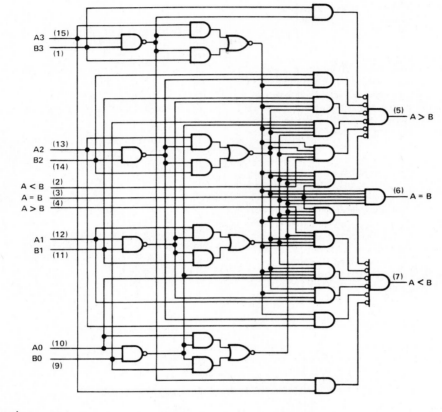

logic symbol†

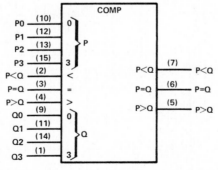

†This symbol is in accordancae with ANSI/IEEE Std 91-1984 and IEC Publication 617-12.
Pin numbers shown are for D, J, N, and W packages.

TEXAS INSTRUMENTS

POST OFFICE BOX 655012 • DALLAS. TEXAS 75265

TYPICAL APPLICATION DATA

COMPARISON OF TWO N-BIT WORDS

This application demonstrates how these magnitude comparators can be cascaded to compare longer words. The example illustrated shows the comparison of two 24-bit words; however, the design is expandable to n-bits. As an example, one comparator can be used with five of the 24-bit comparators illustrated to expand the word length to 120-bits. Typical comparison times for various word lengths using the '85, 'LS85, or 'S85 are:

WORD LENGTH	NUMBER OF PKGS	'85	'LS85	'S85
1-4 bits	1	23 ns	24 ns	11 ns
5-24 bits	2-6	46 ns	48 ns	22 ns
25-120 bits	8-31	69 ns	72 ns	33 ns

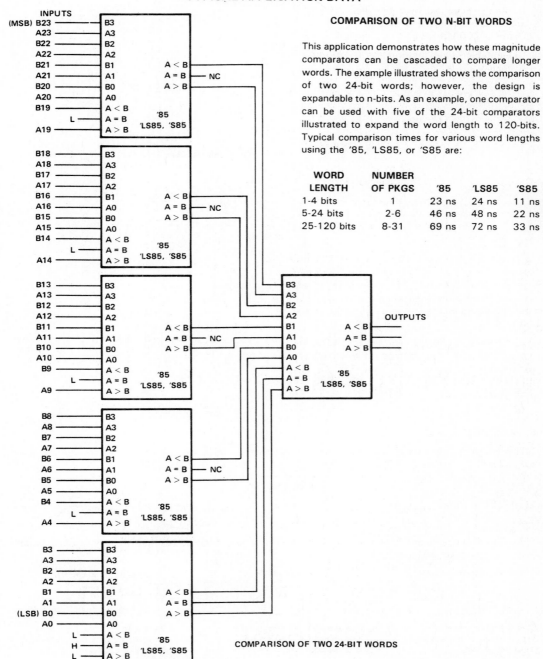

COMPARISON OF TWO 24-BIT WORDS

TTL Devices

2

- Package Options Include Plastic "Small Outline" Packages, Ceramic Chip Carriers and Flat Packages, and Standard Plastic and Ceramic 300-mil DIPs

- Dependable Texas Instruments Quality and Reliability

TYPE	TYPICAL AVERAGE PROPAGATION DELAY TIME	TYPICAL TOTAL POWER DISSIPATION
'86	14 ns	150 mW
'LS86A	10 ns	30.5 mW
'S86	7 ns	250 mW

description

These devices contain four independent 2-input Exclusive-OR gates. They perform the Boolean functions $Y = A \oplus B = \overline{A}B + A\overline{B}$ in positive logic.

A common application is as a true/complement element. If one of the inputs is low, the other input will be reproduced in true form at the output. If one of the inputs is high, the signal on the other input will be reproduced inverted at the output.

The SN5486, 54LS86A, and the SN54S86 are characterized for operation over the full military temperature range of −55°C to 125°C. The SN7486, SN74LS86A, and the SN74S86 are characterized for operation from 0°C to 70°C.

SN5486, SN54LS86A, SN54S86 . . . J OR W PACKAGE
SN7486 . . . N PACKAGE
SN74LS86A, SN74S86 . . . D OR N PACKAGE
(TOP VIEW)

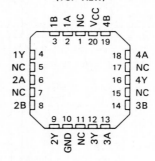

SN54LS86A, SN54S86 . . . FK PACKAGE
(TOP VIEW)

NC – No internal connection

2

TTL Devices

exclusive-OR logic

An exclusive-OR gate has many applications, some of which can be represented better by alternative logic symbols.

EXCLUSIVE-OR

These are five equivalent Exclusive-OR symbols valid for an '86 or 'LS86A gate in positive logic; negation may be shown at any two ports.

LOGIC IDENTITY ELEMENT	EVEN-PARITY	ODD-PARITY ELEMENT
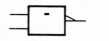		
The output is active (low) if all inputs stand at the same logic level (i.e., A = B).	The output is active (low) if an even number of inputs (i.e., 0 or 2) are active.	The output is active (high) if an odd number of inputs (i.e., only 1 of the 2) are active.

TEXAS
INSTRUMENTS

POST OFFICE BOX 655012 • DALLAS, TEXAS 75265

SN5486, SN54LS86A, SN54S86,
SN7486, SN74LS86A, SN74S86
QUADRUPLE 2-INPUT EXCLUSIVE-OR GATES

schematics of inputs and outputs

'86

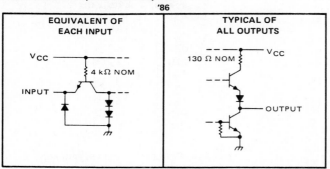

'LS86A

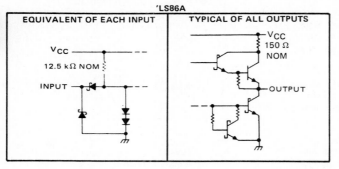

'S86

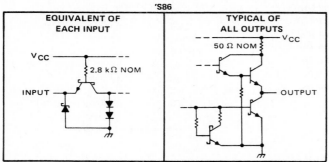

logic symbol†

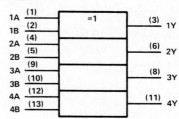

†This symbol is in accordance with
ANSI/IEEE Std. 91-1984 and IEC Publication 617-12.
Pin numbers shown are for D, J, N, and W packages.

FUNCTION TABLE

INPUTS		OUTPUT
A	B	Y
L	L	L
L	H	H
H	L	H
H	H	L

H = high level, L = low level

TEXAS
INSTRUMENTS

POST OFFICE BOX 655012 • DALLAS. TEXAS 75265

SN5490A, SN5492A, SN5493A, SN54LS90, SN54LS92, SN54LS93, SN7490A, SN7492A, SN7493A, SN74LS90, SN74LS92, SN74LS93
DECADE, DIVIDE-BY-TWELVE AND BINARY COUNTERS

MARCH 1974—REVISED MARCH 1988

'90A, 'LS90 . . . Decade Counters

'92A, 'LS92 . . . Divide By-Twelve Counters

'93A, 'LS93 . . . 4-Bit Binary Counters

TYPES	TYPICAL POWER DISSIPATION
'90A	145 mW
'92A, '93A	130 mW
'LS90, 'LS92, 'LS93	45 mW

description

Each of these monolithic counters contains four master-slave flip-flops and additional gating to provide a divide-by-two counter and a three-stage binary counter for which the count cycle length is divide-by-five for the '90A and 'LS90, divide-by-six for the '92A and 'LS92, and the divide-by-eight for the '93A and 'LS93.

All of these counters have a gated zero reset and the '90A and 'LS90 also have gated set-to-nine inputs for use in BCD nine's complement applications.

To use their maximum count length (decade, divide-by-twelve, or four-bit binary) of these counters, the CKB input is connected to the Q_A output. The input count pulses are applied to CKA input and the outputs are as described in the appropriate function table. A symmetrical divide-by-ten count can be obtained from the '90A or 'LS90 counters by connecting the Q_D output to the CKA input and applying the input count to the CKB input which gives a divide-by-ten square wave at output Q_A.

SN5490A, SN54LS90 . . . J OR W PACKAGE
SN7490A . . . N PACKAGE
SN74LS90 . . . D OR N PACKAGE
(TOP VIEW)

CKB	1	14 CKA
R0(1)	2	13 NC
R0(2)	3	12 Q_A
NC	4	11 Q_D
V_{CC}	5	10 GND
R9(1)	6	9 Q_B
R9(2)	7	8 Q_C

SN5492A, SN54LS92 . . . J OR W PACKAGE
SN7492A . . . N PACKAGE
SN74LS92 . . . D OR N PACKAGE
(TOP VIEW)

CKB	1	14 CKA
NC	2	13 NC
NC	3	12 Q_A
NC	4	11 Q_B
V_{CC}	5	10 GND
R0(1)	6	9 Q_C
R0(2)	7	8 Q_D

SN5493A, SN54LS93 . . . J OR W PACKAGE
SN7493 . . . N PACKAGE
SN74LS93 . . . D OR N PACKAGE
(TOP VIEW)

CKB	1	14 CKA
R0(1)	2	13 NC
R0(2)	3	12 Q_A
NC	4	11 Q_D
V_{CC}	5	10 GND
NC	6	9 Q_B
NC	7	8 Q_C

NC—No internal connection

2 TTL Devices

TEXAS INSTRUMENTS

POST OFFICE BOX 655012 • DALLAS. TEXAS 75265

SN5490A, '92A, '93A, SN54LS90, 'LS92, 'LS93, SN7490A, '92A, '93A, SN74LS90, 'LS92, 'LS93
DECADE, DIVIDE-BY-TWELVE, AND BINARY COUNTERS

logic symbols†

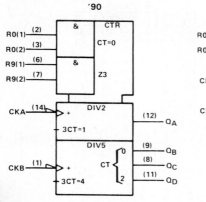

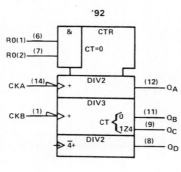

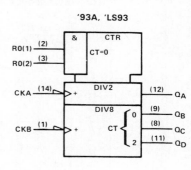

†These symbols are in accordance with ANSI/IEEE Std. 91-1984 and IEC Publication 617-12.

2

TTL Devices

TEXAS
INSTRUMENTS
POST OFFICE BOX 655012 • DALLAS, TEXAS 75265

'90A, 'LS90 BCD COUNT SEQUENCE
(See Note A)

COUNT	OUTPUT			
	Q_D	Q_C	Q_B	Q_A
0	L	L	L	L
1	L	L	L	H
2	L	L	H	L
3	L	L	H	H
4	L	H	L	L
5	L	H	L	H
6	L	H	H	L
7	L	H	H	H
8	H	L	L	L
9	H	L	L	H

'90A, 'LS90 BI-QUINARY (5-2)
(See Note B)

COUNT	OUTPUT			
	Q_A	Q_D	Q_C	Q_B
0	L	L	L	L
1	L	L	L	H
2	L	L	H	L
3	L	L	H	H
4	L	H	L	L
5	H	L	L	L
6	H	L	L	H
7	H	L	H	L
8	H	L	H	H
9	H	H	L	L

'92A, 'LS92 COUNT SEQUENCE
(See Note C)

COUNT	OUTPUT			
	Q_D	Q_C	Q_B	Q_A
0	L	L	L	L
1	L	L	L	H
2	L	L	H	L
3	L	L	H	H
4	L	H	L	L
5	L	H	L	H
6	H	L	L	L
7	H	L	L	H
8	H	L	H	L
9	H	L	H	H
10	H	H	L	L
11	H	H	L	H

'90A, 'LS90 RESET/COUNT FUNCTION TABLE

RESET INPUTS				OUTPUT			
$R_{0(1)}$	$R_{0(2)}$	$R_{9(1)}$	$R_{9(2)}$	Q_D	Q_C	Q_B	Q_A
H	H	L	X	L	L	L	L
H	H	X	L	L	L	L	L
X	X	H	H	H	L	L	H
X	L	X	L	COUNT			
L	X	L	X	COUNT			
L	X	X	L	COUNT			
X	L	L	X	COUNT			

'92A, 'LS92, '93A, 'LS93 RESET/COUNT FUNCTION TABLE

RESET INPUTS		OUTPUT			
$R_{0(1)}$	$R_{0(2)}$	Q_D	Q_C	Q_B	Q_A
H	H	L	L	L	L
L	X	COUNT			
X	L	COUNT			

'93A, 'LS93 COUNT SEQUENCE
(See Note C)

COUNT	OUTPUT			
	Q_D	Q_C	Q_B	Q_A
0	L	L	L	L
1	L	L	L	H
2	L	L	H	L
3	L	L	H	H
4	L	H	L	L
5	L	H	L	H
6	L	H	H	L
7	L	H	H	H
8	H	L	L	L
9	H	L	L	H
10	H	L	H	L
11	H	L	H	H
12	H	H	L	L
13	H	H	L	H
14	H	H	H	L
15	H	H	H	H

NOTES: A. Output Q_A is connected to input CKB for BCD count.
B. Output Q_D is connected to input CKA for bi-quinary count.
C. Output Q_A is connected to input CKB.
D. H = high level, L = low level, X = irrelevant

TEXAS INSTRUMENTS
POST OFFICE BOX 655012 • DALLAS, TEXAS 75265

2

TTL Devices

logic diagrams (positive logic)

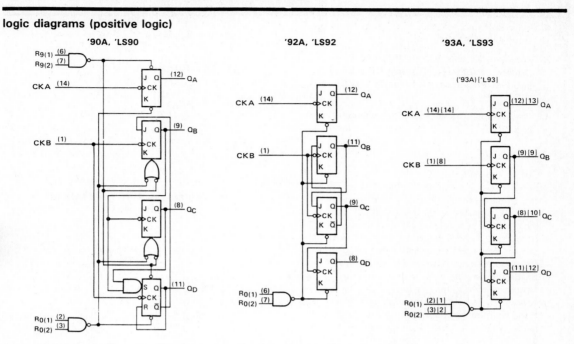

'90A, 'LS90   '92A, 'LS92   '93A, 'LS93

The J and K inputs shown without connection are for reference only and are functionally at a high level.
Pin numbers shown in ( ) are for the 'LS93 and '93A and pin numbers shown in [ ] are for the 54L93.

schematics of inputs and outputs

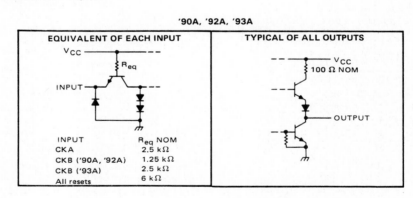

'90A, '92A, '93A

EQUIVALENT OF EACH INPUT	TYPICAL OF ALL OUTPUTS

INPUT	R_{eq} NOM
CKA	2.5 kΩ
CKB ('90A, '92A)	1.25 kΩ
CKB ('93A)	2.5 kΩ
All resets	6 kΩ

TEXAS
INSTRUMENTS
POST OFFICE BOX 655012 • DALLAS, TEXAS 75265

2

TTL Devices

- Fully Buffered to Offer Maximum Isolation from External Disturbance

- Package Options Include Plastic "Small Outline" Packages, Ceramic Chip Carriers and Flat Packages, and Plastic and Ceramic DIPs

- Dependable Texas Instruments Quality and Reliability

description

These devices contain two independent J-K negative-edge-triggered flip-flops. A low level at the preset and clear inputs sets or resets the outputs regardless of the levels of the other inputs. When preset and clear are inactive (high), data at the J and K inputs meeting the setup time requirements are transferred to the outputs on the negative-going edge of the clock pulse. Clock triggering occurs at a voltage level and is not directly related to the rise time of the clock pulse. Following the hold time interval, data at the J and K inputs may be changed without affecting the levels at the outputs. These versatile flip-flops can perform as toggle flip-flops by tying J and K high.

The SN54LS112A and SN54S112 are characterized for operation over the full military temperature range of −55°C to 125°C. The SN74LS112A and SN74S112A are characterized for operation from 0°C to 70°C.

SN54LS112A, SN54S112 . . . J OR W PACKAGE
SN74LS112A, SN74S112A . . . D OR N PACKAGE
(TOP VIEW)

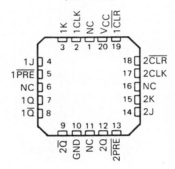

```
1CLK [ 1      16 ] VCC
  1K [ 2      15 ] 1CLR
  1J [ 3      14 ] 2CLR
1PRE [ 4      13 ] 2CLK
  1Q [ 5      12 ] 2K
  1Q̄ [ 6      11 ] 2J
  2Q̄ [ 7      10 ] 2PRE
 GND [ 8       9 ] 2Q
```

SN54LS112A, SN54S112 . . . FK PACKAGE
(TOP VIEW)

```
           1K 1CLK NC VCC 1CLR
            3   2   1  20  19
      1J [ 4              18 ] 2CLR
    1PRE [ 5              17 ] 2CLK
      NC [ 6              16 ] NC
      1Q [ 7              15 ] 2K
      1Q̄ [ 8              14 ] 2J
            9  10  11  12  13
           2Q̄ GND NC  2Q 2PRE
```

NC—No internal connection

logic symbol‡

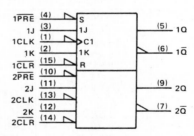

```
1PRE  (4)  ──▷ S
1J    (3)  ──   1J
1CLK  (1)  ──▷ C1        (5)  1Q
1K    (2)  ──   1K        (6)  1Q̄
1CLR  (15) ──▷ R
2PRE  (10) ──▷
2J    (11) ──             (9)  2Q
2CLK  (13) ──▷            (7)  2Q̄
2K    (12) ──
2CLR  (14) ──▷
```

‡This symbol is in accordance with ANSI/IEEE Std 91-1984 and IEC Publication 617-12.
Pin numbers shown are for D, J, N, and W packages.

FUNCTION TABLE (each flip-flop)

INPUTS					OUTPUTS	
$\overline{PRE}$	$\overline{CLR}$	CLK	J	K	Q	$\overline{Q}$
L	H	X	X	X	H	L
H	L	X	X	X	L	H
L	L	X	X	X	H†	H†
H	H	↓	L	L	Q_0	$\overline{Q}_0$
H	H	↓	H	L	H	L
H	H	↓	L	H	L	H
H	H	↓	H	H	TOGGLE	
H	H	H	X	X	Q_0	$\overline{Q}_0$

† The output levels in this configuration are not guaranteed to meet the minimum levels for V_{OH} if the lows at preset and clear are near V_{IL} minimum. Furthermore, this configuration is nonstable; that is, it will not persist when either preset or clear returns to its inactive (high) level.

Copyright © 1982, Texas Instruments Incorporated

TEXAS INSTRUMENTS
POST OFFICE BOX 655012 • DALLAS, TEXAS 75265

TTL Devices

2

SN54LS112A, SN54S112, SN74LS112A, SN74S112A
DUAL J-K NEGATIVE-EDGE-TRIGGERED
FLIP-FLOPS WITH PRESET AND CLEAR

logic diagrams (positive logic)

'LS112A

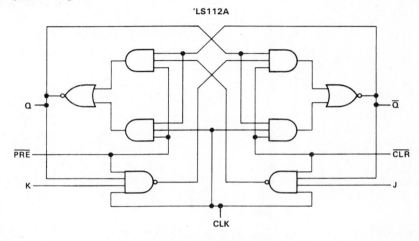

SN54S112, SN74LS112A

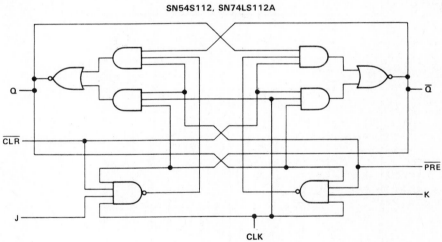

TTL Devices

2

TEXAS
INSTRUMENTS

POST OFFICE BOX 655012 • DALLAS, TEXAS 75265

schematics of inputs and outputs

'LS112A

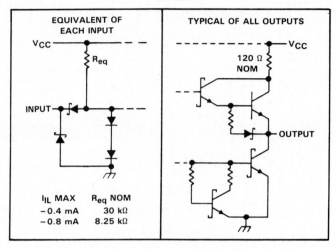

SN54S112, SN74S112A

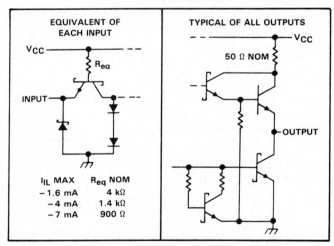

absolute maximum ratings over operating free-air temperature range (unless otherwise noted)

Supply voltage, V_{CC} (see Note 1) . . . . 7 V
Input voltage: 'LS112A . . . . 7 V
　　　　　　　SN54LS112, SN74LS112A . . . . 5.5 V
Operating free-air temperature range: SN54' . . . . −55°C to 125°C
　　　　　　　　　　　　　　　　　　　SN74' . . . . 0°C to 70°C
Storage temperature range . . . . −65°C to 150°C

NOTE 1: Voltage values are with respect to network ground terminal.

2

TTL Devices

SN54LS112A, SN74LS112A
DUAL J-K NEGATIVE-EDGE-TRIGGERED
FLIP-FLOPS WITH PRESET AND CLEAR

recommended operating conditions

			SN54LS112A MIN	SN54LS112A NOM	SN54LS112A MAX	SN74LS112A MIN	SN74LS112A NOM	SN74LS112A MAX	UNIT
V_{CC}	Supply voltage		4.5	5	5.5	4.75	5	5.25	V
V_{IH}	High-level input voltage		2			2			V
V_{IL}	Low-level input voltage				0.7			0.8	V
I_{OH}	High-level output current				−0.4			−0.4	mA
I_{OL}	Low-level output current				4			8	mA
f_{clock}	Clock frequency		0		30	0		30	MHz
t_w	Pulse duration	CLK high	20			20			ns
		$\overline{PRE}$ or $\overline{CLR}$ low	25			25			
t_{su}	Set up time–before CLK↓	Data high or low	20			20			ns
		$\overline{CLR}$ inactive	25			25			
		$\overline{PRE}$ inactive	20			20			
t_h	Hold time–data after CLK↓		0			0			ns
T_A	Operating free-air temperature		−55		125	0		70	°C

electrical characteristics over recommended operating free-air temperature range (unless otherwise noted)

PARAMETER		TEST CONDITIONS[†]	SN54LS112A MIN	SN54LS112A TYP[‡]	SN54LS112A MAX	SN74LS112A MIN	SN74LS112A TYP[‡]	SN74LS112A MAX	UNIT
V_{IK}		V_{CC} = MIN, I_I = −18 mA			−1.5			−1.5	V
V_{OH}		V_{CC} = MIN, V_{IH} = 2 V, V_{IL} = MAX, I_{OH} = −0.4 mA	2.5	3.4		2.7	3.4		V
V_{OL}		V_{CC} = MIN, V_{IL} = MAX, V_{IH} = 2 V, I_{OL} = 4 mA		0.25	0.4		0.25	0.4	V
		V_{CC} = MIN, V_{IL} = MAX, V_{IH} = 2 V, I_{OL} = 8 mA					0.35	0.5	
I_I	J or K	V_{CC} = MAX, V_I = 7 V			0.1			0.1	mA
	$\overline{CLR}$ or $\overline{PRE}$				0.3			0.3	
	CLK				0.4			0.4	
I_{IH}	J or K	V_{CC} = MAX, V_I = 2.7 V			20			20	μA
	$\overline{CLR}$ or $\overline{PRE}$				60			60	
	CLK				80			80	
I_{IL}	J or K	V_{CC} = MAX, V_I = 0.4 V			−0.4			−0.4	mA
	All other				−0.8			−0.8	
I_{OS}[§]		V_{CC} = MAX, see Note 2	−20		−100	−20		−100	mA
I_{CC} (Total)		V_{CC} = MAX, see Note 3		4	6		4	6	mA

[†] For conditions shown as MIN or MAX, use the appropriate value specified under recommended operating conditions.
[‡] All typical values are at V_{CC} = 5 V, T_A = 25°C.
[§] Not more than one output should be shorted at a time, and the duration of the short-circuit should not exceed one second.
NOTES: 2. For certain devices where state commutation can be caused by shorting an output to ground, an equivalent test may be performed with V_O = 2.25 V and 2.125 V for the '54 family and the '74 family, respectively, with the minimum and maximum limits reduced to one half of their stated values.
3. With all outputs open, I_{CC} is measured with the Q and $\overline{Q}$ outputs high in turn. At the time of measurement, the clock input is grounded.

TEXAS
INSTRUMENTS
POST OFFICE BOX 655012 • DALLAS TEXAS 75265

switching characteristics, V_{CC} = 5 V, T_A = 25°C (see Note 4)

PARAMETER	FROM (INPUT)	TO (OUTPUT)	TEST CONDITIONS	MIN	TYP	MAX	UNIT
f_{max}			R_L = 2 kΩ, C_L = 15 pF	30	45		MHz
t_{PLH}	$\overline{CLR}$, $\overline{PRE}$ or CLK	Q or $\overline{Q}$			15	20	ns
t_{PHL}					15	20	ns

NOTE 4: Load circuits and voltage waveforms are shown in Section 1.

- **Designed Specifically for High-Speed:**
  Memory Decoders
  Data Transmission Systems

- **3 Enable Inputs to Simplify Cascading and/or Data Reception**

- **Schottky-Clamped for High Performance**

description

These Schottky-clamped TTL MSI circuits are designed to be used in high-performance memory decoding or data-routing applications requiring very short propagation delay times. In high-performance memory systems, these docoders can be used to minimize the effects of system decoding. When employed with high-speed memories utilizing a fast enable circuit, the delay times of these decoders and the enable time of the memory are usually less than the typical access time of the memory. This means that the effective system delay introduced by the Schottky-clamped system decoder is negligible.

The 'LS138, SN54S138, and SN74S138A decode one of eight lines dependent on the conditions at the three binary select inputs and the three enable inputs. Two active-low and one active-high enable inputs reduce the need for external gates or inverters when expanding. A 24-line decoder can be implemented without external inverters and a 32-line decoder requires only one inverter. An enable input can be used as a data input for demultiplexing applications.

All of these decoder/demultiplexers feature fully buffered inputs, each of which represents only one normalized load to its driving circuit. All inputs are clamped with high-performance Schottky diodes to suppress line-ringing and to simplify system design.

The SN54LS138 and SN54S138 are characterized for operation over the full military temperature range of −55 °C to 125 °C. The SN74LS138 and SN74S138A are characterized for operation from 0 °C to 70 °C.

SN54LS138, SN54S138 . . . J OR W PACKAGE
SN74LS138, SN74S138A . . . D OR N PACKAGE
(TOP VIEW)

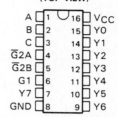

A	1	16	V$_{CC}$
B	2	15	Y0
C	3	14	Y1
$\overline{G}$2A	4	13	Y2
$\overline{G}$2B	5	12	Y3
G1	6	11	Y4
Y7	7	10	Y5
GND	8	9	Y6

SN54LS138, SN54S138 . . . FK PACKAGE
(TOP VIEW)

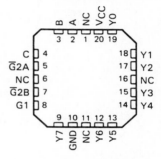

NC—No internal connection

logic symbols[†]

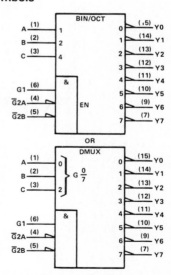

[†]These symbols are in accordance with ANSI/IEEE Std 91-1984 and IEC Publication 617-12.
Pin numbers shown are for D, J, N, and W packages.

TEXAS
INSTRUMENTS
POST OFFICE BOX 655012 • DALLAS. TEXAS 75265

Copyright © 1972, Texas Instruments Incorporated

2

TTL Devices

SN54LS138, SN54S138, SN74LS138, SN74S138A
3-LINE-TO 8-LINE DECODERS/DEMULTIPLEXERS

logic diagram and function table

'LS138, SN54S138, SN74S138A

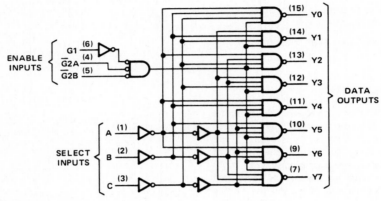

Pin numbers shown are for D, J, N, and W packages.

'LS138, SN54138, SN74S138A
FUNCTION TABLE

INPUTS					OUTPUTS							
ENABLE		SELECT										
G1	G̅2*	C	B	A	Y0	Y1	Y2	Y3	Y4	Y5	Y6	Y7
X	H	X	X	X	H	H	H	H	H	H	H	H
L	X	X	X	X	H	H	H	H	H	H	H	H
H	L	L	L	L	L	H	H	H	H	H	H	H
H	L	L	L	H	H	L	H	H	H	H	H	H
H	L	L	H	L	H	H	L	H	H	H	H	H
H	L	L	H	H	H	H	H	L	H	H	H	H
H	L	H	L	L	H	H	H	H	L	H	H	H
H	L	H	L	H	H	H	H	H	H	L	H	H
H	L	H	H	L	H	H	H	H	H	H	L	H
H	L	H	H	H	H	H	H	H	H	H	H	L

* $\overline{G2} = \overline{G2A} + \overline{G2B}$
H = high level, L = low level, X = irrelevant

'147, 'LS147

- Encodes 10-Line Decimal to 4-Line BCD

- Applications Include:

  Keyboard Encoding
  Range Selection: '148, 'LS148

- Encodes 8 Data Lines to 3-Line Binary (Octal)

- Applications Include:

  N-Bit Encoding
  Code Converters and Generators

TYPE	TYPICAL DATA DELAY	TYPICAL POWER DISSIPATION
'147	10 ns	225 mW
'148	10 ns	190 mW
'LS147	15 ns	60 mW
'LS148	15 ns	60 mW

description

These TTL encoders feature priority decoding of the inputs to ensure that only the highest-order data line is encoded. The '147 and 'LS147 encode nine data lines to four-line (8-4-2-1) BCD. The implied decimal zero condition requires no input condition as zero is encoded when all nine data lines are at a high logic level. The '148 and 'LS148 encode eight data lines to three-line (4-2-1) binary (octal). Cascading circuitry (enable input EI and enable output EO) has been provided to allow octal expansion without the need for external circuitry. For all types, data inputs and outputs are active at the low logic level. All inputs are buffered to represent one normalized Series 54/74 or 54LS/74LS load, respectively.

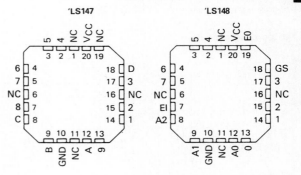

SN54147, SN54LS147,
SN54148, SN54LS148 . . . J OR W PACKAGE
SN74147, SN74148 . . . N PACKAGE
SN74LS147, SN74LS148 . . . D OR N PACKAGE
(TOP VIEW)

SN54LS147, SN54LS148 . . . FK PACKAGE
(TOP VIEW)

NC - No internal connection

TTL Devices

2

'147, 'LS147 FUNCTION TABLE

INPUTS									OUTPUTS			
1	2	3	4	5	6	7	8	9	D	C	B	A
H	H	H	H	H	H	H	H	H	H	H	H	H
X	X	X	X	X	X	X	X	L	L	H	H	L
X	X	X	X	X	X	X	L	H	L	H	H	H
X	X	X	X	X	X	L	H	H	H	L	L	L
X	X	X	X	X	L	H	H	H	H	L	L	H
X	X	X	X	L	H	H	H	H	H	L	H	L
X	X	X	L	H	H	H	H	H	H	L	H	H
X	X	L	H	H	H	H	H	H	H	H	L	L
X	L	H	H	H	H	H	H	H	H	H	L	H
L	H	H	H	H	H	H	H	H	H	H	H	L

'148, 'LS148 FUNCTION TABLE

INPUTS									OUTPUTS				
EI	0	1	2	3	4	5	6	7	A2	A1	A0	GS	EO
H	X	X	X	X	X	X	X	X	H	H	H	H	H
L	H	H	H	H	H	H	H	H	H	H	H	H	L
L	X	X	X	X	X	X	X	L	L	L	L	L	H
L	X	X	X	X	X	X	L	H	L	L	H	L	H
L	X	X	X	X	X	L	H	H	L	H	L	L	H
L	X	X	X	X	L	H	H	H	L	H	H	L	H
L	X	X	X	L	H	H	H	H	H	L	L	L	H
L	X	X	L	H	H	H	H	H	H	L	H	L	H
L	X	L	H	H	H	H	H	H	H	H	L	L	H
L	L	H	H	H	H	H	H	H	H	H	H	L	H

H = high logic level, L = low logic level, X = irrelevant

TEXAS
INSTRUMENTS

POST OFFICE BOX 655012 • DALLAS, TEXAS 75265

SN54147, SN54148, SN54LS147, SN54LS148,
SN74147, SN74148 (TIM9907), SN74LS147, SN74LS148
10-LINE TO 4-LINE AND 8-LINE TO 3-LINE PRIORITY ENCODERS

logic symbols[†]

'147, 'LS147

'148, 'LS148

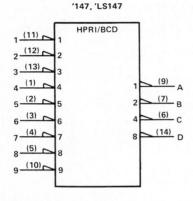

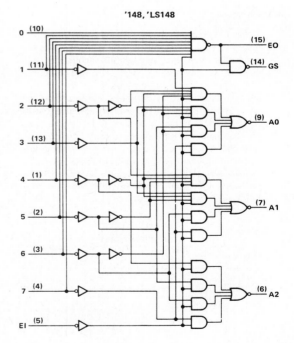

[†]These symbols are in accordance with ANSI/IEEE Std. 91-1984 and IEC Publication 617-12.

Pin numbers shown are for D, J, N, and W packages.

logic diagrams

'147, 'LS147

'148, 'LS148

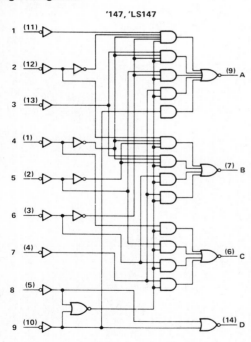

Pin numbers shown are for D, J, N, and W packages.

TEXAS
INSTRUMENTS
POST OFFICE BOX 655012 • DALLAS. TEXAS 75265

SN54147, SN54148 (TIM9907), SN54LS147, SN54LS148, SN74147, SN74148, SN74LS147, SN74LS148
10-LINE TO 4-LINE AND 8-LINE TO 3-LINE PRIORITY ENCODERS

TYPICAL APPLICATION DATA

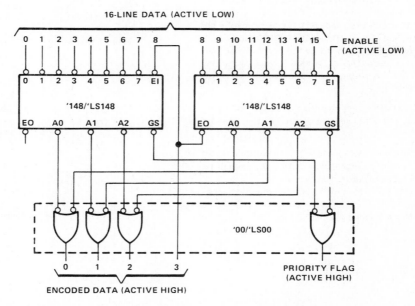

Since the '147/'LS147 and '148/'LS148 are combinational logic circuits, wrong addresses can appear during input transients. Moreover, for the '148/'LS148 a change from high to low at input EI can cause a transient low on the GS output when all inputs are high. This must be considered when strobing the outputs.

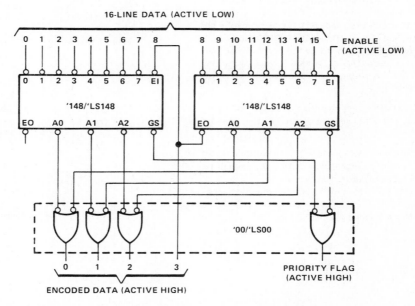

TEXAS
INSTRUMENTS

POST OFFICE BOX 655012 • DALLAS, TEXAS 75265

SN54150, SN54151A, SN54LS151, SN54S151, SN74150, SN74151A, SN74LS151, SN74S151
DATA SELECTORS/MULTIPLEXERS

DECEMBER 1972–REVISED MARCH 1988

- '150 Selects One-of-Sixteen Data Sources
- Others Select One-of-Eight Data Sources
- All Perform Parallel-to-Serial Conversion
- All Permit Multiplexing from N Lines to One Line
- Also For Use as Boolean Function Generator
- Input-Clamping Diodes Simplify System Design
- Fully Compatible with Most TTL Circuits

TYPE	TYPICAL AVERAGE PROPAGATION DELAY TIME DATA INPUT TO W OUTPUT	TYPICAL POWER DISSIPATION
'150	13 ns	200 mW
'151A	8 ns	145 mW
'LS151	13 ns	30 mW
'S151	4.5 ns	225 mW

description

These monolithic data selectors/multiplexers contain full on-chip binary decoding to select the desired data source. The '150 selects one-of-sixteen data sources; the '151A, 'LS151, and 'S151 select one-of-eight data sources. The '150, '151A, 'LS151, and 'S151 have a strobe input which must be at a low logic level to enable these devices. A high level at the strobe forces the W output high, and the Y output (as applicable) low.

The '150 has only an inverted W output; the '151A, 'LS151, and 'S151 feature complementary W and Y outputs.

The '151A and '152A incorporate address buffers that have symmetrical propagation delay times through the complementary paths. This reduces the possibility of transients occurring at the output(s) due to changes made at the select inputs, even when the '151A outputs are enabled (i.e., strobe low).

SN54150 . . . J OR W PACKAGE
SN74150 . . . N PACKAGE
(TOP VIEW)

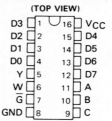

SN54151A, SN54LS151, SN54S151 . . . J OR W PACKAGE
SN74151A . . . N PACKAGE
SN74LS151, SN74S151 . . . D OR N PACKAGE
(TOP VIEW)

SN54LS151, SN54S151 . . . FK PACKAGE
(TOP VIEW)

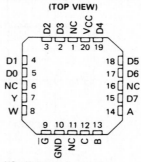

NC - No internal connection

TEXAS INSTRUMENTS
POST OFFICE BOX 655012 • DALLAS, TEXAS 75265

TTL Devices

2

SN54150, SN54151A, SN54LS151, SN54S151,
SN74150, SN74151A, SN74LS151, SN74S151
DATA SELECTORS/MULTIPLEXERS

logic symbols[†]

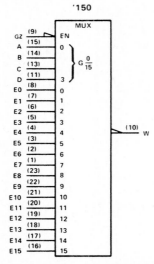

'150

'151A, 'LS151, 'S151

[†]These symbols are in accordance with ANSI/IEEE Std. 91-1984 and IEC Publication 617-12.
Pin numbers shown are D, J, N, and W packages.

'150

FUNCTION TABLE

SELECT				STROBE	OUTPUT
D	C	B	A	$\overline{G}$	W
X	X	X	X	H	H
L	L	L	L	L	$\overline{E0}$
L	L	L	H	L	$\overline{E1}$
L	L	H	L	L	$\overline{E2}$
L	L	H	H	L	$\overline{E3}$
L	H	L	L	L	$\overline{E4}$
L	H	L	H	L	$\overline{E5}$
L	H	H	L	L	$\overline{E6}$
L	H	H	H	L	$\overline{E7}$
H	L	L	L	L	$\overline{E8}$
H	L	L	H	L	$\overline{E9}$
H	L	H	L	L	$\overline{E10}$
H	L	H	H	L	$\overline{E11}$
H	H	L	L	L	$\overline{E12}$
H	H	L	H	L	$\overline{E13}$
H	H	H	L	L	$\overline{E14}$
H	H	H	H	L	$\overline{E15}$

'151A, 'LS151, 'S151

FUNCTION TABLE

SELECT			STROBE	OUTPUTS	
C	B	A	$\overline{G}$	Y	W
X	X	X	H	L	H
L	L	L	L	D0	$\overline{D0}$
L	L	H	L	D1	$\overline{D1}$
L	H	L	L	D2	$\overline{D2}$
L	H	H	L	D3	$\overline{D3}$
H	L	L	L	D4	$\overline{D4}$
H	L	H	L	D5	$\overline{D5}$
H	H	L	L	D6	$\overline{D6}$
H	H	H	L	D7	$\overline{D7}$

H = high level, L = low level, X = irrelevant
$\overline{E0}, \overline{E1} \ldots \overline{E15}$ = the complement of the level of the respective E input
D0, D1 . . . D7 = the level of the D respective input

TEXAS INSTRUMENTS
POST OFFICE BOX 655012 • DALLAS, TEXAS 75265

SN54150, SN54151A, SN54LS151, SN54S151,
SN74150, SN74151A, SN74LS151, SN74S151
DATA SELECTORS/MULTIPLEXERS

logic diagrams (positive logic)

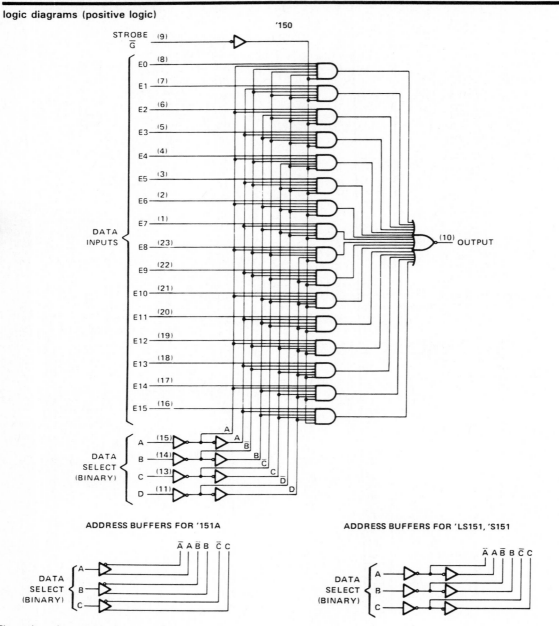

'150

STROBE $\overline{G}$ (9)

DATA INPUTS
E0 (8)
E1 (7)
E2 (6)
E3 (5)
E4 (4)
E5 (3)
E6 (2)
E7 (1)
E8 (23)
E9 (22)
E10 (21)
E11 (20)
E12 (19)
E13 (18)
E14 (17)
E15 (16)

(10) OUTPUT

DATA SELECT (BINARY)
A (15)
B (14)
C (13)
D (11)

ADDRESS BUFFERS FOR '151A

DATA SELECT (BINARY)
A
B
C

$\overline{A}$ A $\overline{B}$ B $\overline{C}$ C

ADDRESS BUFFERS FOR 'LS151, 'S151

DATA SELECT (BINARY)
A
B
C

$\overline{A}$ A $\overline{B}$ B $\overline{C}$ C

Pin numbers shown are for D, J, N, and W packages.

TEXAS INSTRUMENTS

POST OFFICE BOX 655012 • DALLAS, TEXAS 75265

'151A, 'LS151, 'S151

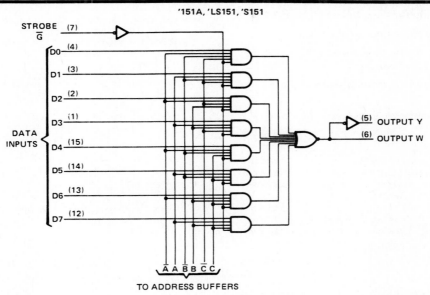

TO ADDRESS BUFFERS

absolute maximum ratings over operating free-air temperature range (unless otherwise noted)

Supply voltage, V_{CC} (see Note 1) . . . . 7 V
Input voltage (see Note 2): '150, '151A, 'S151 . . . . 5.5 V
'LS151 . . . . 7 V
Operating free-air temperature range: SN54' . . . . −55°C to 125°C
SN74' . . . . 0°C to 70°C
Storage temperature range . . . . −65°C to 150°C

NOTES: 1: Voltage values are with respect to network ground terminal.
2. For the '150, input voltages must be zero or positive with respect to network ground terminal.

TTL Devices

2

- **Permits Multiplexing from N lines to 1 line**
- **Performs Parallel-to-Serial Conversion**
- **Strobe (Enable) Line Provided for Cascading (N lines to n lines)**
- **High-Fan-Out, Low-Impedance, Totem-Pole Outputs**
- **Fully Compatible with most TTL Circuits**

SN54153, SN54LS153, SN54S153 . . . J OR W PACKAGE
SN74153 . . . N PACKAGE
SN74LS153, SN74S153 . . . D OR N PACKAGE
(TOP VIEW)

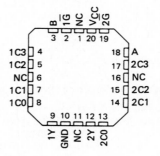

TYPE	TYPICAL AVERAGE PROPAGATION DELAY TIMES			TYPICAL POWER DISSIPATION
	FROM DATA	FROM STROBE	FROM SELECT	
'153	14 ns	17 ns	22 ns	180 mW
'LS153	14 ns	19 ns	22 ns	31 mW
'S153	6 ns	9.5 ns	12 ns	225 mW

SN54LS153, SN54S153 . . . FK PACKAGE
(TOP VIEW)

NC – No internal connection

description

Each of these monolithic, data selectors/multiplexers contains inverters and drivers to supply fully complementary, on-chip, binary decoding data selection to the AND-OR gates. Separate strobe inputs are provided for each of the two four-line sections.

FUNCTION TABLE

SELECT INPUTS		DATA INPUTS				STROBE	OUTPUT
B	A	C0	C1	C2	C3	$\overline{G}$	Y
X	X	X	X	X	X	H	L
L	L	L	X	X	X	L	L
L	L	H	X	X	X	L	H
L	H	X	L	X	X	L	L
L	H	X	H	X	X	L	H
H	L	X	X	L	X	L	L
H	L	X	X	H	X	L	H
H	H	X	X	X	L	L	L
H	H	X	X	X	H	L	H

Select inputs A and B are common to both sections.
H = high level, L = low level, X = irrelevant

absolute maximum ratings over operating free-air temperature range (unless otherwise noted)

Supply voltage, V$_{CC}$ (See Note 1) . . . . 7 V
Input voltage: '153, 'S153 . . . . 5.5 V
            'LS153 . . . . 7 V
Operating free-air temperature range: SN54' . . . . –55°C to 125°C
                   SN74' . . . . 0°C to 70°C
Storage temperature range . . . . –65°C to 150°C

NOTE 1: Voltage values are with respect to network ground terminal.

TEXAS
INSTRUMENTS

POST OFFICE BOX 655012 • DALLAS, TEXAS 75265

2

TTL Devices

SN54153, SN54LS153, SN54S153
SN74153, SN74LS153, SN74S153
DUAL 4-LINE TO 1-LINE DATA SELECTORS/MULTIPLEXERS

logic symbol†

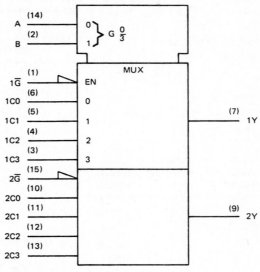

†This symbol is in accordance with ANSI/IEEE Std. 91-1984 and IEC Publication 617-12.

logic diagrams (positive logic)

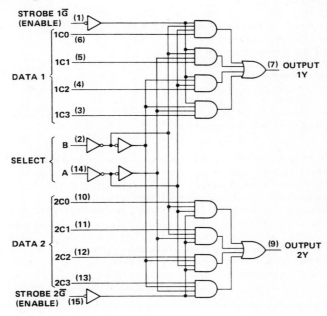

Pin numbers shown are for D, J, N, and W packages.

TEXAS
INSTRUMENTS

POST OFFICE BOX 655012 • DALLAS, TEXAS 75265

'160, '161, 'LS160A, 'LS161A . . . SYNCHRONOUS COUNTERS WITH DIRECT CLEAR
'162, '163, 'LS162A, 'LS163A, 'S162, 'S163 . . . FULLY SYNCHRONOUS COUNTERS

- Internal Look-Ahead for Fast Counting
- Carry Output for n-Bit Cascading
- Synchronous Counting
- Synchronously Programmable
- Load Control Line
- Diode-Clamped Inputs

TYPE	TYPICAL PROPAGATION TIME, CLOCK TO Q OUTPUT	TYPICAL MAXIMUM CLOCK FREQUENCY	TYPICAL POWER DISSIPATION
'160 thru '163	14 ns	32 MHz	305 mW
'LS162A thru 'LS163A	14 ns	32 MHz	93 mW
'S162 and 'S163	9 ns	70 MHz	475 mW

SERIES 54', 54LS' 54S' . . . J OR W PACKAGE
SERIES 74' . . . N PACKAGE
SERIES 74LS', 74S' . . . D OR N PACKAGE
(TOP VIEW)

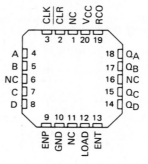

NC—No internal connection

SERIES 54LS', 54S' . . . FK PACKAGE
(TOP VIEW)

NC—No internal connection

description

These synchronous, presettable counters feature an internal carry look-ahead for application in high-speed counting designs. The '160, '162, 'LS160A, 'LS162A, and 'S162 are decade counters and the '161, '163, 'LS161A, 'LS163A, and 'S163 are 4-bit binary counters. Synchronous operation is provided by having all flip-flops clocked simultaneously so that the outputs change coincident with each other when so instructed by the count-enable inputs and internal gating. This mode of operation eliminates the output counting spikes that are normally associated with asynchronous (ripple clock) counters, however counting spikes may occur on the (RCO) ripple carry output. A buffered clock input triggers the four flip-flops on the rising edge of the clock input waveform.

These counters are fully programmable; that is, the outputs may be preset to either level. As presetting is synchronous, setting up a low level at the load input disables the counter and causes the outputs to agree with the setup data after the next clock pulse regardless of the levels of the enable inputs. Low-to-high transitions at the load input of the '160 thru '163 should be avoided when the clock is low if the enable inputs are high at or before the transition. This restriction is not applicable to the 'LS160A thru 'LS163À or 'S162 or 'S163. The clear function for the '160, '161, 'LS160A, and 'LS161A is asynchronous and a low level at the clear input sets all four of the flip-flop outputs low regardless of the levels of clock, load, or enable inputs. The clear function for the '162, '163, 'LS162A, 'LS163A, 'S162, and 'S163 is synchronous and a low level at the clear input sets all four of the flip-flop outputs low after the next clock pulse, regardless of the levels of the enable inputs. This synchronous clear allows the count length to be modified easily as decoding the maximum count desired can be accomplished with one external NAND gate. The gate output is connected to the clear input to synchronously clear the counter to 0000 (LLLL). Low-to-high transitions at the clear input of the '162 and '163 should be avoided when the clock is low if the enable and load inputs are high at or before the transition.

TEXAS
INSTRUMENTS

POST OFFICE BOX 655012 • DALLAS, TEXAS 75265

2-493

TTL Devices

2

SN54160 THRU SN54163, SN54LS160A THRU SN54LS163A, SN54S162, SN54S163, SN74160 THRU SN74163, SN74LS160A THRU SN74LS163A, SN74S162, SN74S163 SYNCHRONOUS 4-BIT COUNTERS

The carry look-ahead circuitry provides for cascading counters for n-bit synchronous applications without additional gating. Instrumental in accomplishing this function are two count-enable inputs and a ripple carry output. Both count-enable inputs (P and T) must be high to count, and input T is fed forward to enable the ripple carry output. The ripple carry output thus enabled will produce a high-level output pulse with a duration approximately equal to the high-level portion of the Q_A output. This high-level overflow ripple carry pulse can be used to enable successive cascaded stages. High-to-low-level transitions at the enable P or T inputs of the '160 thru '163 should occur only when the clock input is high. Transitions at the enable P or T inputs of the 'LS160A thru 'LS163A or 'S162 and 'S163 are allowed regardless of the level of the clock input.

'LS160A thru 'LS163A, 'S162 and 'S163 feature a fully independent clock circuit. Changes at control inputs (enable P or T, or load) that will modify the operating mode have no effect until clocking occurs. The function of the counter (whether enabled, disabled, loading, or counting) will be dictated solely by the conditions meeting the stable setup and hold times.

logic symbols†

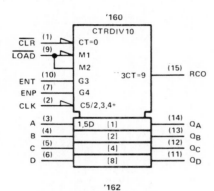

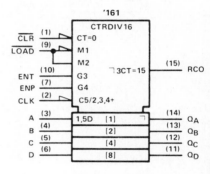

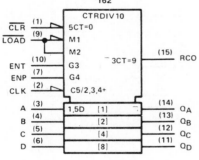

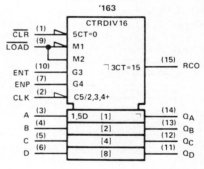

†These symbols are in accordance with ANSI/IEEE Std 91-1984 and IEC Publication 617-12.

Pin numbers shown are for D, J, N, and W packages.

TEXAS INSTRUMENTS

POST OFFICE BOX 655012 • DALLAS, TEXAS 75265

logic symbols (continued)[†]

'LS160A

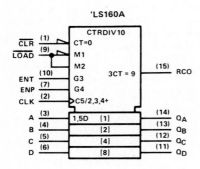

'LS161A

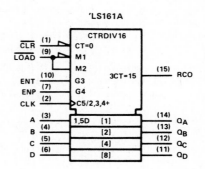

'LS162A, 'S162

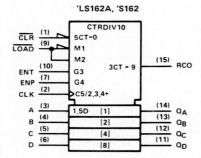

'LS163A, 'S163

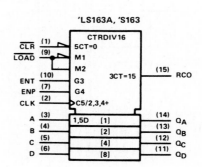

[†]These symbols are in accordance with ANSI/IEEE Std 91-1984 and
IEC Publication 617-12.

Pin numbers shown are for D, J, N, and W packages.

TEXAS
INSTRUMENTS
POST OFFICE BOX 655012 • DALLAS, TEXAS 75265

TTL Devices

2

SN54LS160A, SN54LS162A, SN74LS160A, SN74LS162A
SYNCHRONOUS 4-BIT COUNTERS

logic diagram (positive logic)

SN54LS160A, SN74LS160A SYNCHRONOUS
DECADE COUNTERS

SN54LS162A, SN74LS162A synchronous decade counters are similar; however the clear is synchronous as shown for the SN54LS163A, SN74LS163A binary counters at right.

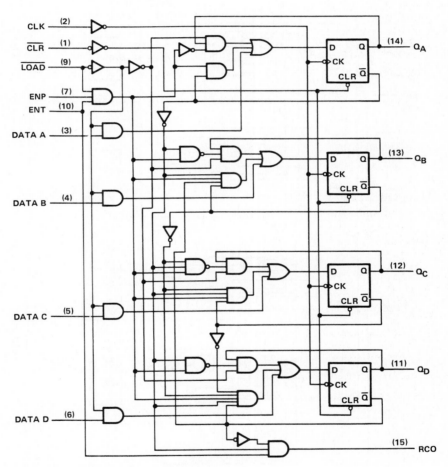

Pin numbers shown are for D, J, N, and W packages.

TEXAS
INSTRUMENTS
POST OFFICE BOX 655012 • DALLAS, TEXAS 75265

SN54LS161A, SN54LS163A, SN74LS161A, SN74LS163A
SYNCHRONOUS 4-BIT COUNTERS

logic diagram (positive logic)

SN54LS163A, SN74LS163A SYNCHRONOUS BINARY COUNTERS

SN54LS161A, SN74LS161A synchronous binary counters are similar; however, the clear is asynchronous as shown for the SN54LS160A, SN74LS160A decade counters at left.

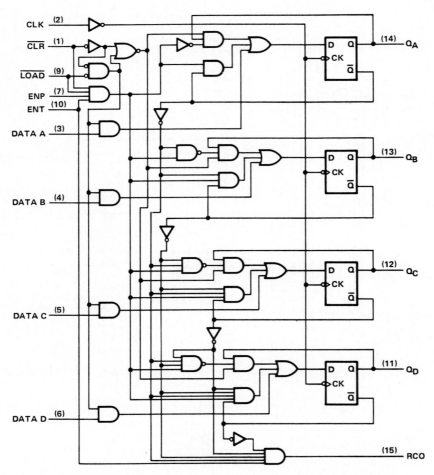

Pin numbers shown are for D, J, N, and W packages.

TEXAS INSTRUMENTS
POST OFFICE BOX 655012 • DALLAS, TEXAS 75265

TTL Devices

2

SN54160, SN54162, SN54LS160A, SN54LS162A, SN54S162, SN74160, SN74162, SN74LS160A, SN74LS162A, SN74S162 SYNCHRONOUS 4-BIT COUNTERS

'160, '162, 'LS160A, 'LS162A, 'S162 DECADE COUNTERS

typical clear, preset, count, and inhibit sequences

Illustrated below is the following sequence:

1. Clear outputs to zero ('160 and 'LS160A are asynchronous; '162, 'LS162A, and 'S162 are synchronous)
2. Preset to BCD seven
3. Count to eight, nine, zero, one, two, and three
4. Inhibit

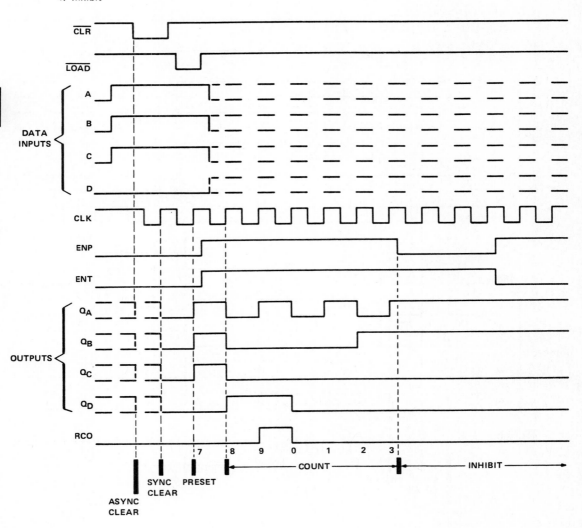

TEXAS
INSTRUMENTS
POST OFFICE BOX 655012 • DALLAS, TEXAS 75265

'161, 'LS161A, '163, 'LS163A, 'S163 BINARY COUNTERS

typical clear, preset, count, and inhibit sequences

Illustrated below is the following sequence:

1. Clear outputs to zero ('161 and 'LS161A are asynchronous; '163, 'LS163A, and 'S163 are synchronous)
2. Preset to binary twelve
3. Count to thirteen, fourteen fifteen, zero, one, and two
4. Inhibit

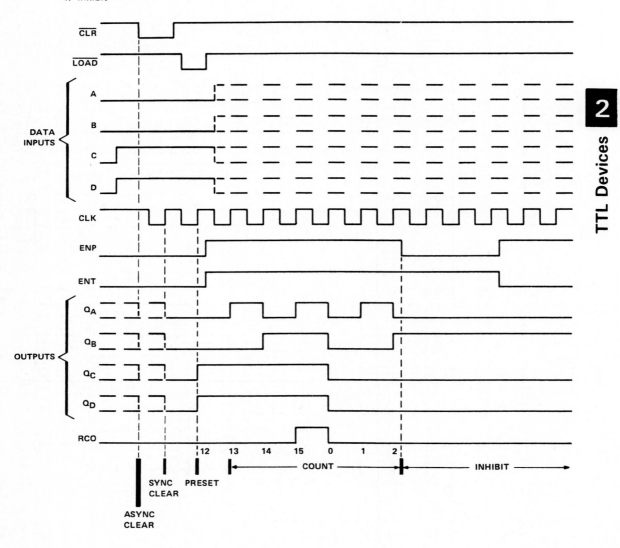

2

TTL Devices

SN54LS160A THRU SN54LS163A, SN74LS160A THRU SN74LS163A
SYNCHRONOUS 4-BIT COUNTERS

schematics of inputs and outputs

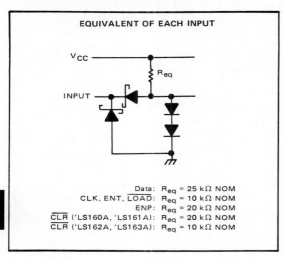

EQUIVALENT OF EACH INPUT

Data: R_{eq} = 25 kΩ NOM
CLK, ENT, $\overline{LOAD}$: R_{eq} = 10 kΩ NOM
ENP: R_{eq} = 20 kΩ NOM
$\overline{CLR}$ ('LS160A, 'LS161A): R_{eq} = 20 kΩ NOM
$\overline{CLR}$ ('LS162A, 'LS163A): R_{eq} = 10 kΩ NOM

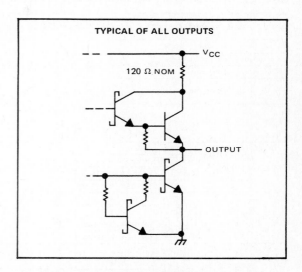

TYPICAL OF ALL OUTPUTS

120 Ω NOM

absolute maximum ratings over operating free-air temperature range (unless otherwise noted)

Supply voltage, V_{CC} (see Note 7) . . . . 7 V
Input voltage . . . . 7 V
Operating free-air temperature range: SN54LS' Circuits . . . . -55°C to 125°C
                                        SN74LS' Circuits . . . . 0°C to 70°C
Storage temperature range . . . . -65°C to 150°C

NOTE 7: Voltage values are with respect to network ground terminal.

recommended operating conditions

		SN54LS'			SN74LS'			UNIT
		MIN	NOM	MAX	MIN	NOM	MAX	
V_{CC}	Supply voltage	4.5	5	5.5	4.75	5	5.25	V
I_{OH}	High-level output current			−400			−400	µA
I_{OL}	Low-level output current			4			8	mA
f_{clock}	Clock frequency	0		25	0		25	MHz
$t_{w(clock)}$	Width of clock pulse	25			25			ns
$t_{w(clear)}$	Width of clear pulse	20			20			ns
t_{su}	Setup time, (see Figures 1 and 2)	Data inputs A, B, C, D	20			20			ns
		ENP or ENT	20			20		
		$\overline{LOAD}$	20			20		
		$\overline{LOAD}$ inactive state	20			20		
		$\overline{CLR}$†	20			20		
		$\overline{CLR}$ inactive state	25			25		
t_h	Hold time at any input	3			3			ns
T_A	Operating free-air temperature	−55		125	0		70	°C

† This applies only for 'LS162 and 'LS163, which have synchronous clear inputs.

TEXAS
INSTRUMENTS

POST OFFICE BOX 655012 • DALLAS, TEXAS 75265

electrical characteristics over recommended operating free-air temperature range (unless otherwise noted)

PARAMETER			TEST CONDITIONS†		SN54LS' MIN	SN54LS' TYP‡	SN54LS' MAX	SN74LS' MIN	SN74LS' TYP‡	SN74LS' MAX	UNIT
V_{IH}	High-level input voltage				2			2			V
V_{IL}	Low-level input voltage						0.7			0.8	V
V_{IK}	Input clamp voltage		V_{CC} = MIN,	I_I = −18 mA			−1.5			−1.5	V
V_{OH}	High-level output voltage		V_{CC} = MIN, V_{IH} = 2 V, V_{IL} = V_{IL} max, I_{OH} = −400 µA		2.5	3.4		2.7	3.4		V
V_{OL}	Low-level output voltage		V_{CC} = MIN, V_{IH} = 2 V, V_{IL} = V_{IL} max	I_{OL} = 4 mA		0.25	0.4		0.25	0.4	V
				I_{OL} = 8 mA					0.35	0.5	
I_I	Input current at maximum input voltage	Data or ENP	V_{CC} = MAX, V_I = 7 V				0.1			0.1	mA
		$\overline{LOAD}$, CLK, or ENT					0.2			0.2	
		$\overline{CLR}$ ('LS160A, 'LS161A)					0.1			0.1	
		$\overline{CLR}$ ('LS162A, 'LS163A)					0.2			0.2	
I_{IH}	High-level input current	Data or ENP	V_{CC} = MAX, V_I = 2.7 V				20			20	µA
		$\overline{LOAD}$, CLK, or ENT					40			40	
		$\overline{CLR}$ ('LS160A, 'LS161A)					20			20	
		$\overline{CLR}$ ('LS162A, 'LS163A)					40			40	
I_{IL}	Low-level input current	Data or ENP	V_{CC} = MAX, V_I = 0.4 V				−0.4			−0.4	mA
		$\overline{LOAD}$, CLK, or ENT					−0.8			−0.8	
		$\overline{CLR}$ ('LS160A, 'LS161A)					−0.4			−0.4	
		$\overline{CLR}$ ('LS162A, 'LS163A)					−0.8			−0.8	
I_{OS}	Short-circuit output current§		V_{CC} = MAX		−20		−100	−20		−100	mA
I_{CCH}	Supply current, all outputs high		V_{CC} = MAX, See Note 3			18	31		18	31	mA
I_{CCL}	Supply current, all outputs low		V_{CC} = MAX, See Note 4			19	32		19	32	mA

†For conditions shown as MIN or MAX, use the appropriate value specified under recommended operating conditions.
‡All typical values are at V_{CC} = 5 V, T_A = 25°C.
§Not more than one output should be shorted at a time, and duration of the short-circuit should not exceed one second.
NOTES: 3. I_{CCH} is measured with the load input high, then again with the load input low, with all other inputs high and all outputs open.
       4. I_{CCL} is measured with the clock input high, then again with the clock input low, with all other inputs low and all outputs open.

switching characteristics, V_{CC} = 5 V, T_A = 25°C

PARAMETER¶	FROM (INPUT)	TO (OUTPUT)	TEST CONDITIONS	MIN	TYP	MAX	UNIT
f_{max}				25	32		MHz
t_{PLH}	CLK	RCO			20	35	ns
t_{PHL}					18	35	
t_{PLH}	CLK ($\overline{LOAD}$ input high)	Any Q	C_L = 15 pF, R_L = 2 kΩ, See figures 1 and 2 and Note 8		13	24	ns
t_{PHL}					18	27	
t_{PLH}	CLK ($\overline{LOAD}$ input low)	Any Q			13	24	ns
t_{PHL}					18	27	
t_{PLH}	ENT	RCO			9	14	ns
t_{PHL}					9	14	
t_{PHL}	$\overline{CLR}$	Any Q			20	28	ns

¶f_{max} = Maximum clock frequency
t_{PLH} = propagation delay time, low-to-high-level output.
t_{PHL} = propagation delay time, high-to-low-level output.
NOTE 8: Propagation delay for clearing is measured from the clear input for the 'LS160A and 'LS161A or from the clock transition for the 'LS162A and 'LS163A.

TEXAS
INSTRUMENTS
POST OFFICE BOX 655012 • DALLAS, TEXAS 75265

2-507

SN54160 THRU SN54163, SN54LS160A THRU SN54LS163A, SN54S162, SN54S163, SN74160 THRU SN74163, SN74LS160A THRU SN74LS163A, SN74S162, SN74S163 SYNCHRONOUS 4-BIT COUNTERS

PARAMETER MEASUREMENT INFORMATION

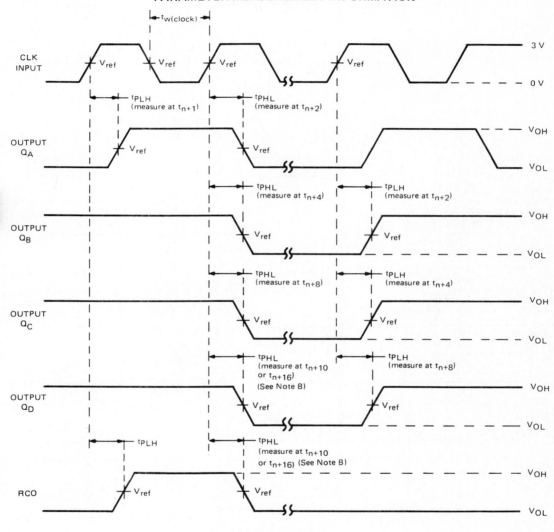

VOLTAGE WAVEFORMS

NOTES: A. The input pulses are supplied by a generator having the following characteristics: PRR ≤ 1 MHz, duty cycle ≤ 50%, $Z_{out} \approx 50\ \Omega$; for '160 thru '163, $t_r \leq 10$ ns, $t_f \leq 10$ ns; for 'LS160A thru 'LS163A, $t_r \leq 15$ ns, $t_f \leq 6$ ns; and for 'S162, 'S163, $t_r \leq 2.5$ ns, $t_f \leq 2.5$ ns. Vary PRR to measure f_{max}.
B. Outputs Q_D and carry are tested at t_{n+10} for '160, '162, 'LS160A, 'LS162A, and 'S162, and at t_{n+16} for '161, '163, 'LS161A, 'LS163A, and 'S163, where t_n is the bit time when all outputs are low.
C. For '160 thru '163, 'S162, and 'S163, $V_{ref} = 1.5$ V; for 'LS160A thru 'LS163A, $V_{ref} = 1.3$ V.

FIGURE 1—SWITCHING TIMES

TEXAS INSTRUMENTS

POST OFFICE BOX 655012 • DALLAS, TEXAS 75265

PARAMETER MEASUREMENT INFORMATION

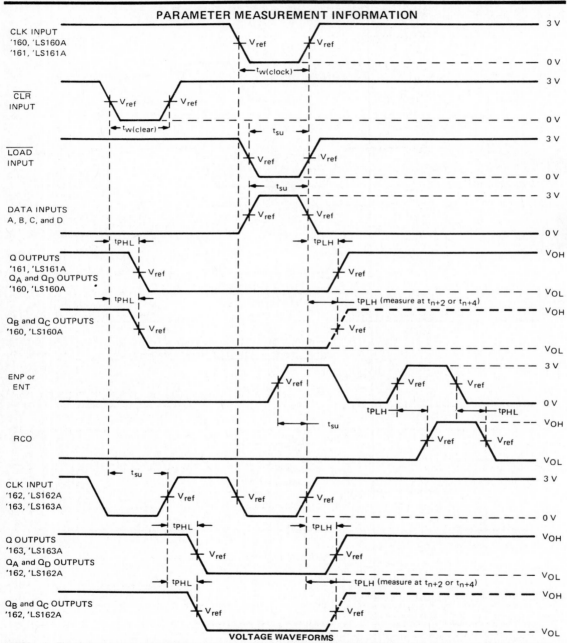

VOLTAGE WAVEFORMS

NOTES: A. The input pulses are supplied by generators having the following characteristics: PRR ≤ 1 MHz, duty cycle ≤ 50%, $Z_{out} \approx 50\ \Omega$; for '160 thru '163, $t_r \le 10$ ns, $t_f \le 10$ ns; and for 'LS160A thru 'LS163A, $t_r \le 15$ ns, $t_f \le 6$ ns.

B. Enable P and enable T setup times are measured at t_{n+0}.

C. For '160 thru '163, $V_{ref} = 1.5$ V; for 'LS160A thru 'LS163A, $V_{ref} = 1.3$ V.

FIGURE 2—SWITCHING TIMES

TTL Devices

TEXAS
INSTRUMENTS

POST OFFICE BOX 655012 • DALLAS, TEXAS 75265

PARAMETER MEASUREMENT INFORMATION

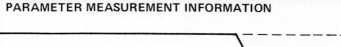

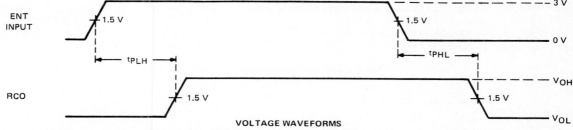

VOLTAGE WAVEFORMS

NOTES: A. The input pulse is supplied by a generator having the following characteristics: $t_r \leq 2.5$ ns, $t_f \leq 2.5$ ns, PRR $\leq$ 1 MHz, duty cycle $\leq$ 50%, $Z_{out} \approx 50$ Ω.

B. t_{PLH} and t_{PHL} from enable T input to carry output assume that the counter is at the maximum count (Q_A and Q_D high for 'S162, all Q outputs high for 'S163).

FIGURE 3–PROPAGATION DELAY TIMES FROM ENABLE T INPUT TO CARRY OUTPUT

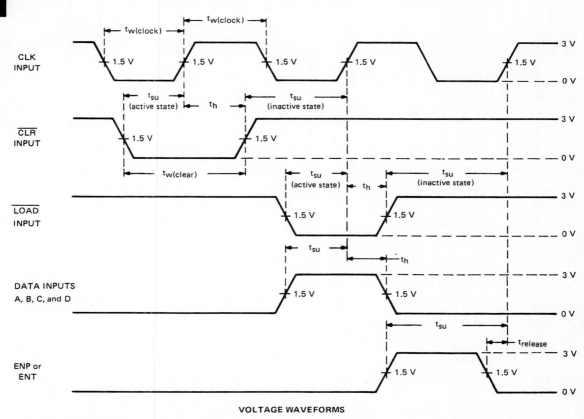

VOLTAGE WAVEFORMS

NOTE A: The input pulses are supplied by generators having the following characteristics: $t_r \leq 2.5$ ns, $t_f \leq 2.5$ ns, PRR $\leq$ 1 MHz, duty cycle $\leq$ 50%, $Z_{out} \approx 50$ Ω.

FIGURE 4–PULSE WIDTHS, SETUP TIMES, HOLD TIMES, AND RELEASE TIME

TEXAS INSTRUMENTS

POST OFFICE BOX 655012 • DALLAS, TEXAS 75265

2

TTL Devices

TYPICAL APPLICATION DATA

This application demonstrates how the ripple mode carry circuit (Figure 1) and the carry-look-ahead circuit (Figure 2) can be used to implement a high-speed N-bit counter. The '160, '162, 'LS160A, 'LS162A, or 'S162 will count in BCD and the '161, '163, 'LS161A, 'LS163A, or 'S163 will count in binary. When additional stages are added the f_{MAX} decreases in Figure 1, but remains unchanged in Figure 2.

N-BIT SYNCHRONOUS COUNTERS

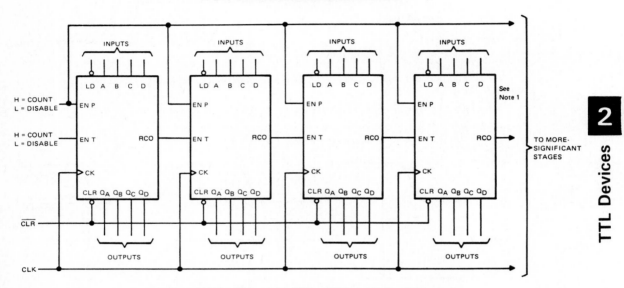

$$f_{MAX} = 1/(\text{CLK to RCO } t_{PLH}) + (\text{ENT to RCO } t_{PLH})(N-2) + (\text{ENT } t_{su})$$

FIGURE 1

TEXAS INSTRUMENTS
POST OFFICE BOX 655012 • DALLAS, TEXAS 75265

TTL Devices

2

SN54160 THRU SN54163, SN54LS160A THRU SN54LS163A, SN54S162, SN54S163, SN74160 THRU SN74163, SN74LS160A THRU SN74LS163A, SN74S162, SN74S163
SYNCHRONOUS 4-BIT COUNTERS

TYPICAL APPLICATION DATA

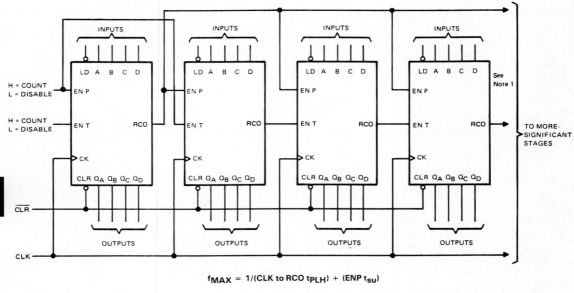

$$f_{MAX} = 1/(\text{CLK to RCO } t_{PLH}) + (\text{ENP } t_{su})$$

FIGURE 2

TEXAS
INSTRUMENTS
POST OFFICE BOX 655012 • DALLAS, TEXAS 75265

- **Gated Serial Inputs**
- **Fully Buffered Clock and Serial Inputs**
- **Asynchronous Clear**

TYPE	TYPICAL MAXIMUM CLOCK FREQUENCY	TYPICAL POWER DISSIPATION
'164	36 MHz	21 mW per bit
'LS164	36 MHz	10 mW per bit

description

These 8-bit shift registers feature gated serial inputs and an asynchronous clear. The gated serial inputs (A and B) permit complete control over incoming data as a low at either input inhibits entry of the new data and resets the first flip-flop to the low level at the next clock pulse. A high-level input enables the other input which will then determine the state of the first flip-flop. Data at the serial inputs may be changed while the clock is high or low, but only information meeting the setup-time requirements will be entered. Clocking occurs on the low-to-high-level transition of the clock input. All inputs are diode-clamped to minimize transmission-line effects.

The SN54164 and SN54LS164 are characterized for operation over the full military temperature range of −55°C to 125°C. The SN74164 and SN74LS164 are characterized for operation from 0°C to 70°C.

SN54164, SN54LS164 . . . J OR W PACKAGE
SN74164 . . . N PACKAGE
SN74LS164 . . . D OR N PACKAGE
(TOP VIEW)

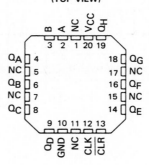

SN54LS164 . . . FK PACKAGE
(TOP VIEW)

NC — No internal connection

FUNCTION TABLE

INPUTS				OUTPUTS		
CLEAR	CLOCK	A	B	Q_A	Q_B $\cdots$	Q_H
L	X	X	X	L	L	L
H	L	X	X	Q_{A0}	Q_{B0}	Q_{H0}
H	↑	H	H	H	Q_{An}	Q_{Gn}
H	↑	L	X	L	Q_{An}	Q_{Gn}
H	↑	X	L	L	Q_{An}	Q_{Gn}

H = high level (steady state), L = low level (steady state)
X = irrelevant (any input, including transitions)
↑ = transition from low to high level.
Q_{A0}, Q_{B0}, Q_{H0} = the level of Q_A, Q_B, or Q_H, respectively, before the indicated steady-state input conditions were established.
Q_{An}, Q_{Gn} = the level of Q_A or Q_G before the most-recent ↑ transition of the clock; indicates a one-bit shift.

schematics of inputs and outputs

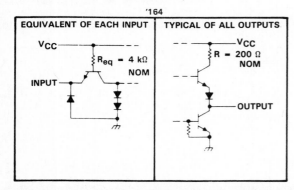

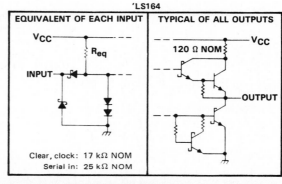

2

TTL Devices

SN54164, SN54LS164, SN74164, SN74LS164
8-BIT PARALLEL-OUT SERIAL SHIFT REGISTERS

typical clear, shift, and clear sequences

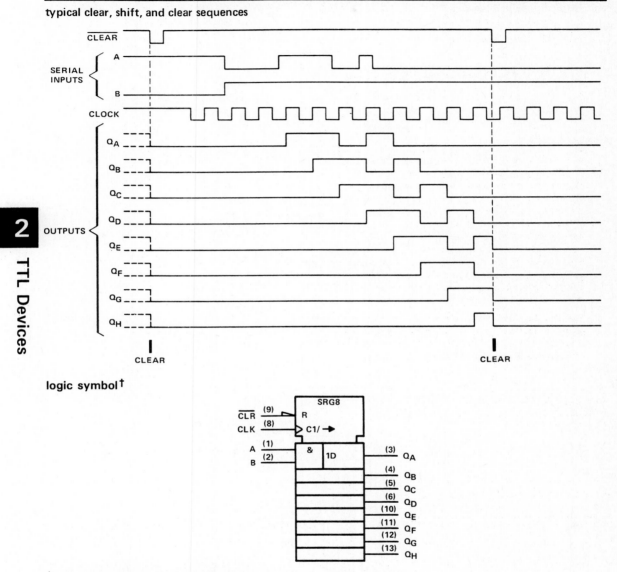

logic symbol†

†This symbol is in accordance with ANSI/IEEE Std. 91-1984 and IEC Publication 617-12.
Pin numbers shown are for D, J, N, and W packages.

TEXAS
INSTRUMENTS
POST OFFICE BOX 655012 • DALLAS, TEXAS 75265

logic diagram (positive logic)

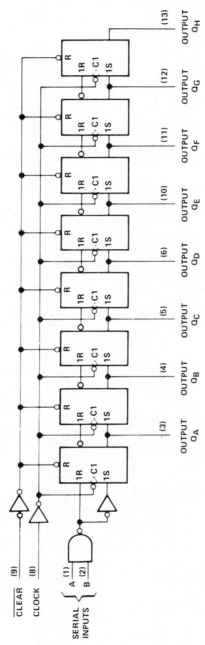

Pin numbers shown are for D, J, N, and W packages.

2

TTL Devices

TEXAS
INSTRUMENTS
POST OFFICE BOX 655012 • DALLAS, TEXAS 75265

SN54166, SN54LS166A, SN74166, SN74LS166A
PARALLEL-LOAD 8-BIT SHIFT REGISTERS

OCTOBER 1976 — REVISED MARCH 1988

- **Synchronous Load**
- **Direct Overriding Clear**
- **Parallel to Serial Conversion**

TYPE	TYPICAL MAXIMUM CLOCK FREQUENCY	TYPICAL POWER DISSIPATION
'166	35 MHz	360 mW
'LS166A	35 MHz	100 mW

description

The '166 and 'LS166A 8-bit shift registers are compatible with most other TTL logic families. All '166 and 'LS166A inputs are buffered to lower the drive requirements to one Series 54/74 or Series 54LS/74LS standard load, respectively. Input clamping diodes minimize switching transients and simplify system design.

These parallel-in or serial-in, serial-out shift registers have a complexity of 77 equivalent gates on a monolithic chip. They feature gated clock inputs and an overriding clear input. The parallel-in or serial-in modes are established by the shift/load input. When high, this input enables the serial data input and couples the eight flip-flops for serial shifting with each clock pulse. When low, the parallel (broadside) data inputs are enabled and synchronous loading occurs on the next clock pulse. During parallel loading, serial data flow is inhibited. Clocking is accomplished on the low-to-high-level edge of the clock pulse through a two-input positive NOR gate permitting one input to be used as a clock-enable or clock-inhibit function. Holding either of the clock inputs high inhibits clocking; holding either low enables the other clock input. This, of course, allows the system clock to be free-running and the register can be stopped on command with the other clock input. The clock inhibit input should be changed to the high level only while the clock input is high. A buffered, direct clear input overrides all other inputs, including the clock, and sets all flip-flops to zero.

SN54166, SN54LS166A . . . J OR W PACKAGE
SN74166 . . . N PACKAGE
SN74LS166A . . . D OR N PACKAGE
(TOP VIEW)

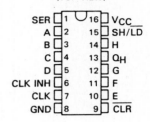

```
SER    [1   16] VCC
A      [2   15] SH/LD
B      [3   14] H
C      [4   13] QH
D      [5   12] G
CLK INH[6   11] F
CLK    [7   10] E
GND    [8    9] CLR
```

SN54LS166A . . . FK PACKAGE
(TOP VIEW)

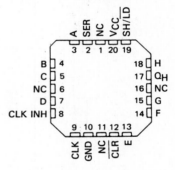

NC - No internal connection

logic symbol†

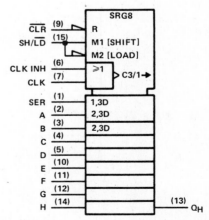

†This symbol is in accordance with ANSI/IEEE Std 91-1984 and IEC Publication 617-12.

Pin numbers shown are for D, J, N, and W packages.

FUNCTION TABLE

INPUTS						INTERNAL OUTPUTS		OUTPUT
CLEAR	SHIFT/ LOAD	CLOCK INHIBIT	CLOCK	SERIAL	PARALLEL A...H	QA	QB	QH
L	X	X	X	X	X	L	L	L
H	X	L	L	X	X	QA0	QB0	QH0
H	L	L	↑	X	a...h	a	b	h
H	H	L	↑	H	X	H	QAn	QGn
H	H	L	↑	L	X	L	QAn	QGn
H	X	H	↑	X	X	QA0	QB0	QH0

TEXAS INSTRUMENTS

POST OFFICE BOX 655012 • DALLAS, TEXAS 75265

2-529

TTL Devices

2

typical clear, shift, load, inhibit, and shift sequences

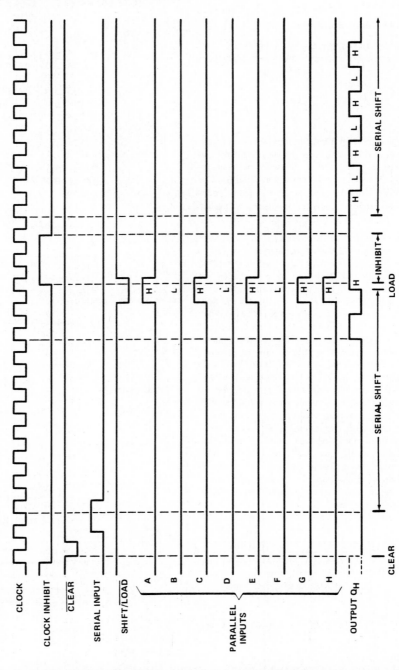

TEXAS
INSTRUMENTS
POST OFFICE BOX 655012 • DALLAS, TEXAS 75265

SN54166, SN54LS166A, SN74166, SN74LS166A
PARALLEL-LOAD 8-BIT SHIFT REGISTERS

logic diagram (positive logic)

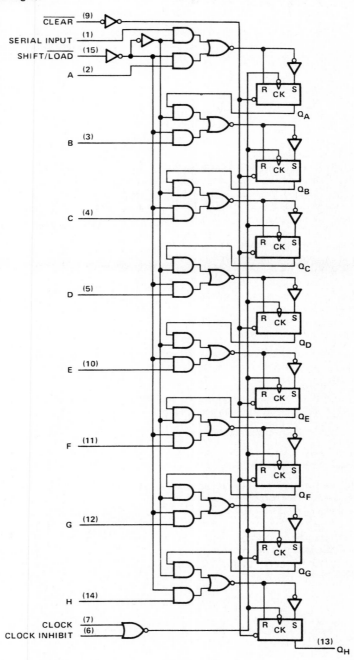

Pin numbers shown are for D, J, N, and W packages.

TEXAS
INSTRUMENTS

POST OFFICE BOX 655012 • DALLAS, TEXAS 75265

SN54184, SN54185A, SN74184, SN74185A
BCD-TO-BINARY AND BINARY-TO-BCD CONVERTERS

FEBRUARY 1971 — REVISED MARCH 1988

SN54184, SN74184 BCD-TO-BINARY CONVERTERS
SN54185A, SN74185A BINARY-TO-BCD CONVERTERS

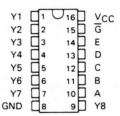

SN54184, SN54185A . . . J OR W PACKAGE
SN74L184, SN74185A . . . N PACKAGE
(TOP VIEW)

Y1	1	16	V_CC
Y2	2	15	$\overline{G}$
Y3	3	14	E
Y4	4	13	D
Y5	5	12	C
Y6	6	11	B
Y7	7	10	A
GND	8	9	Y8

description

These monolithic converters are derived from the custom MSI 256-bit read-only memories SN5488 and SN7488. Emitter connections are made to provide direct read-out of converted codes at outputs Y8 through Y1 as shown in the function tables. These converters demonstrate the versatility of a read-only memory in that an unlimited number of reference tables or conversion tables may be built into a system using economical, customized read-only memories. Both of these converters comprehend that the least significant bits (LSB) of the binary and BCD codes are logically equal, and in each case the LSB bypasses the converter as illustrated in the typical applications. This means that a 6-bit converter is produced in each case. Both devices are cascadable to N bits.

TABLE I
SN54184, SN74184
PACKAGE COUNT AND DELAY TIMES
FOR BCD-TO-BINARY CONVERSION

INPUT (DECADES)	PACKAGES REQUIRED	TOTAL DELAY TIMES (ns)	
		TYP	MAX
2	2	56	80
3	6	140	200
4	11	196	280
5	19	280	400
6	28	364	520

An overriding enable input is provided on each converter which, when taken high, inhibits the function, causing all outputs to go high. For this reason, and to minimize power consumption, unused outputs Y7 and Y8 of the '185A and all "don't care" conditions of the '184 are programmed high. The outputs are of the open-collector type.

The SN54184 and SN54185A are characterized for operation over the full military temperature range of −55°C to 125°C; the SN74184 and SN74185A are characterized for operation from 0°C to 70°C.

SN54184 and SN74184 BCD-to-binary converters

The 6-bit BCD-to-binary function of the SN54184 and SN74184 is analogous to the algorithm:

   a. Shift BCD number right one bit and examine each decade. Subtract three from each 4-bit decade containing a binary value greater than seven.

   b. Shift right, examine, and correct after each shift until the least significant decade contains a number smaller than eight and all other converted decades contain zeros.

In addition to BCD-to-binary conversion, the SN54184 and SN74184 are programmed to generate BCD 9's complement or BCD 10's complement. Again, in each case, one bit of the complement code is logically equal to one of the BCD bits; therefore, these complements can be produced on three lines. As outputs Y6, Y7, and Y8 are not required in the BCD-to-binary conversion, they are utilized to provide these complement codes as specified in the function table (following page, right) when the devices are connected as shown above the function table.

TEXAS
INSTRUMENTS

POST OFFICE BOX 655012 • DALLAS, TEXAS 75265

SN54184, SN74184
BCD-TO-BINARY AND BINARY-TO-BCD CONVERTERS

SN54184 and SN74184 BCD-to-binary converters (continued)

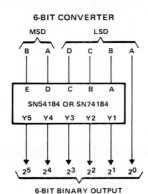

6-BIT CONVERTER

6-BIT BINARY OUTPUT

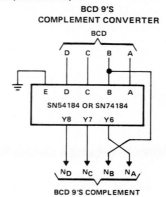

BCD 9'S COMPLEMENT CONVERTER

BCD 9'S COMPLEMENT

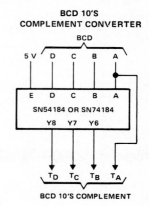

BCD 10'S COMPLEMENT CONVERTER

BCD 10'S COMPLEMENT

FUNCTION TABLE BCD-TO-BINARY CONVERTER

BCD WORDS	INPUTS (See Note A)						OUTPUTS (See Note B)				
	E	D	C	B	A	Ḡ	Y5	Y4	Y3	Y2	Y1
0·1	L	L	L	L	L	L	L	L	L	L	L
2·3	L	L	L	L	H	L	L	L	L	L	H
4·5	L	L	L	H	L	L	L	L	L	H	L
6·7	L	L	L	H	H	L	L	L	L	H	H
8·9	L	L	H	L	L	L	L	L	H	L	L
10·11	L	H	L	L	L	L	L	L	H	L	H
12·13	L	H	L	L	H	L	L	L	H	H	L
14·15	L	H	L	H	L	L	L	L	H	H	H
16·17	L	H	L	H	H	L	L	H	L	L	L
18·19	L	H	H	L	L	L	L	H	L	L	H
20·21	H	L	L	L	L	L	L	H	L	H	L
22·23	H	L	L	L	H	L	L	H	L	H	H
24·25	H	L	L	H	L	L	L	H	H	L	L
26·27	H	L	L	H	H	L	L	H	H	L	H
28·29	H	L	H	L	L	L	L	H	H	H	L
30·31	H	H	L	L	L	L	L	H	H	H	H
32·33	H	H	L	L	H	L	H	L	L	L	L
34·35	H	H	L	H	L	L	H	L	L	L	H
36·37	H	H	L	H	H	L	H	L	L	H	L
38·39	H	H	H	L	L	L	H	L	L	H	H
ANY	X	X	X	X	X	H	H	H	H	H	H

H = high level, L = low level, X = irrelevant

NOTES: A. Input conditions other than those shown produce highs at outputs Y1 through Y5.

B. Outputs Y6, Y7, and Y8 are not used for BCD-to-binary conversion.

FUNCTION TABLE BCD 9'S OR BCD 10'S COMPLEMENT CONVERTER

BCD WORD	INPUTS (See Note C)						OUTPUTS (See Note D)		
	E†	D	C	B	A	Ḡ	Y8	Y7	Y6
0	L	L	L	L	L	L	H	L	H
1	L	L	L	L	H	L	H	L	L
2	L	L	L	H	L	L	L	H	H
3	L	L	L	H	H	L	L	H	L
4	L	L	H	L	L	L	L	H	L
5	L	L	H	L	H	L	L	H	L
6	L	L	H	H	L	L	L	L	H
7	L	L	H	H	H	L	L	L	L
8	L	H	L	L	L	L	L	L	L
9	L	H	L	L	H	L	L	L	L
0	H	L	L	L	L	L	L	L	L
1	H	L	L	L	H	L	H	L	L
2	H	L	L	H	L	L	H	L	L
3	H	L	L	H	H	L	L	H	L
4	H	L	H	L	L	L	L	H	H
5	H	L	H	L	H	L	L	H	L
6	H	L	H	H	L	L	L	H	L
7	H	L	H	H	H	L	L	L	H
8	H	H	L	L	L	L	L	L	L
9	H	H	L	L	H	L	L	L	L
ANY	X	X	X	X	X	H	H	H	H

H = high level, L = low level, X = irrelevant

NOTES: C. Input conditions other than those shown produce highs at outputs Y6, Y7, and Y8.

D. Outputs Y1 through Y5 are not used for BCD 9's or BCD 10's complement conversion.

†When these devices are used as complement converters, input E is used as a mode control. With this input low, the BCD 9's complement is generated; when it is high, the BCD 10's complement is generated.

TEXAS INSTRUMENTS
POST OFFICE BOX 655012 • DALLAS, TEXAS 75265

SN54185A and SN74185A binary-to-BCD converters

The function performed by these 6-bit binary-to-BCD converters is analogous to the algorithm:

a. Examine the three most significant bits. If the sum is greater than four, add three and shift left one bit.

b. Examine each BCD decade. If the sum is greater than four, add three and shift left one bit.

c. Repeat step b until the least-significant binary bit is in the least-significant BCD location.

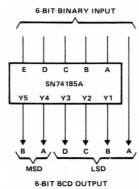

6-BIT CONVERTER

6-BIT BINARY INPUT

SN74185A

6-BIT BCD OUTPUT

TABLE II

SN54185A, SN74185A

PACKAGE COUNT AND DELAY TIMES

FOR BINARY-TO-BCD CONVERSION

INPUT (BITS)	PACKAGES REQUIRED	TOTAL DELAY TIME (ns)	
		TYP	MAX
4 to 6	1	25	40
7 or 8	3	50	80
9	4	75	120
10	6	100	160
11	7	125	200
12	8	125	200
13	10	150	240
14	12	175	280
15	14	175	280
16	16	200	320
17	19	225	360
18	21	225	360
19	24	250	400
20	27	275	440

FUNCTION TABLE

BINARY WORDS	INPUTS						OUTPUTS							
	BINARY SELECT					ENABLE								
	E	D	C	B	A	$\overline{G}$	Y8	Y7	Y6	Y5	Y4	Y3	Y2	Y1
0 - 1	L	L	L	L	L	L	H	H	L	L	L	L	L	L
2 - 3	L	L	L	L	H	L	H	H	L	L	L	L	L	H
4 - 5	L	L	L	H	L	L	H	H	L	L	L	L	H	L
6 - 7	L	L	L	H	H	L	H	H	L	L	L	L	H	H
8 - 9	L	L	H	L	L	L	H	H	L	L	L	H	L	L
10 - 11	L	L	H	L	H	L	H	H	L	L	L	H	L	H
12 - 13	L	L	H	H	L	L	H	H	L	L	H	L	L	H
14 - 15	L	L	H	H	H	L	H	H	L	L	H	L	H	L
16 - 17	L	H	L	L	L	L	H	H	L	L	H	L	H	H
18 - 19	L	H	L	L	H	L	H	H	L	L	H	H	L	L
20 - 21	L	H	L	H	L	L	H	H	L	H	L	L	L	L
22 - 23	L	H	L	H	H	L	H	H	L	H	L	L	L	H
24 - 25	L	H	H	L	L	L	H	H	L	H	L	L	H	L
26 - 27	L	H	H	L	H	L	H	H	L	H	L	L	H	H
28 - 29	L	H	H	H	L	L	H	H	L	H	L	H	L	L
30 - 31	L	H	H	H	H	L	H	H	L	H	H	L	L	L
32 - 33	H	L	L	L	L	L	H	H	L	H	H	L	L	H
34 - 35	H	L	L	L	H	L	H	H	L	H	H	L	H	L
36 - 37	H	L	L	H	L	L	H	H	L	H	H	L	H	H
38 - 39	H	L	L	H	H	L	H	H	L	H	H	H	L	L
40 - 41	H	L	H	L	L	L	H	H	H	L	L	L	L	L
42 - 43	H	L	H	L	H	L	H	H	H	L	L	L	L	H
44 - 45	H	L	H	H	L	L	H	H	H	L	L	L	H	L
46 - 47	H	L	H	H	H	L	H	H	H	L	L	L	H	H
48 - 49	H	H	L	L	L	L	H	H	H	L	L	H	L	L
50 - 51	H	H	L	L	H	L	H	H	H	L	H	L	L	L
52 - 53	H	H	L	H	L	L	H	H	H	L	H	L	L	H
54 - 55	H	H	L	H	H	L	H	H	H	L	H	L	H	L
56 - 57	H	H	H	L	L	L	H	H	H	L	H	L	H	H
58 - 59	H	H	H	L	H	L	H	H	H	L	H	H	L	L
60 - 61	H	H	H	H	L	L	H	H	H	H	L	L	L	L
62 - 63	H	H	H	H	H	L	H	H	H	H	L	L	L	H
ALL	X	X	X	X	X	H	H	H	H	H	H	H	H	H

H = high level, L = low level, X = irrelevant

SN54184, SN54185A, SN74184, SN74185A
BCD-TO-BINARY AND BINARY-TO-BCD CONVERTERS

logic symbols[†]

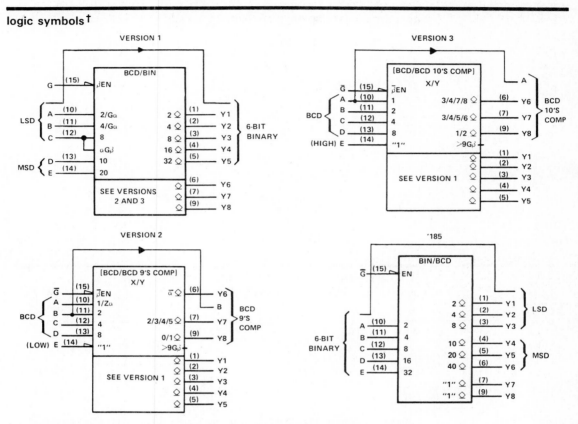

[†]These symbols are in accordance with ANSI/IEEE Std. 91-1984 and IEC Publication 617-12.

absolute maximum ratings over operating free-air temperature range (unless otherwise noted)

Supply voltage, V_{CC} (see Note 1)	7 V
Input voltage	5.5 V
Operating free-air temperature range: SN54184, SN54185A	−55°C to 125°C
SN74184, SN74185A	0°C to 70°C
Storage temperature range	−65°C to 150°C

NOTE 1: Voltage values are with respect to network ground terminal.

recommended operating conditions

	SN54184, SN54185A			SN74184, SN74185A			UNIT
	MIN	NOM	MAX	MIN	NOM	MAX	
Supply voltage, V_{CC}	4.5	5	5.5	4.75	5	5.25	V
Low-level output current, I_{OL}			12			12	mA
Operating free-air temperature, T_A	−55		125	0		70	C

TEXAS INSTRUMENTS
POST OFFICE BOX 655012 • DALLAS. TEXAS 75265

SN54184, SN74184
BCD-TO-BINARY CONVERTERS

PARAMETER MEASUREMENT INFORMATION

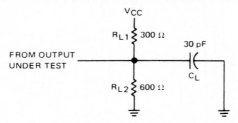

C_L includes probe and jig capacitance.

LOAD CIRCUIT
FIGURE 1

NOTE 2: Load circuits and voltage waveforms are shown in Section 1.

TYPICAL APPLICATION DATA
SN54184, SN74184

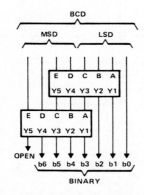

FIGURE 2—BCD-TO-BINARY CONVERTER
FOR TWO BCD DECADES

MSD—most significant decade
LSD—least significant decade
Each rectangle represents an SN54184 or SN74184

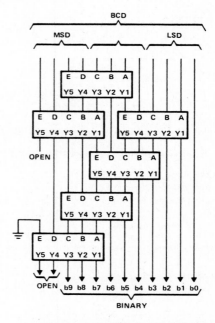

FIGURE 3—BCD-TO-BINARY CONVERTER
FOR THREE BCD DECADES

SN54185, SN74185A
BCD-TO-BINARY CONVERTERS

TYPICAL APPLICATION DATA
SN54185A, SN74185A

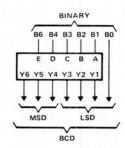

FIGURE 5—6-BIT BINARY-TO-BCD
CONVERTER

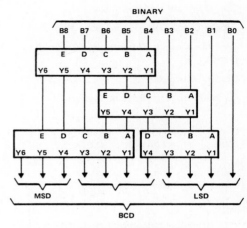

FIGURE 7—9-BIT BINARY-TO-BCD
CONVERTER

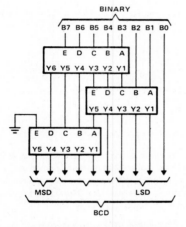

FIGURE 6—8-BIT BINARY-TO-BCD
CONVERTER

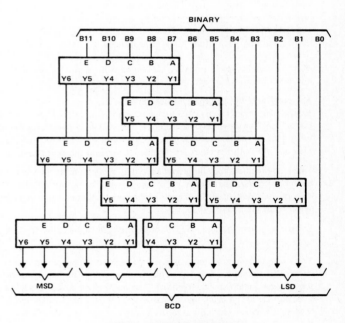

FIGURE 8—12-BIT BINARY-TO-BCD
CONVERTER (SEE NOTE B)

MSD—Most significant decade
LSD—Least significant decade
NOTES: A. Each rectangle represents an SN54185A or an SN74185A.
  B. All unused E inputs are grounded.

TEXAS
INSTRUMENTS
POST OFFICE BOX 655012 • DALLAS, TEXAS 75265

SN54190, SN54191, SN54LS190, SN54LS191, SN74190, SN74191, SN74LS190, SN74LS191
SYNCHRONOUS UP/DOWN COUNTERS WITH DOWN/UP MODE CONTROL

DECEMBER 1972—REVISED MARCH 1988

- **Counts 8-4-2-1 BCD or Binary**
- **Single Down/Up Count Control Line**
- **Count Enable Control Input**
- **Ripple Clock Output for Cascading**
- **Asynchronously Presettable with Load Control**
- **Parallel Outputs**
- **Cascadable for n-Bit Applications**

TYPE	AVERAGE PROPAGATION DELAY	TYPICAL MAXIMUM CLOCK FREQUENCY	TYPICAL POWER DISSIPATION
'190,'191	20 ns	25 MHz	325 mW
'LS190,'LS191	20 ns	25 MHz	100 mW

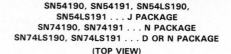

**SN54190, SN54191, SN54LS190,
SN54LS191 . . . J PACKAGE
SN74190, SN74191 . . . N PACKAGE
SN74LS190, SN74LS191 . . . D OR N PACKAGE
(TOP VIEW)**

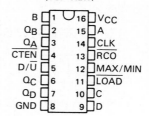

description

The '190, 'LS190, '191, and 'LS191 are synchronous, reversible up/down counters having a complexity of 58 equivalent gates. The '191 and 'LS191 are 4-bit binary counters and the '190 and 'LS190 are BCD counters. Synchronous operation is provided by having all flip-flops clocked simultaneously so that the outputs change coincident with each other when so instructed by the steering logic. This mode of operation eliminates the output counting spikes normally associated with asynchronous (ripple clock) counters.

**SN54LS190, SN54LS191 . . . FK PACKAGE
(TOP VIEW)**

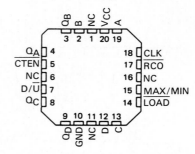

NC - No internal connection

The outputs of the four master-slave flip-flops are triggered on a low-to-high transition of the clock input if the enable input is low. A high at the enable input inhibits counting. Level changes at the enable input should be made only when the clock input is high. The direction of the count is determined by the level of the down/up input. When low, the counter count up and when high, it counts down. A false clock may occur if the down/up input changes while the clock is low. A false ripple carry may occur if both the clock and enable are low and the down/up input is high during a load pulse.

These counters are fully programmable; that is, the outputs may be preset to either level by placing a low on the load input and entering the desired data at the data inputs. The output will change to agree with the data inputs independently of the level of the clock input. This feature allows the counters to be used as modulo-N dividers by simply modifying the count length with the preset inputs.

The clock, down/up, and load inputs are buffered to lower the drive requirement which significantly reduces the number of clock drivers, etc., required for long parallel words.

Two outputs have been made available to perform the cascading function: ripple clock and maximum/minimum count. The latter output produces a high-level output pulse with a duration approximately equal to one complete cycle of the clock when the counter overflows or underflows. The ripple clock output produces a low-level output pulse equal in width to the low-level portion of the clock input when an overflow or underflow condition exists. The counters can be easily cascaded by feeding the ripple clock output to the enable input of the succeeding counter if parallel clocking is used, or to the clock input if parallel enabling is used. The maximum/minimum count output can be used to accomplish look-ahead for high-speed operation.

Series 54' and 54LS' are characterized for operation over the full military temperature range of −55°C to 125°C; Series 74' and 74LS' are characterized for operation from 0°C to 70°C.

**TEXAS
INSTRUMENTS**

POST OFFICE BOX 655012 • DALLAS, TEXAS 75265

2

TTL Devices

SN54190, SN54191, SN54LS190, SN54LS191, SN74190, SN74191, SN74LS190, SN74LS191
SYNCHRONOUS UP/DOWN COUNTERS WITH DOWN/UP MODE CONTROL

logic symbols†

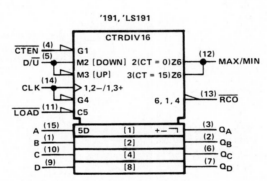

†These symbols are accordance with ANSI/IEEE Std 91-1984 and IEC Publication 617-12.
Pin numbers shown are for D, J, and N packages.

Texas
INSTRUMENTS
POST OFFICE BOX 655012 • DALLAS, TEXAS 75265

logic diagram (positive logic)

'190, 'LS190 DECADE COUNTERS

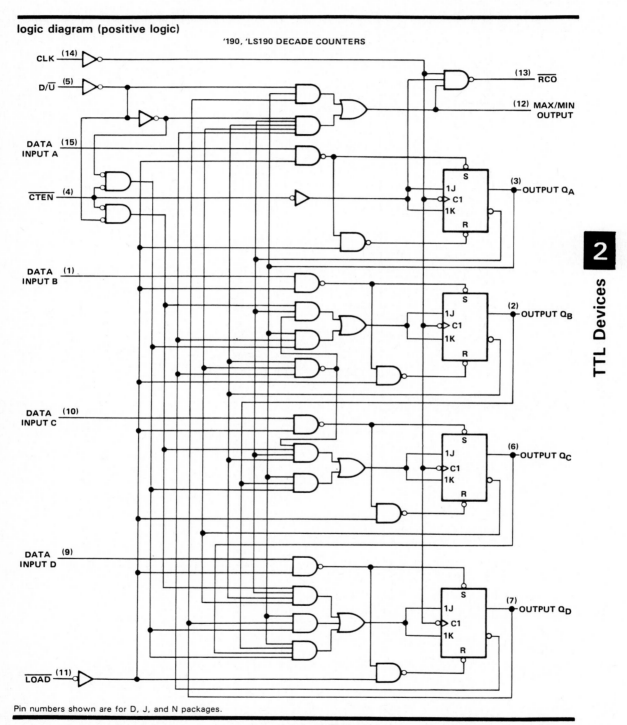

Pin numbers shown are for D, J, and N packages.

2

TTL Devices

TEXAS INSTRUMENTS
POST OFFICE BOX 655012 • DALLAS, TEXAS 75265

SN54191, SN54LS191, SN74191, SN74LS191
SYNCHRONOUS UP/DOWN COUNTERS WITH DOWN/UP MODE CONTROL

logic diagram (positive logic)

'191, 'LS191 BINARY COUNTERS

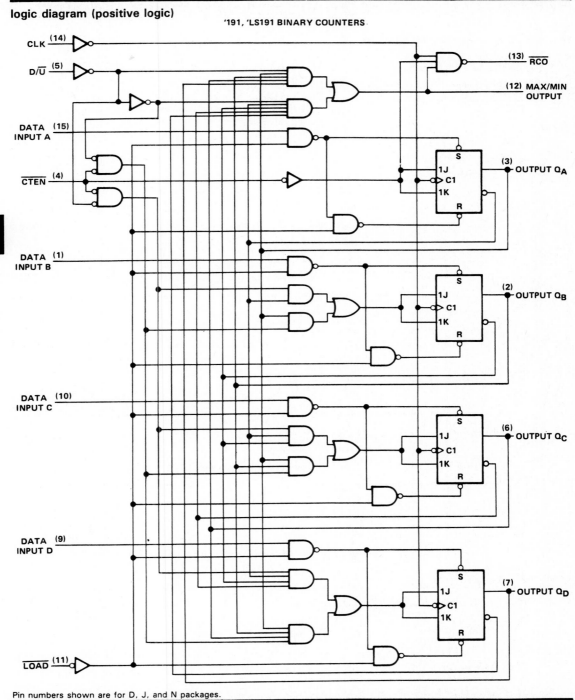

Pin numbers shown are for D, J, and N packages.

TEXAS
INSTRUMENTS

POST OFFICE BOX 655012 • DALLAS. TEXAS 75265

'190, 'LS190 DECADE COUNTERS

typical load, count, and inhibit sequences

Illustrated below is the following sequence:

1. Load (preset) to BCD seven.
2. Count up to eight, nine (maximum), zero, one, and two.
3. Inhibit.
4. Count down to one, zero (minimum), nine, eight, and seven.

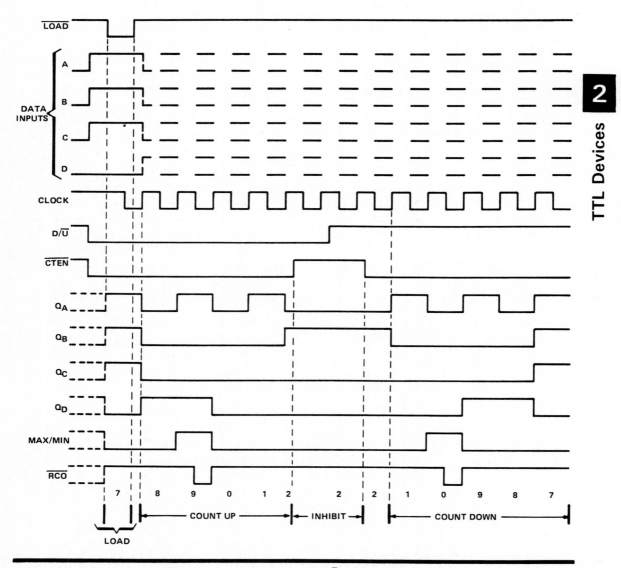

2

TTL Devices

'191, 'LS191 BINARY COUNTERS

typical load, count, and inhibit sequences

Illustrated below is the following sequence:

1. Load (preset) to binary thirteen.
2. Count up to fourteen, fifteen (maximum), zero, one, and two.
3. Inhibit.
4. Count down to one, zero (minimum), fifteen, fourteen, and thirteen.

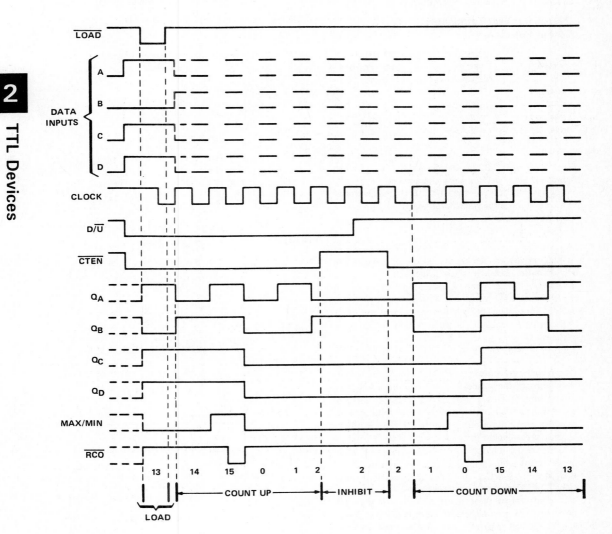

TEXAS
INSTRUMENTS

POST OFFICE BOX 655012 • DALLAS, TEXAS 75265

- **SN54221, SN54LS221, SN74221 and SN74LS221 Are Dual Versions of Highly Stable SN54121, SN74121 One-Shots on a Monolithic Chip**

- **SN54221 and SN74221 Demonstrate Electrical and Switching Characteristics That Are Virtually Identical to the SN54121, SN74121 One-Shots**

- **Pin-Out Is Identical to the SN54123, SN74123, SN54LS123, SN74LS123**

- **Overriding Clear Terminates Output Pulse**

TYPE	TYPICAL POWER DISSIPATION	MAXIMUM OUTPUT PULSE LENGTH
SN54221	130 mW	21 s
SN74221	130 mW	28 s
SN54LS221	23 mW	49 s
SN74LS221	23 mW	70 s

SN54221, SN54LS221 . . . J OR W PACKAGE
SN74221 . . . N PACKAGE
SN74LS221 . . . D OR N PACKAGE
(TOP VIEW)

```
        ____  ____
1A   [ 1      16 ] VCC
1B   [ 2      15 ] 1Rext/Cext
1CLR [ 3      14 ] 1Cext
1Q   [ 4      13 ] 1Q
2Q   [ 5      12 ] 2Q
2Cext[ 6      11 ] 2CLR
2Rext/Cext[ 7  10 ] 2B
GND  [ 8       9 ] 2A
```

SN54LS221 . . . FK PACKAGE
(TOP VIEW)

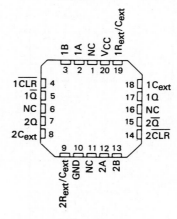

description

The '221 and 'LS221 are monolithic dual multivibrators with performance characteristics virtually identical to those of the '121. Each multivibrator features a negative-transition-triggered input and a positive-transition-triggered input either of which can be used as an inhibit input.

Pulse triggering occurs at a particular voltage level and is not directly related to the transition time of the input pulse. Schmitt-trigger input circuitry (TTL hysteresis) for B input allows jitter-free triggering from inputs with transition rates as slow as 1 volt/second, providing the circuit with excellent noise immunity of typically 1.2 volts. A high immunity to V_{CC} noise of typically 1.5 volts is also provided by internal latching circuitry.

Once fired, the outputs are independent of further transitions of the A and B inputs and are a function of the timing components, or the output pulses can be terminated by the overriding clear. Input pulses may be of any duration relative to the output pulse. Output pulse length may be varied from 35 nanoseconds to the maximums shown in the above table by choosing appropriate timing components. With $R_{ext} = 2$ kΩ and $C_{ext} = 0$, an output pulse of typically 30 nanoseconds is achieved which may be used as a d-c-triggered reset signal. Output rise and fall times are TTL compatible and independent of pulse length. Typical triggering and clearing sequences are illustrated as a part of the switching characteristics waveforms.

FUNCTION TABLE
(EACH MONOSTABLE)

INPUTS			OUTPUTS	
CLEAR	A	B	Q	Q̄
L	X	X	L	H
X	H	X	L	H
X	X	L	L	H
H	L	↑	⊓‡	⊔‡
H	↓	H	⊓‡	⊔‡
↑	L	H	⊓‡	⊔‡

Also see description and switching characteristics

†This condition is true only if the output of the latch formed by the two NAND gates has been conditioned to the logic 1 state prior to CLR going high. This latch is conditioned by taking either A high or B low while CLR is inactive (high).

‡Pulsed output patterns are tested during AC switching at 25°C, with $R_{ext} = 2$ kΩ, $C_{ext} = 80$ pF.

TEXAS INSTRUMENTS
POST OFFICE BOX 655012 • DALLAS, TEXAS 75265

2-681

2

TTL Devices

SN54221, SN54LS221, SN74221, SN74LS221
DUAL MONOSTABLE MULTIVIBRATORS
WITH SCHMITT-TRIGGER INPUTS

description (continued)

Pulse width stability is achieved through internal compensation and is virtually independent of V_{CC} and temperature. In most applications, pulse stability will only be limited by the accuracy of external timing components.

Jitter-free operation is maintained over the full temperature and V_{CC} ranges for more than six decades of timing capacitance (10 pF to 10 μF) and more than one decade of timing resistance (2 kΩ to 30 kΩ for the SN54221, 2 kΩ to 40 kΩ for the SN74221, 2 kΩ to 70 kΩ for the SN54LS221, and 2 kΩ to 100 kΩ for the SN74LS221). Throughout these ranges, pulse width is defined by the relationship: $t_w(out) = C_{ext}R_{ext} \, ln2 \approx 0.7 \, C_{ext}R_{ext}$. In circuits where pulse cutoff is not critical, timing capacitance up to 1000 μF and timing resistance as low as 1.4 kΩ may be used. Also, the range of jitter-free output pulse widths is extended if V_{CC} is held to 5 volts and free-air temperature is 25°C. Duty cycles as high as 90% are achieved when using maximum recommended R_T. Higher duty cycles are available if a certain amount of pulse-width jitter is allowed.

The variance in output pulse width from device to device is typically less than $\pm$ 0.5% for given external timing components. An example of this distribution for the '221 is shown in Figure 2. Variations in output pulse width versus supply voltage and temperature for the '221 are shown in Figure 3 and 4, respectively.

Pin assignments for these devices are identical to those of the SN54123/SN74123 or SN54LS123/SN74LS123 so that the '221 or 'LS221 can be substituted for those products in systems not using the retrigger by merely changing the value of R_{ext} and/or C_{ext}, however the polarity of the capacitor will have to be changed.

TIMING COMPONENT CONNECTIONS

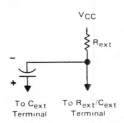

NOTE: Due to the internal circuit, the R_{ext}/C_{ext} pin will never be more positive than the C_{ext} pin.

Pin numbers shown are for D, J, N, and W packages.

logic symbol†

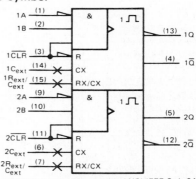

†This symbol is in accordance with ANSI/IEEE Std. 91-1984 and IEC Publication 617-12.

schematics of inputs and outputs

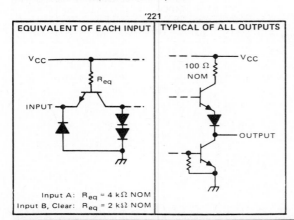

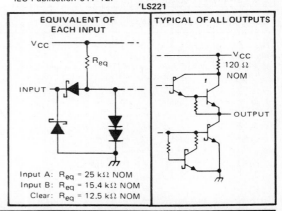

Texas
Instruments
POST OFFICE BOX 655012 • DALLAS. TEXAS 75265

recommended operating conditions

		SN54LS221 MIN	NOM	MAX	SN74LS221 MIN	NOM	MAX	UNIT
Supply voltage, V_{CC}		4.5	5	5.5	4.75	5	5.25	V
High-level input voltage at A input, V_{IH}		2			2			V
Low-level input voltage at B input, V_{IL}				0.7			0.8	V
High-level output current, I_{OH}				−400			−400	μA
Low-level output current, I_{OL}				4			8	mA
Rate of rise or fall of input pulse, dv/dt	Schmitt, B	1			1			V/s
	Logic input, A	1			1			V/μs
Input pulse width	A or B, $t_{w(in)}$	50			50			ns
	Clear, $t_{w(clear)}$	40			40			
Clear-inactive-state setup time, t_{su}		15			15			ns
External timing resistance, R_{ext}		1.4		70	1.4		100	kΩ
External timing capacitance, C_{ext}		0		1000	0		1000	μF
Output duty cycle	R_T = 2 kΩ			50			50	%
	R_T = MAX R_{ext}			90			90	
Operating free-air temperature, T_A		−55		125	0		70	°C

recommended operating conditions

PARAMETER		TEST CONDITIONS†	SN54LS221 MIN	TYP‡	MAX	SN74LS221 MIN	TYP‡	MAX	UNIT
V_{T+}	Positive-going threshold voltage at B input	V_{CC} = MIN		1.0	2		1.0	2	V
V_{T-}	Negative-going threshold voltage at B input	V_{CC} = MIN	0.7	0.9		0.8	0.9		V
V_{IK}	Input clamp voltage	V_{CC} = MIN, I_I = −18 mA			−1.5			−1.5	V
V_{OH}	High-level output voltage	V_{CC} = MIN, I_{OH} = −400 μA	2.5	3.4		2.7	3.4		V
V_{OL}	Low-level output voltage	V_{CC} = MIN, I_{OL} = 4 mA		0.25	0.4		0.25	0.4	V
		I_{OL} = 8 mA					0.35	0.5	
I_I	Input current at maximum input voltage	V_{CC} = MAX, V_I = 7 V			0.1			0.1	mA
I_{IH}	High-level input current	V_{CC} = MAX, V_I = 2.7 V			20			20	μA
I_{IL}	Low-level input current	Input A, V_{CC} = MAX, V_I = 0.4 V			−0.4			−0.4	mA
		Input B			−0.8			−0.8	
		Clear			−0.8			−0.8	
I_{OS}	Short-circuit output current§	V_{CC} = MAX	−20		−100	−20		−100	mA
I_{CC}	Supply current	V_{CC} = MAX, Quiescent		4.7	11		4.7	11	mA
		Triggered		19	27		19	27	

†For conditions shown as MIN or MAX, use the appropriate value specified under recommended operating conditions.
‡All typical values are at V_{CC} = 5 V, T_A = 25 °C.
§Not more than one output should be shorted at a time and duration of the short-circuit should not exceed one second.

2

TTL Devices

TEXAS
INSTRUMENTS
POST OFFICE BOX 655012 • DALLAS. TEXAS 75265

SN54LS221, SN74LS221
DUAL MONOSTABLE MULTIVIBRATORS
WITH SCHMITT-TRIGGER INPUTS

switching characteristics, V_{CC} = 5 V, T_A = 25°C

PARAMETER[†]	FROM (INPUT)	TO (OUTPUT)	TEST CONDITIONS		MIN	TYP	MAX	UNIT
t_{PLH}	A	Q				45	70	ns
	B	Q				35	55	
t_{PHL}	A	$\overline{Q}$	C_{ext} = 80 pF, R_{ext} = 2 kΩ			50	80	ns
	B	$\overline{Q}$				40	65	
t_{PHL}	Clear	Q	C_L = 15 pF,			35	55	ns
t_{PLH}	Clear	$\overline{Q}$	R_L = 2 kΩ, See Figure 1			44	65	ns
$t_{W(out)}$	A or B	Q or $\overline{Q}$	and Note 3	C_{ext} = 80 pF, R_{ext} = 2 kΩ	70	120	150	ns
				C_{ext} = 0, R_{ext} = 2 kΩ	20	47	70	
				C_{ext} = 100 pF, R_{ext} = 10 kΩ	670	740	810	
				C_{ext} = 1 μF, R_{ext} = 10 kΩ	6	6.9	7.5	ms

[†]t_{PLH} ≡ Propagation delay time, low-to-high-level output

t_{PHL} ≡ Propagation delay time, high-to-low-level output

$t_{W(out)}$ ≡ Output pulse width

NOTE 3: Load circuits and voltage waveforms are shown in Section 1.

TEXAS
INSTRUMENTS

POST OFFICE BOX 655012 • DALLAS, TEXAS 75265

TYPICAL CHARACTERISTICS ('221 ONLY)†

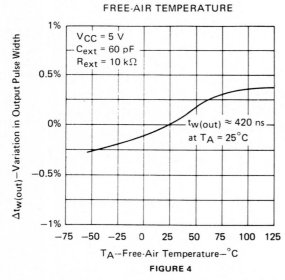

DISTRIBUTION OF UNITS
for
OUTPUT PULSE WIDTH

FIGURE 2

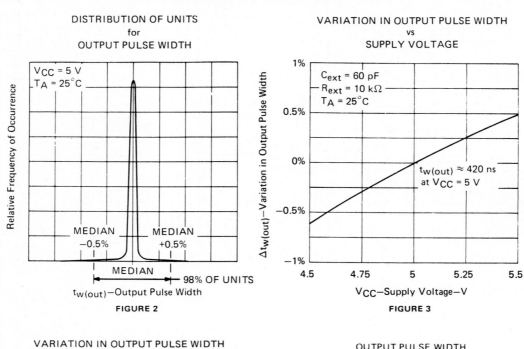

VARIATION IN OUTPUT PULSE WIDTH
vs
SUPPLY VOLTAGE

FIGURE 3

VARIATION IN OUTPUT PULSE WIDTH
vs
FREE-AIR TEMPERATURE

FIGURE 4

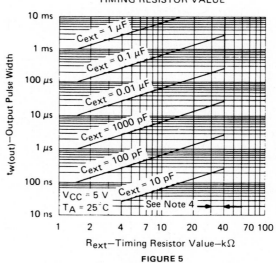

OUTPUT PULSE WIDTH
vs
TIMING RESISTOR VALUE

FIGURE 5

2

TTL Devices

NOTE 4: These values of resistance exceed the maximum recommended for use over the full temperature range of the SN54221.

†Data for temperatures below 0°C and above 70°C, and for supply voltages below 4.75 V and above 5.25 V are applicable for the SN54221 only.

SN54LS240, SN54LS241, SN54LS244, SN54S240, SN54S241, SN54S244, SN74LS240, SN74LS241, SN74LS244, SN74S240, SN74S241, SN74S244
OCTAL BUFFERS AND LINE DRIVERS WITH 3-STATE OUTPUTS

APRIL 1985 – REVISED MARCH 1988

- **3-State Outputs Drive Bus Lines or Buffer Memory Address Registers**
- **PNP Inputs Reduce D-C Loading**
- **Hysteresis at Inputs Improves Noise Margins**

description

These octal buffers and line drivers are designed specifically to improve both the performance and density of three-state memory address drivers, clock drivers, and bus-oriented receivers and transmitters. The designer has a choice of selected combinations of inverting and noninverting outputs, symmetrical $\overline{G}$ (active-low output control) inputs, and complementary G and $\overline{G}$ inputs. These devices feature high fan-out, improved fan-in, and 400-mV noise-margin. The SN74LS' and SN74S' can be used to drive terminated lines down to 133 ohms.

The SN54' family is characterized for operation over the full military temperature range of $-55°C$ to $125°C$. The SN74' family is characterized for operation from $0°C$ to $70°C$.

SN54LS', SN54S' . . . J OR W PACKAGE
SN74LS', SN74S' . . . DW OR N PACKAGE
(TOP VIEW)

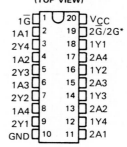

1$\overline{G}$	1	20	V$_{CC}$
1A1	2	19	2G/2G*
2Y4	3	18	1Y1
1A2	4	17	2A4
2Y3	5	16	1Y2
1A3	6	15	2A3
2Y2	7	14	1Y3
1A4	8	13	2A2
2Y1	9	12	1Y4
GND	10	11	2A1

SN54LS', SN54S' . . . FK PACKAGE
(TOP VIEW)

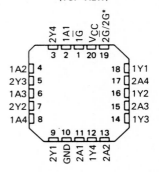

*2G for 'LS241 and 'S241 or $\overline{2G}$ for all other drivers.

schematics of inputs and outputs

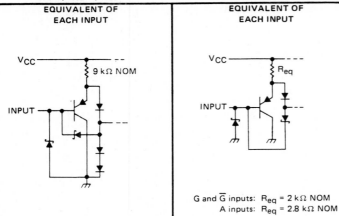

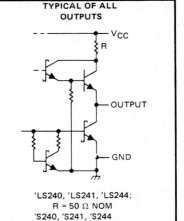

'LS240, 'LS241, 'LS244	'S240, 'S241, 'S244	TYPICAL OF ALL OUTPUTS
EQUIVALENT OF EACH INPUT	EQUIVALENT OF EACH INPUT	

9 kΩ NOM

G and $\overline{G}$ inputs: R$_{eq}$ = 2 kΩ NOM
A inputs: R$_{eq}$ = 2.8 kΩ NOM

'LS240, 'LS241, 'LS244;
R = 50 Ω NOM
'S240, 'S241, 'S244
R = 25 Ω NOM

TEXAS INSTRUMENTS

POST OFFICE BOX 655012 • DALLAS, TEXAS 75265

SN54LS240, SN54LS241, SN54LS244, SN54S240, SN54S241, SN54S244, SN74SL240, SN74LS241, SN74LS244, SN74S240, SN74S241, SN74S244
OCTAL BUFFERS AND LINE DRIVERS WITH 3-STATE OUTPUTS

logic symbols†

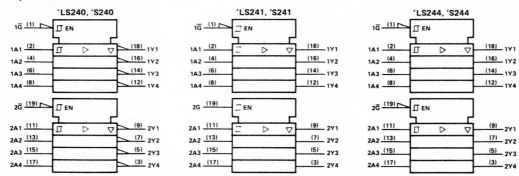

†These symbols are in accordance with ANSI/IEEE Std. 91-1984 and IEC Publication 617-12.

logic diagrams (positive logic)

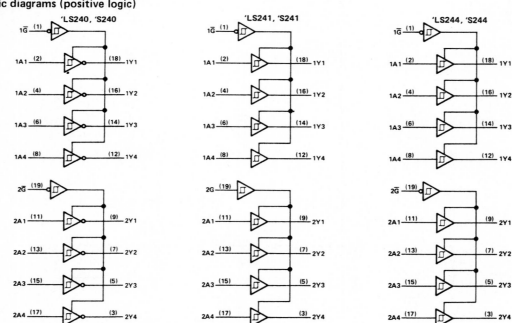

Pin numbers shown are for DW, J, N, and W packages.

absolute maximum ratings over operating free-air temperature range (unless otherwise noted)

Supply voltage, V$_{CC}$ (see Note 1)..7 V
Input voltage: 'LS Circuits..7 V
                'S Circuits..5.5 V
Off-state output voltage..5.5 V
Operating free-air temperature range: SN54LS', SN54S' Circuits...............................−55°C to 125°C
                             SN74LS', SN74S' Circuits...............................0°C to 70°C
Storage temperature range..−65°C to 150°C

NOTE 1: Voltage values are with respect to network ground terminal.

TEXAS
INSTRUMENTS
POST OFFICE BOX 655012 • DALLAS. TEXAS 75265

SN54S260, SN74S260
DUAL 5-INPUT POSITIVE-NOR GATES

DECEMBER 1983 — REVISED MARCH 1988

- **Package Options Include Ceramic Chip Carriers and Flat Packages in Addition to Plastic and Ceramic DIPs**

- **Dependable Texas Instruments Quality and Reliability**

description

These devices contain two independent 5-input positive -NOR gates. They perform the Boolean function $Y = \overline{A + B + C + D + E}$ in positive logic.

The SN54S260 is characterized for operation over the full military temperature range of $-55°C$ to $125°C$. The SN74S260 is characterized for operation from $0°C$ to $70°C$.

logic diagram (each gate)

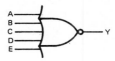

logic symbol†

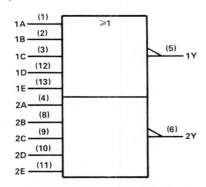

†This symbol is in accordance with ANSI/IEEE Std. 91-1984 and IEC Publication 617-12.
Pin numbers shown are for D, J, N, and W packages.

SN54S260 . . . J OR W PACKAGE
SN74S260 . . . D OR N PACKAGE
(TOP VIEW)

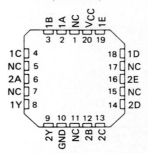

SN54S260 . . . FK PACKAGE
(TOP VIEW)

NC - No internal connection

2

TTL Devices

TEXAS
INSTRUMENTS

POST OFFICE BOX 655012 • DALLAS, TEXAS 75265

SN54LS373, SN54LS374, SN54S373, SN54S374, SN74LS373, SN74LS374, SN74S373, SN74S374
OCTAL D-TYPE TRANSPARENT LATCHES AND EDGE-TRIGGERED FLIP-FLOPS

OCTOBER 1975—REVISED MARCH 1988

- Choice of 8 Latches or 8 D-Type Flip-Flops In a Single Package
- 3-State Bus-Driving Outputs
- Full Parallel-Access for Loading
- Buffered Control Inputs
- Clock/Enable Input Has Hysteresis to Improve Noise Rejection ('S373 and 'S374)
- P-N-P Inputs Reduce D-C Loading on Data Lines ('S373 and 'S374)

'LS373, 'S373 FUNCTION TABLE

OUTPUT ENABLE	ENABLE LATCH	D	OUTPUT
L	H	H	H
L	H	L	L
L	L	X	Q_0
H	X	X	Z

'LS374, 'S374 FUNCTION TABLE

OUTPUT ENABLE	CLOCK	D	OUTPUT
L	↑	H	H
L	↑	L	L
L	L	X	Q_0
H	X	X	Z

description

These 8-bit registers feature three-state outputs designed specifically for driving highly-capacitive or relatively low-impedance loads. The high-impedance third state and increased high-logic-level drive provide these registers with the capability of being connected directly to and driving the bus lines in a bus-organized system without need for interface or pull-up components. They are particularly attractive for implementing buffer registers, I/O ports, bidirectional bus drivers, and working registers.

The eight latches of the 'LS373 and 'S373 are transparent D-type latches meaning that while the enable (C) is high the Q outputs will follow the data (D) inputs. When the enable is taken low the output will be latched at the level of the data that was set up.

SN54LS373, SN54LS374, SN54S373, SN54S374 . . . J OR W PACKAGE
SN74LS373, SN74LS374, SN74S373, SN74S374 . . . DW OR N PACKAGE
(TOP VIEW)

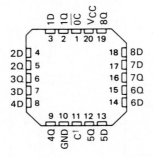

SN54LS373, SN54LS374, SN54S373, SN54S374 . . . FK PACKAGE
(TOP VIEW)

†C for 'LS373 and 'S373; CLK for 'LS374 and 'S374.

TEXAS
INSTRUMENTS

POST OFFICE BOX 655012 • DALLAS, TEXAS 75265

2

TTL Devices

SN54LS373, SN54LS374, SN54S373, SN54S374,
SN74LS373, SN74LS374, SN74S373, SN74S374
OCTAL D-TYPE TRANSPARENT LATCHES AND EDGE-TRIGGERED FLIP-FLOPS

description (continued)

The eight flip-flops of the 'LS374 and 'S374 are edge-triggered D-type flip-flops. On the positive transition of the clock, the Q outputs will be set to the logic states that were setup at the D inputs.

Schmitt-trigger buffered inputs at the enable/clock lines of the 'S373 and 'S374 devices, simplify system design as ac and dc noise rejection is improved by typically 400 mV due to the input hysteresis. A buffered output control input can be used to place the eight outputs in either a normal logic state (high or low logic levels) or a high-impedance state. In the high-impedance state the outputs neither load nor drive the bus lines significantly.

The output control does not affect the internal operation of the latches or flip-flops. That is, the old data can be retained or new data can be entered even while the outputs are off.

logic diagrams (positive logic)

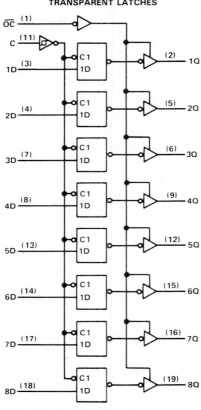

'LS373, 'S373
TRANSPARENT LATCHES

⊐⊏ for 'S373 only

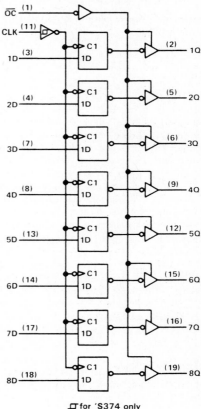

'LS374, 'S374
POSITIVE-EDGE-TRIGGERED FLIP-FLOPS

⊐⊏ for 'S374 only

Pin numbers shown are for DW, J, N, and W packages.

TEXAS
INSTRUMENTS
POST OFFICE BOX 655012 • DALLAS, TEXAS 75265

SN54390, SN54LS390, SN54393, SN54LS393, SN74390, SN74LS390, SN74393, SN74LS393
DUAL 4-BIT DECADE AND BINARY COUNTERS

OCTOBER 1976 — REVISED MARCH 1988

- Dual Versions of the Popular '90A, 'LS90 and '93A, 'LS93

- '390, 'LS390 . . . Individual Clocks for A and B Flip-Flops Provide Dual ÷ 2 and ÷ 5 Counters

- '393, 'LS393 . . . Dual 4-Bit Binary Counter with Individual Clocks

- All Have Direct Clear for Each 4-Bit Counter

- Dual 4-Bit Versions Can Significantly Improve System Densities by Reducing Counter Package Count by 50%

- Typical Maximum Count Frequency . . . 35 MHz

- Buffered Outputs Reduce Possibility of Collector Commutation

description

Each of these monolithic circuits contains eight master-slave flip-flops and additional gating to implement two individual four-bit counters in a single package. The '390 and 'LS390 incorporate dual divide-by-two and divide-by-five counters, which can be used to implement cycle lengths equal to any whole and/or cumulative multiples of 2 and/or 5 up to divide-by-100. When connected as a bi-quinary counter, the separate divide-by-two circuit can be used to provide symmetry (a square wave) at the final output stage. The '393 and 'LS393 each comprise two independent four-bit binary counters each having a clear and a clock input. N-bit binary counters can be implemented with each package providing the capability of divide-by-256. The '390, 'LS390, '393, and 'LS393 have parallel outputs from each counter stage so that any submultiple of the input count frequency is available for system-timing signals.

Series 54 and Series 54LS circuits are characterized for operation over the full military temperature range of −55°C to 125°C; Series 74 and Series 74LS circuits are characterized for operation from 0°C to 70°C.

SN54390, SN54LS390 . . . J OR W PACKAGE
SN74390 . . . N PACKAGE
SN74LS390 . . . D OR N PACKAGE
(TOP VIEW)

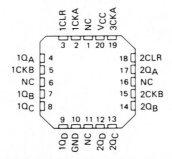

SN54LS390 . . . FK PACKAGE
(TOP VIEW)

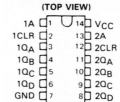

SN54393, SN54LS393 . . . J OR W PACKAGE
SN74393 . . . N PACKAGE
SN74LS393 . . . D OR N PACKAGE
(TOP VIEW)

SN54LS393 . . . FK PACKAGE
(TOP VIEW)

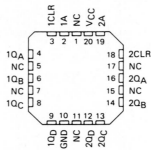

NC - No internal connection

TEXAS
INSTRUMENTS

POST OFFICE BOX 655012 • DALLAS, TEXAS 75265

2-919

TTL Devices

2

SN54390, SN54LS390, SN54393, SN54LS393, SN74390, SN74LS390, SN74393, SN74LS393
DUAL 4-BIT DECADE AND BINARY COUNTERS

FUNCTION TABLES

'390, 'LS390
BCD COUNT SEQUENCE
(EACH COUNTER)
(See Note A)

COUNT	OUTPUT			
	Q_D	Q_C	Q_B	Q_A
0	L	L	L	L
1	L	L	L	H
2	L	L	H	L
3	L	L	H	H
4	L	H	L	L
5	L	H	L	H
6	L	H	H	L
7	L	H	H	H
8	H	L	L	L
9	H	L	L	H

'390, 'LS390
BI-QUINARY (5-2)
(EACH COUNTER)
(See Note B)

COUNT	OUTPUT			
	Q_A	Q_D	Q_C	Q_B
0	L	L	L	L
1	L	L	L	H
2	L	L	H	L
3	L	L	H	H
4	L	H	L	L
5	H	L	L	L
6	H	L	L	H
7	H	L	H	L
8	H	L	H	H
9	H	H	L	L

'393, 'LS393
COUNT SEQUENCE
(EACH COUNTER)

COUNT	OUTPUT			
	Q_D	Q_C	Q_B	Q_A
0	L	L	L	L
1	L	L	L	H
2	L	L	H	L
3	L	L	H	H
4	L	H	L	L
5	L	H	L	H
6	L	H	H	L
7	L	H	H	H
8	H	L	L	L
9	H	L	L	H
10	H	L	H	L
11	H	L	H	H
12	H	H	L	L
13	H	H	L	H
14	H	H	H	L
15	H	H	H	H

NOTES: A. Output Q_A is connected to input B for BCD count.
B. Output Q_D is connected to input A for bi-quinary count.
C. H = high level, L = low level.

logic diagrams (positive logic)

logic symbols†

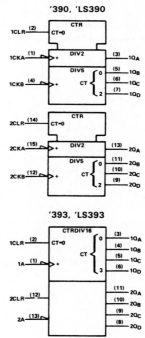

†These symbols are in accordance with ANSI/IEEE Std. 91-1984 and IEC Publication 617-12.

Pin numbers shown are for D, J, N, and W packages.

TEXAS INSTRUMENTS
POST OFFICE BOX 655012 • DALLAS, TEXAS 75265

2

TTL Devices

logic diagrams (continued)

'393, 'LS393

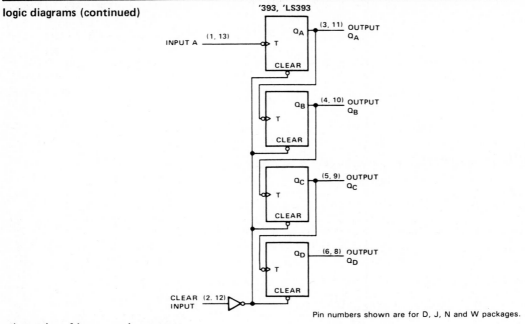

Pin numbers shown are for D, J, N and W packages.

schematics of inputs and outputs

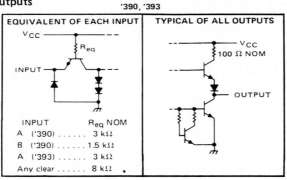

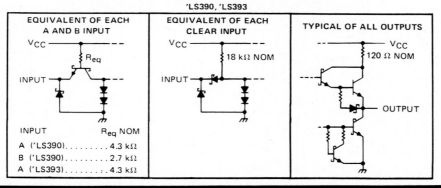

TTL Devices

2

MOS
LSI

TMS2114, TMS2114L
1024-WORD BY 4-BIT STATIC RAMS

DECEMBER 1979 – REVISED AUGUST 1983

- Previously Called TMS4045/TMS40L45
- 1024 X 4 Organization
- Single +5-V Supply
- High Density 300-mil (7.62 mm) 18-Pin Package
- Fully Static Operation (No Clocks, No Refresh, No Timing Strobe)
- 4 Performance Ranges:

		ACCESS READ OR WRITE	
		TIME	CYCLE
		(MAX)	(MIN)
TMS2114-15, TMS2114L-15		150 ns	150 ns
TMS2114-20, TMS2114L-20		200 ns	200 ns
TMS2114-25, TMS2114L-25		250 ns	250 ns
TMS2114-45, TMS2114L-45		450 ns	450 ns

```
A6   [ 1    18 ]  VCC
A5   [ 2    17 ]  A7
A4   [ 3    16 ]  A8
A3   [ 4    15 ]  A9
A0   [ 5    14 ]  DQ1
A1   [ 6    13 ]  DQ2
A2   [ 7    12 ]  DQ3
S‾   [ 8    11 ]  DQ4
VSS  [ 9    10 ]  W‾
```

- 400-mV Guaranteed DC Noise Immunity with Standard TTL Loads – No Pull-Up Resistors Required
- Common I/O Capability
- 3-State Outputs and Chip Select Control for OR-Tie Capability
- Fan-Out to 2 Series 74, 1 Series 74S, or 8 Series 74LS TTL Loads
- Low Power Dissipation

PIN NOMENCLATURE	
A0 – A9	Addresses
DQ1 – DQ4	Data In/Data Out
S‾	Chip Select
VCC	+5-V Supply
VSS	Ground
W‾	Write Enable

	MAX
	(OPERATING)
TMS2114	550 mW
TMS2114L	330 mW

description

This series of static random-access memories is organized as 1024 words of 4 bits each. Static design results in reducing overhead costs by elimination of refresh-clocking circuitry and by simplification of timing requirements. Because this series is fully static, chip select may be tied low to further simplify system timing. Output data is always available during a read cycle.

All inputs and outputs are fully compatible with Series 74, 74S or 74LS TTL. No pull-up resistors are required. This 4K Static RAM series is manufactured using TI's reliable N-channel silicon-gate technology to optimize the cost/performance relationship.

The TMS2114/2114L series is offered in the 18-pin dual-in-line plastic (NL suffix) package designed for insertion in mounting-hole rows on 300-mil (7.62 mm) centers. The series is guaranteed for operation from 0°C to 70°C.

Static RAM and Memory Support Devices

8

TEXAS INSTRUMENTS
POST OFFICE BOX 225012 • DALLAS, TEXAS 75265

TMS2114, TMS2114L
1024-WORD BY 4-BIT STATIC RAMS

operation

addresses (A0 – A9)

The ten address inputs select one of the 1024 4-bit words in the RAM. The address inputs must be stable for the duration of a write cycle. The address inputs can be driven directly from standard Series 54/74 TTL with no external pull-up resistors.

chip select ($\overline{S}$)

The chip-select terminal, which can be driven directly from standard TTL circuits, affects the data-in and data-out terminals. When chip select is at a logic low level, both terminals are enabled. When chip select is high, data-in is inhibited and data-out is in the floating or high-impedance state.

write enable ($\overline{W}$)

The read or write mode is selected through the write enable terminal. A logic high selects the read mode; a logic low selects the write mode. $\overline{W}$ or $\overline{S}$ must be high when changing addresses to prevent erroneously writing data into a memory location. The $\overline{W}$ input can be driven directly from standard TTL circuits.

data-in/data-out (DQ1 – DQ4)

Data can be written into a selected device when the write enable input is low. The DQ terminal can be driven directly from standard TTL circuits. The three-state output buffer provides direct TTL compatibility with a fan-out of two Series 74 TTL gates, one Series 74S TTL gate, or eight Series 74LS TTL gates. The DQ terminals are in the high-impedance state when chip select ($\overline{S}$) is high or whenever a write operation is being performed. Data-out is the same polarity as data-in.

Static RAM and Memory Support Devices

8

TEXAS
INSTRUMENTS
POST OFFICE BOX 225012 • DALLAS, TEXAS 75265

logic symbol†

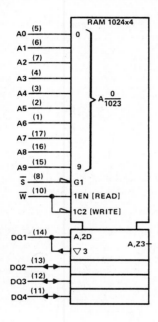

FUNCTION TABLE			
$\overline{W}$	$\overline{S}$	DQ1 – DQ4	MODE
L	L	VALID DATA	WRITE
H	L	DATA OUTPUT	READ
X	H	HI-Z	DEVICE DISABLED

†This symbol is in accordance with IEEE Std 91/ANSI Y32.14 and recent decisions by IEEE and IEC. See explanation on page 10-1.

absolute maximum ratings over operating free-air temperature (unless otherwise noted)†

Supply voltage, V_{CC} (see Note 1) . . . . −0.5 V to 7 V
Input voltage (any input) (see Note 1) . . . . −1 V to 7 V
Continuous power dissipation . . . . 1 W
Operating free-air temperature range . . . . 0 °C to 70 °C
Storage temperature range . . . . −55 °C to 150 °C

* Stresses beyond those listed under ''Absolute Maximum Rating'' may cause permanent damage to the device. This is a stress rating only and functional operation of the device at these or any other conditions beyond those indicated in the ''Recommended Operating Conditions'' section of this specification is not implied. Exposure to absolute-maximum-rated conditions for extended periods may affect device reliability.

NOTE 1: Voltage values are with respect to the ground material.

recommended operating conditions

PARAMETER	TMS2114 TMS2114L			UNIT
	MIN	NOM	MAX	
Supply voltage, V_{CC}	4.5	5	5.5	V
Supply voltage, V_{SS}		0		V
High-level input voltage, V_{IH}	2		5.5	V
Low-level input voltage, V_{IL} (see Note 2)	−1		0.8	V
Operating free-air temperature, T_A	0		70	°C

NOTE 2: The algebraic convention, where the more negative (less positive) limit is designated as minium, is used in this data sheet for logic voltage levels only.

TEXAS INSTRUMENTS
POST OFFICE BOX 225012 • DALLAS TEXAS 75265

TMS2114, TMS2114L
1024-WORD BY 4-BIT STATIC RAMS

electrical characteristics over recommended operating free-air temperature range (unless otherwise noted)

	PARAMETER	TEST CONDITIONS[†]			MIN	TYP[‡]	MAX	UNIT
V_{OH}	High-level voltage	$I_{OH} = -1$ mA	V_{CC} = MIN (operating)		2.4			V
V_{OL}	Low-level voltage	$I_{OL} = 3.2$ mA	V_{CC} = MIN (operating)				0.4	V
I_I	Input current	$V_I = 0$ V to MAX					10	μA
I_{OZ}	Off-state output current	$\overline{S}$ at 2 V or $\overline{W}$ at 0.8 V	$V_O = 0$ V to MAX				±10	μA
I_{CC}	Supply current from V_{CC}	$I_O = 0$ mA, $T_A = 0°C$ (worst case)	TMS 2114	V_{CC} = MAX		90	100	mA
			TMS 2114L	V_{CC} = MAX		50	60	
C_i	Input capacitance	$V_I = 0$ V, f = 1 MHz					8	pF
C_o	Output capacitance	$V_O = 0$ V, f = 1 MHz					8	pF

† For conditions shown as MIN or MAX, use the appropriate value specified under recommended operating conditions.
‡ All typical values are at $V_{CC} = 5$ V, $T_A = 25°C$.

timing requirements over recommended supply voltage range, $T_A = 0°C$ to 70°C, 1 Series 74 TTL load, $C_L = 100$ pF

	PARAMETER	TMS2114-15 TMS2114L-15		TMS2114-20 TMS2114L-20		TMS2114-25 TMS2114L-25		TMS2114-45 TMS2114L-45		UNIT
		MIN	MAX	MIN	MAX	MIN	MAX	MIN	MAX	
$t_{c(rd)}$	Read cycle time	150		200		250		450		ns
$t_{c(wr)}$	Write cycle time	150		200		250		450		ns
$t_{w(W)}$	Write pulse width	80		100		100		200		ns
$t_{su(A)}$	Address set up time	0		0		0		0		ns
$t_{su(S)}$	Chip select set up time	80		100		100		200		ns
$t_{su(D)}$	Data set up time	80		100		100		200		ns
$t_{h(D)}$	Data hold time	0		0		0		0		ns
$t_{h(A)}$	Address hold time	0		0		0		20		ns

TEXAS
INSTRUMENTS
POST OFFICE BOX 225012 ● DALLAS, TEXAS 75265

switching characteristics over recommended voltage range, T_A = 0°C to 70°C, 1 Series 74 TTL load, C_L = 100 pF

	PARAMETER	TMS2114-15 TMS2114L-15		TMS2114-20 TMS2114L-20		TMS2114-25 TMS2114L-25		TMS2114-45 TMS2114L-45		UNIT
		MIN	MAX	MIN	MAX	MIN	MAX	MIN	MAX	
$t_{a(A)}$	Access time from address		150		200		250		450	ns
$t_{a(S)}$	Access time from chip select (or output enable) low		70		85		100		120	ns
$t_{a(W)}$	Access time from write enable high		70		85		100		120	ns
$t_{v(A)}$	Output data valid after address change	20		20		20		20		ns
$t_{dis(S)}$	Output disable time after chip select (or output enable) high		50		60		60		100	ns
$t_{dis(W)}$	Output disable time after write enable low		50		60		60		100	ns

read cycle timing†

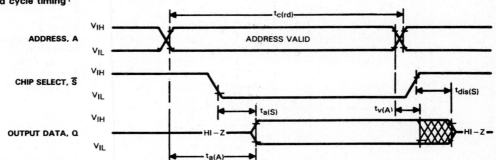

All timing reference points are 0.8 V and 2.0 V on inputs and 0.6 V and 2.2 V on outputs (90% points). Input rise and fall times equal 10 nanoseconds.

†Write enable is high for a read cycle.

early write cycle timing

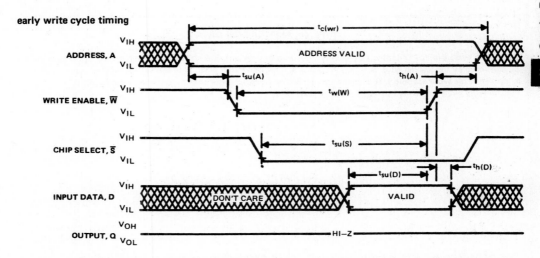

TEXAS INSTRUMENTS
POST OFFICE BOX 225012 ● DALLAS, TEXAS 75265

Static RAM and Memory Support Devices

8

TMS2114, TMS2114L
1024-WORD BY 4-BIT STATIC RAMS

read-write cycle timing

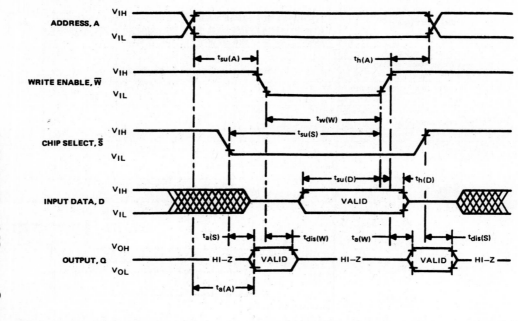

TYPICAL APPLICATION DATA

Early write cycle avoids DQ conflicts by controlling the write time with $\overline{S}$. On the diagram above, the write operation will be controlled by the leading edge of $\overline{S}$, not $\overline{W}$. Data can only be written when both $\overline{S}$ and $\overline{W}$ are low. Either $\overline{S}$ or $\overline{W}$ being high inhibits the write operation. To prevent erroneous data being written into the array, the addresses must be stable during the write cycle as defined by $t_{su(A)}$, $t_{w(W)}$, and $t_{h(A)}$.

Texas Instruments reserves the right to make changes at any time in order to improve design and to supply the best product possible.

Texas Instruments
POST OFFICE BOX 225012 ● DALLAS, TEXAS 75265

- Timing from Microseconds to Hours
- Astable or Monostable Operation
- Adjustable Duty Cycle
- TTL-Compatible Output Can Sink or Source Up to 200 mA
- Functionally Interchangeable with the Signetics SE555, SE555C, SA555, NE555; Have Same Pinout

SE555C FROM TI IS NOT RECOMMENDED FOR NEW DESIGNS

description

These devices are monolithic timing circuits capable of producing accurate time delays or oscillation. In the time-delay or monostable mode of operation, the timed interval is controlled by a single external resistor and capacitor network. In the astable mode of operation, the frequency and duty cycle may be independently controlled with two external resistors and a single external capacitor.

The threshold and trigger levels are normally two-thirds and one-third, respectively, of V_{CC}. These levels can be altered by use of the control voltage terminal. When the trigger input falls below the trigger level, the flip-flop is set and the output goes high. If the trigger input is above the trigger level and the threshold input is above the threshold level, the flip-flop is reset and the output is low. The reset input can override all other inputs and can be used to initiate a new timing cycle. When the reset input goes low, the flip-flop is reset and the output goes low. Whenever the output is low, a low-impedance path is provided between the discharge terminal and ground.

The output circuit is capable of sinking or sourcing current up to 200 mA. Operation is specified for supplies of 5 to 15 V. With a 5-V supply, output levels are compatible with TTL inputs.

The SE555 and SE555C are characterized for operation over the full military range of −55 °C to 125 °C. The SA555 is characterized for operation from −40 °C to 85 °C, and the NE555 is characterized for operation from 0 °C to 70 °C.

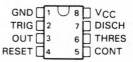

SE555, SE555C . . . JG PACKAGE
SA555, NE555 . . . D, JG, OR P PACKAGE
(TOP VIEW)

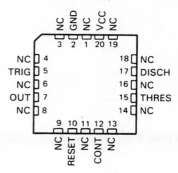

GND	1	8	V_{CC}
TRIG	2	7	DISCH
OUT	3	6	THRES
RESET	4	5	CONT

SE555, SE555C . . . FK PACKAGE
(TOP VIEW)

NC — No internal connection

functional block diagram

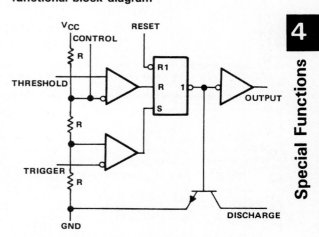

Reset can override Trigger, which can override Threshold.

Copyright © 1983, Texas Instruments Incorporated

TEXAS INSTRUMENTS
POST OFFICE BOX 655012 • DALLAS, TEXAS 75265

4

Special Functions

electrical characteristics at 25 °C free-air temperature, V$_{CC}$ = 5 V to 15 V (unless otherwise noted)

PARAMETER	TEST CONDITIONS		SE555 MIN	SE555 TYP	SE555 MAX	SE555C, SA555, NE555 MIN	SE555C, SA555, NE555 TYP	SE555C, SA555, NE555 MAX	UNIT
Threshold voltage level	V$_{CC}$ = 15 V		9.4	10	10.6	8.8	10	11.2	V
	V$_{CC}$ = 5 V		2.7	3.3	4	2.4	3.3	4.2	
Threshold current (see Note 2)				30	250		30	250	nA
Trigger voltage level	V$_{CC}$ = 15 V		4.8	5	5.2	4.5	5	5.6	V
	V$_{CC}$ = 5 V		1.45	1.67	1.9	1.1	1.67	2.2	
Trigger current	Trigger at 0 V			0.5	0.9		0.5	2	µA
Reset voltage level			0.3	0.7	1	0.3	0.7	1	V
Reset current	Reset at V$_{CC}$			0.1	0.4		0.1	0.4	mA
	Reset at 0 V			−0.4	−1		−0.4	−1.5	
Discharge switch off-state current				20	100		20	100	nA
Control voltage (open circuit)	V$_{CC}$ = 15 V		9.6	10	10.4	9	10	11	V
	V$_{CC}$ = 5 V		2.9	3.3	3.8	2.6	3.3	4	
Low-level output voltage	V$_{CC}$ = 15 V	I$_{OL}$ = 10 mA		0.1	0.15		0.1	0.25	V
		I$_{OL}$ = 50 mA		0.4	0.5		0.4	0.75	
		I$_{OL}$ = 100 mA		2	2.2		2	2.5	
		I$_{OL}$ = 200 mA		2.5			2.5		
	V$_{CC}$ = 5 V	I$_{OL}$ = 5 mA		0.1	0.2		0.1	0.35	
		I$_{OL}$ = 8 mA		0.15	0.25		0.15	0.4	
High-level output voltage	V$_{CC}$ = 15 V	I$_{OH}$ = −100 mA	13	13.3		12.75	13.3		V
		I$_{OH}$ = −200 mA		12.5			12.5		
	V$_{CC}$ = 5 V	I$_{OH}$ = −100 mA	3	3.3		2.75	3.3		
Supply current	Output low, No load	V$_{CC}$ = 15 V		10	12		10	15	mA
		V$_{CC}$ = 5 V		3	5		3	6	
	Output high, No load	V$_{CC}$ = 15 V		9	10		9	13	
		V$_{CC}$ = 5 V		2	4		2	5	

NOTE 2: This parameter influences the maximum value of the timing resistors R$_A$ and R$_B$ in the circuit of Figure 12. For example, when V$_{CC}$ = 5 V, the maximum value is R = R$_A$ + R$_B$ ≈ 3.4 MΩ, and for V$_{CC}$ = 15 V, the maximum value is 10 MΩ.

operating characteristics, V$_{CC}$ = 5 V and 15 V

PARAMETER		TEST CONDITIONS[†]	SE555 MIN	SE555 TYP	SE555 MAX	SE555C, SA555, NE555 MIN	SE555C, SA555, NE555 TYP	SE555C, SA555, NE555 MAX	UNIT
Initial error of timing interval[‡]	Each timer, monostable[§]	T$_A$ = 25 °C		0.5	1.5		1	3	%
	Each timer, astable[¶]			1.5			2.25		
Temperature coefficient of timing interval	Each timer, monostable[§]	T$_A$ = MIN to MAX		30	100		50		ppm/°C
	Each timer, astable[¶]			90			150		
Supply voltage sensitivity of timing interval	Each timer, monostable[§]	T$_A$ = 25 °C		0.05	0.2		0.1	0.5	%/V
	Each timer, astable[¶]			0.15			0.3		
Output pulse rise time		C$_L$ = 15 pF,		100	200		100	300	ns
Output pulse fall time		T$_A$ = 25 °C		100	200		100	300	

[†]For conditions shown as MIN or MAX, use the appropriate value specified under recommended operating conditions.

[‡]Timing interval error is defined as the difference between the measured value and the average value of a random sample from each process run.

[§]Values specified are for a device in a monostable circuit similar to Figure 9, with component values as follow: R$_A$ = 2 kΩ to 100 kΩ, C = 0.1 µF.

[¶]Values specified are for a device in an astable circuit similar to Figure 12, with component values as follow: R$_A$ = 1 kΩ to 100 kΩ, C = 0.1 µF.

TEXAS
INSTRUMENTS
POST OFFICE BOX 655012 • DALLAS, TEXAS 75265

4

Special Functions

SE555, SE555C, SA555, NE555
PRECISION TIMERS

TYPICAL APPLICATION DATA

monostable operation

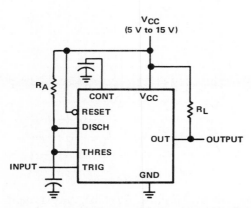

FIGURE 9. CIRCUIT FOR MONOSTABLE OPERATION

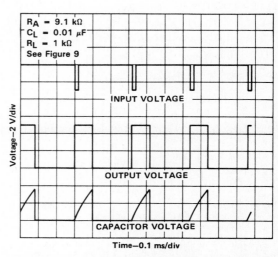

FIGURE 10. TYPICAL MONOSTABLE WAVEFORMS

For monostable operation, any of these timers may be connected as shown in Figure 9. If the output is low, application of a negative-going pulse to the trigger input sets the flip-flop ($\overline{Q}$ goes low), drives the output high, and turns off Q1. Capacitor C is then charged through R_A until the voltage across the capacitor reaches the threshold voltage of the threshold input. If the trigger input has returned to a high level, the output of the threshold comparator will reset the flip-flop ($\overline{Q}$ goes high), drive the output low, and discharge C through Q1.

Monostable operation is initiated when the trigger input voltage falls below the trigger threshold. Once initiated, the sequence ends only if the trigger input is high at the end of the timing interval. Because of the threshold level and saturation voltage of Q1, the output pulse duration is approximately $t_W = 1.1\ R_A C$. Figure 11 is a plot of the time constant for various values of R_A and C. The threshold levels and charge rates are both directly proportional to the supply voltage, V_{CC}. The timing interval is therefore independent of the supply voltage, so long as the supply voltage is constant during the time interval.

Applying a negative-going trigger pulse simultaneously to the reset and trigger terminals during the timing interval discharges C and re-initiates the cycle, commencing on the positive edge of the reset pulse. The output is held low as long as the reset pulse is low. To prevent false triggering, when the reset input is not used, it should be connected to V_{CC}.

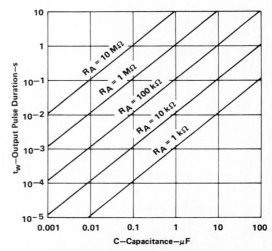

FIGURE 11. OUTPUT PULSE
DURATION vs CAPACITANCE

4

Special Functions

TEXAS
INSTRUMENTS

POST OFFICE BOX 655012 • DALLAS, TEXAS 75265

TYPICAL APPLICATION DATA

astable operation

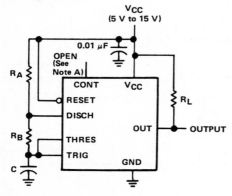

NOTE A: Decoupling the control voltage input to ground with a capacitor may improve operation. This should be evaluated for individual applications.

FIGURE 12. CIRCUIT FOR ASTABLE OPERATION

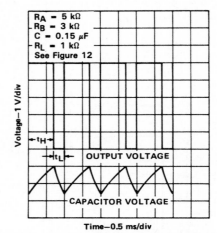

FIGURE 13. TYPICAL ASTABLE WAVEFORMS

As shown in Figure 12, adding a second resistor, R_B, to the circuit of Figure 9 and connecting the trigger input to the threshold input causes the timer to self-trigger and run as a multivibrator. The capacitor C will charge through R_A and R_B and then discharge through R_B only. The duty cycle may be controlled, therefore, by the values of R_A and R_B.

This astable connection results in capacitor C charging and discharging between the threshold-voltage level ($\approx 0.67 \cdot V_{CC}$) and the trigger-voltage level ($\approx 0.33 \cdot V_{CC}$). As in the monostable circuit, charge and discharge times (and therefore the frequency and duty cycle) are independent of the supply voltage.

Figure 13 shows typical waveforms generated during astable operation. The output high-level duration t_H and low-level duration t_L may be calculated as follows:

$$t_H = 0.693 \, (R_A + R_B) \, C$$

$$t_L = 0.693 \, (R_B) \, C$$

Other useful relationships are shown below.

$$\text{period} = t_H + t_L = 0.693 \, (R_A + 2R_B) \, C$$

$$\text{frequency} \approx \frac{1.44}{(R_A + 2R_B) \, C}$$

$$\text{Output driver duty cycle} = \frac{t_L}{t_H + t_L} = \frac{R_B}{R_A + 2R_B}$$

$$\text{Output waveform duty cycle} = \frac{t_H}{t_H + t_L} = 1 - \frac{R_B}{R_A + 2R_B}$$

$$\text{Low-to-high ratio} = \frac{t_L}{t_H} = \frac{R_B}{R_A + R_B}$$

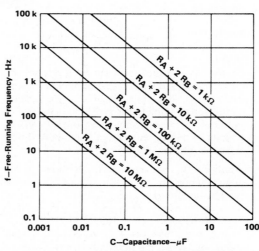

FIGURE 14. FREE-RUNNING FREQUENCY

Special Functions 4

TEXAS
INSTRUMENTS
POST OFFICE BOX 655012 • DALLAS, TEXAS 75265

TYPICAL APPLICATION DATA

sequential timer

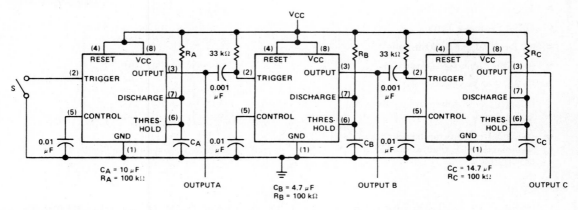

S closes momentarily at t = 0.

FIGURE 22. SEQUENTIAL TIMER CIRCUIT

Many applications, such as computers, require signals for initializing conditions during start-up. Other applications, such as test equipment, require activation of test signals in sequence. These timing circuits may be connected to provide such sequential control. The timers may be used in various combinations of astable or monostable circuit connections, with or without modulation, for extremely flexible waveform control. Figure 22 illustrates a sequencer circuit with possible applications in many systems, and Figure 23 shows the output waveforms.

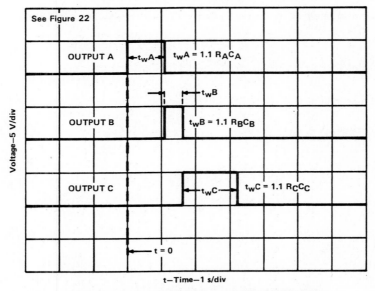

FIGURE 23. SEQUENTIAL TIMER WAVEFORMS

Special Functions 4

- **8-Bit Resolution**

- **Ratiometric Conversion**

- **100-μs Conversion Time**

- **135-ns Access Time**

- **No Zero Adjust Requirement**

- **On-Chip Clock Generator**

- **Single 5-V Power Supply**

- **Operates with Microprocessor or as Stand-Alone**

- **Designed to be Interchangeable with National Semiconductor and Signetics ADC0804**

N DUAL-IN-LINE PACKAGE
(TOP VIEW)

```
         $\overline{CS}$  [ 1    20 ]  V_CC (OR REF)
         $\overline{RD}$  [ 2    19 ]  CLK OUT
         $\overline{WR}$  [ 3    18 ]  DB0 (LSB)
       CLK IN  [ 4    17 ]  DB1
       $\overline{INTR}$  [ 5    16 ]  DB2
         IN +  [ 6    15 ]  DB3      DATA
         IN −  [ 7    14 ]  DB4      OUTPUTS
     ANLG GND  [ 8    13 ]  DB5
        REF/2  [ 9    12 ]  DB6
     DGTL GND  [ 10   11 ]  DB7 (MSB)
```

description

The ADC0804 is a CMOS 8-bit successive-approximation analog-to-digital converter that uses a modified potentiometric (256R) ladder. The ADC0804 is designed to operate from common microprocessor control buses, with the three-state output latches driving the data bus. The ADC0804 can be made to appear to the microprocessor as a memory location or an I/O port. Detailed information on interfacing to most popular microprocessors is readily available from the factory.

A differential analog voltage input allows increased common-mode rejection and offset of the zero-input analog voltage value. Although a reference input (REF/2) is available to allow 8-bit conversion over smaller analog voltage spans or to make use of an external reference, ratiometric conversion is possible with the REF/2 input open. Without an external reference, the conversion takes place over a span from V_CC to analog ground (ANLG GND). The ADC0804 can operate with an external clock signal or, with an additional resistor and capacitor, can operate using an on-chip clock generator.

The ADC0804I is characterized for operation from −40 °C to 85 °C. The ADC0804C is characterized for operation from 0 °C to 70 °C.

Data Sheets

2

TEXAS
INSTRUMENTS

POST OFFICE BOX 655012 • DALLAS, TEXAS 75265

ADC0804I, ADC0804C
8-BIT ANALOG-TO-DIGITAL CONVERTER
WITH DIFFERENTIAL INPUTS

functional block diagram (positive logic)

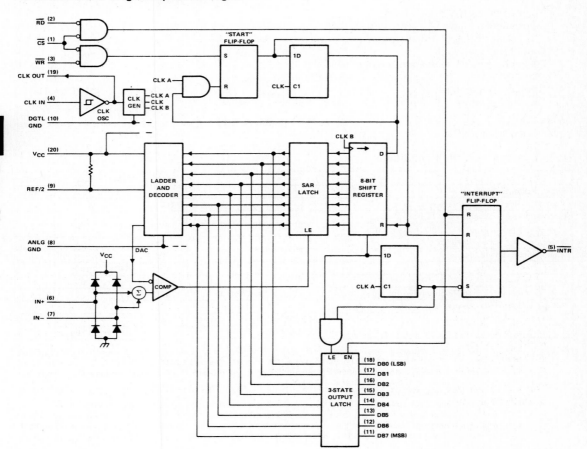

TEXAS
INSTRUMENTS
POST OFFICE BOX 655012 • DALLAS, TEXAS 75265

absolute maximum ratings over operating free-air temperature range (unless otherwise noted)

Supply voltage, V_{CC} (see Note 1) .... 6.5 V
Input voltage range: $\overline{CS}$, $\overline{RD}$, $\overline{WR}$ .... −0.3 V to 18 V
        other inputs .... −0.3 V to V_{CC} + 0.3 V
Output voltage range .... −0.3 V to V_{CC} + 0.3 V
Operating free-air temperature range: ADC0804I .... −40°C to 85°C
                     ADC0804C .... 0°C to 70°C
Storage temperature range .... −65°C to 150°C
Lead temperature 1,6 mm (1/16 inch) from case for 10 seconds .... 260°C

NOTE 1: All voltage values are with respect to digital ground (DGTL GND) with DGTL GND and ANLG GND connected together (unless otherwise noted).

recommended operating conditions

		MIN	NOM	MAX	UNIT
Supply voltage, V_{CC}		4.5	5	6.3	V
Voltage at REF/2, $V_{REF/2}$ (see Note 2)		0.25	2.5		V
High-level input voltage at $\overline{CS}$, $\overline{RD}$, or $\overline{WR}$, V_{IH}		2		15	V
Low-level input voltage at $\overline{CS}$, $\overline{RD}$, or $\overline{WR}$, V_{IL}				0.8	V
Analog ground voltage (see Note 3)		−0.05	0	1	V
Analog input voltage (see Note 4)		−0.05		V_{CC}+0.05	V
Clock input frequency, f_{clock} (see Note 5)		100	640	1460	kHz
Duty cycle for $f_{clock} \geq$ 640 kHz (see Note 5)		40		60	%
Pulse duration clock input (high or low) for $f_{clock} <$ 640 kHz, $t_{w(CLK)}$ (see Note 5)		275	781		ns
Pulse duration, $\overline{WR}$ input low (start conversion), $t_{w(WR)}$		100			ns
Operating free-air temperature, T_A	ADC0804I	−40		85	°C
	ADC0804C	0		70	

NOTES: 2. The internal reference voltage is equal to the voltage applied to REF/2, or approximately equal to one-half of the V_{CC} when REF/2 is left open. The voltage at REF/2 should be one-half the full-scale differential input voltage between the analog inputs. Thus, the differential input voltage when REF/2 is open and V_{CC} = 5 V is 0 to 5 V. VREF/2 for an input voltage range from 0.5 V to 3.5 V (full-scale differential voltage of 3 V) is 1.5 V.
     3. These values are with respect to DGTL GND.
     4. When the differential input voltage ($V_{IN+} - V_{in-}$) is less than or equal to 0 V, the output code is 0000 0000.
     5. Total unadjusted error is specified only at an f_{clock} of 640 kHz with a duty cycle of 40% to 60% (pulse duration 625 ns to 937 ns). For frequencies above this limit or pulse duration below 625 ns, error may increase. The duty cycle limits should be observed for an f_{clock} greater than 640 kHz. Below 640 kHz, this duty cycle limit can be exceeded provided $t_{w(CLK)}$ remains within limits.

Data Sheets

2

electrical characteristics over recommended operating free-air temperature range, V_{CC} = 5 V, f_{clock} = 640 kHz, REF/2 = 2.5 V (unless otherwise noted)

PARAMETER			TEST CONDITIONS	MIN	TYP[†]	MAX	UNIT
V_{OH}	High-level output voltage	All outputs	V_{CC} = 4.75 V, I_{OH} = −360 μA	2.4			V
		DB and $\overline{INTR}$	V_{CC} = 4.75 V, I_{OH} = −10 μA	4.5			
V_{OL}	Low-level output voltage	Data outputs	V_{CC} = 4.75 V, I_{OL} = 1.6 mA			0.4	V
		$\overline{INTR}$ output	V_{CC} = 4.75 V, I_{OL} = 1 mA			0.4	
		CLK OUT	V_{CC} = 4.75 V, I_{OL} = 360 μA			0.4	
V_{T+}	Clock positive-going threshold voltage			2.7	3.1	3.5	V
V_{T-}	Clock negative-going threshold voltage			1.5	1.8	2.1	V
$V_{T+} - V_{T-}$	Clock input hysteresis			0.6	1.3	2	V
I_{IH}	High-level input current				0.005	1	μA
I_{IL}	Low-level input current				−0.005	−1	μA
I_{OZ}	Off-state output current		V_O = 0			−3	μA
			V_O = 5 V			3	
I_{OHS}	Short-circuit output current	Output high	V_O = 0, $\quad$ T_A = 25°C	−4.5	−6		mA
I_{OLS}	Short-circuit output current	Output low	V_O = 5 V, $\quad$ T_A = 25°C	9	16		mA
I_{CC}	Supply current plus reference current		REF/2 open, $\quad$ $\overline{CS}$ at 5 V, T_A = 25°C		1.9	2.5	mA
$R_{REF/2}$	Input resistance to reference ladder		See Note 6	1	1.3		kΩ
C_i	Input capacitance (control)				5	7.5	pF
C_o	Output capacitance (DB)				5	7.5	pF

operating characteristics over recommended operating free-air temperature range, V_{CC} = 5 V, $V_{REF/2}$ = 2.5 V, f_{clock} = 640 kHz (unless otherwise noted)

PARAMETER		TEST CONDITIONS	MIN	TYP[†]	MAX	UNIT
	Supply-voltage-variation error (See Notes 2 and 7)	V_{CC} = 4.5 V to 5.5 V		±1/16	±1/8	LSB
	Total unadjusted error (See Notes 7 and 8)	$V_{REF/2}$ = 2.5 V			±1	LSB
	DC common-mode error (See Note 8)			±1/16	±1/8	LSB
t_{en}	Output enable time	C_L = 100 pF		135	200	ns
t_{dis}	Output disable time	C_L = 10 pF, $\quad$ R_L = 10 kΩ		125	200	ns
$t_{d(INTR)}$	Delay time to reset $\overline{INTR}$			300	450	ns
t_{conv}	Conversion cycle time (See Note 9)	f_{clock} = 100 kHz to 1.46 MHz	65½		72½	clock cycles
	Conversion time			103	114	μs
CR	Free-running conversion rate	$\overline{INTR}$ connected to $\overline{WR}$, $\overline{CS}$ at 0 V			8827	conv/s

[†] All typical values are at T_A = 25°C.

NOTES: 2. The internal reference voltage is equal to the voltage applied to REF/2, or approximately equal to one-half of the V_{CC} when REF/2 is left open. The voltage at REF/2 should be one-half the full-scale differential input voltage between the analog inputs. Thus, the differential input voltage when REF/2 is open and V_{CC} = 5 V is 0 to 5 V. $V_{REF/2}$ for an input voltage range from 0.5 V to 3.5 V (full-scale differential voltage of 3 V) is 1.5 V.

6. The resistance is calculated from the current drawn from a 5-V supply applied to pins 8 and 9.

7. These parameters are specified for the recommended analog input voltage range.

8. All errors are measured with reference to an ideal straight line through the end-points of the analog-to-digital transfer characteristic.

9. Although internal conversion is completed in 64 clock periods, a $\overline{CS}$ or $\overline{WR}$ low-to-high transition is followed by 1 to 8 clock periods before conversion starts. After conversion is completed, part of another clock period is required before a high-to-low transition of $\overline{INTR}$ completes the cycle.

TEXAS INSTRUMENTS
POST OFFICE BOX 655012 • DALLAS, TEXAS 75265

timing diagrams

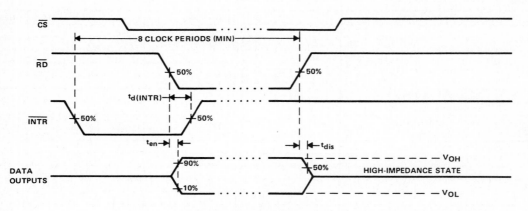

READ OPERATION TIMING DIAGRAM

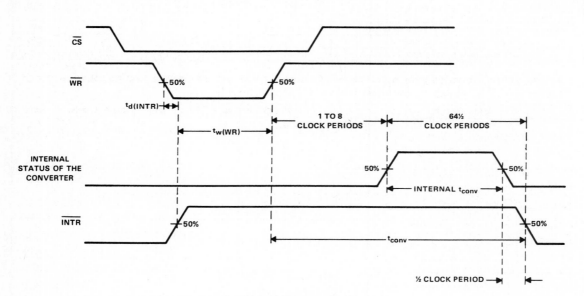

WRITE OPERATION TIMING DIAGRAM

Data Sheets **2**

PRINCIPLES OF OPERATION

The ADC0804 contains a circuit equivalent to a 256-resistor network. Analog switches are sequenced by successive approximation logic to match an analog differential input voltage ($V_{in+} - V_{in-}$) to a corresponding tap on the 256-resistor network. The most-significant bit (MSB) is tested first. After eight comparisons (64 clock periods), an 8-bit binary code (1111 1111 = full scale) is transferred to an output latch and the interrupt ($\overline{INTR}$) output goes low. The device can be operated in a free-running mode by connecting the $\overline{INTR}$ output to the write ($\overline{WR}$) input and holding the conversion start ($\overline{CS}$) input at a low level. To ensure start-up under all conditions, a low-level $\overline{WR}$ input is required during the power-up cycle. Taking $\overline{CS}$ low anytime after that will interrupt a conversion in process.

When the $\overline{WR}$ input goes low, the ADC0804 successive approximation register (SAR) and 8-bit shift register are reset. As long as both $\overline{CS}$ and $\overline{WR}$ remain low, the ADC0804 remains in a reset state. One to eight clock periods after $\overline{CS}$ or $\overline{WR}$ makes a low-to-high transition, conversion starts.

When the $\overline{CS}$ and $\overline{WR}$ inputs are low, the start flip-flop is set and the interrupt flip-flop and 8-bit register are reset. The next clock pulse transfers a logic high to the output of the start flip-flop. The logic high is ANDed with the next clock pulse, placing a logic high on the reset input of the start flip-flop. If either $\overline{CS}$ or $\overline{WR}$ have gone high, the set signal to the start flip-flop is removed, causing it to be reset. A logic high is placed on the D input of the 8-bit shift register and the conversion process is started. If the $\overline{CS}$ and $\overline{WR}$ inputs are still low, the start flip-flop, the 8-bit shift register, and the SAR remain reset. This action allows for wide $\overline{CS}$ and $\overline{WR}$ inputs with conversion starting from one to eight clock periods after one of the inputs goes high.

When the logic high input has been clocked through the 8-bit shift register, completing the SAR search, it is applied to an AND gate controlling the output latches and to the D input of a flip-flop. On the next clock pulse, the digital word is transferred to the three-state output latches and the interrupt flip-flop is set. The output of the interrupt flip-flop is inverted to provide an $\overline{INTR}$ output that is high during conversion and low when the conversion is completed.

When a low is at both the $\overline{CS}$ and $\overline{RD}$ inputs, an output is applied to the DB0 through DB7 outputs and the interrupt flip-flop is reset. When either the $\overline{CS}$ or $\overline{RD}$ inputs return to a high state, the DB0 through DB7 outputs are disabled (returned to the high-impedance state). The interrupt flip-flop remains reset.

TEXAS INSTRUMENTS
POST OFFICE BOX 655012 • DALLAS, TEXAS 75265

DACPORT
Low-Cost Complete
μP-Compatible 8-Bit DAC

AD557

FEATURES
Complete 8-Bit DAC
Voltage Output – 0 to 2.56V
Internal Precision Band-Gap Reference
Single-Supply Operation: +5V (±10%)
Full Microprocessor Interface
Fast: 1μs Voltage Settling to ±1/2LSB
Low Power: 75mW
No User Trims Required
Guaranteed Monotonic Over Temperature
All Errors Specified T_{min} to T_{max}
Small 16-Pin DIP or 20-Pin PLCC Package
Low Cost

AD557 FUNCTIONAL BLOCK DIAGRAM

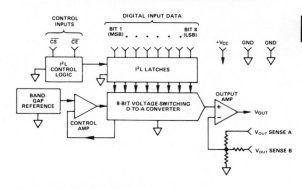

PRODUCT DESCRIPTION
The AD557 DACPORT™ is a complete voltage-output 8-bit digital-to-analog converter, including output amplifier, full microprocessor interface and precision voltage reference on a single monolithic chip. No external components or trims are required to interface, with full accuracy, an 8-bit data bus to an analog system.

The low cost and versatility of the AD557 DACPORT are the result of continued development in monolithic bipolar technologies.

The complete microprocessor interface and control logic is implemented with integrated injection logic (I²L), an extremely dense and low-power logic structure that is process-compatible with linear bipolar fabrication. The internal precision voltage reference is the patented low-voltage band-gap circuit which permits full-accuracy performance on a single +5V power supply. Thin-film silicon-chromium resistors provide the stability required for guaranteed monotonic operation over the entire operating temperature range, while laser-wafer trimming of these thin-film resistors permits absolute calibration at the factory to within ±2.5LSB; thus, no user-trims for gain or offset are required. A new circuit design provides voltage settling to ±1/2LSB for a full-scale step in 800ns.

The AD557 is available in two package configurations. The AD557JN is packaged in a 16-pin plastic, 0.3"-wide DIP. For surface mount applications, the AD557JP is packaged in a 20-pin JEDEC standard PLCC. Both versions are specified over the operating temperature range of 0 to +70°C.

DACPORT is a trademark of Analog Devices, Inc.
Covered by U.S. Patent Nos. 3,887,863; 3,685,045; 4,323,795; other patents pending.

PRODUCT HIGHLIGHTS
1. The 8-bit I²L input register and fully microprocessor-compatible control logic allow the AD557 to be directly connected to 8- or 16-bit data buses and operated with standard control signals. The latch may be disabled for direct DAC interfacing.

2. The laser-trimmed on-chip SiCr thin-film resistors are calibrated for absolute accuracy and linearity at the factory. Therefore, no user trims are necessary for full rated accuracy over the operating temperature range.

3. The inclusion of a precision low-voltage band-gap reference eliminates the need to specify and apply a separate reference source.

4. The AD557 is designed and specified to operate from a single +4.5V to +5.5V power supply.

5. Low digital input currents, 100μA max, minimize bus loading. Input thresholds are TTL/low voltage CMOS compatible.

6. The single-chip, low power I²L design of the AD557 is inherently more reliable than hybrid multichip or conventional single-chip bipolar designs.

SPECIFICATIONS (@ T_A = +25°C, V_{CC} = +5V unless otherwise specified)

Model	Min	AD557J Typ	Max	Units
RESOLUTION			8	Bits
RELATIVE ACCURACY[1]				
0 to +70°C		±1/2	1	LSB
OUTPUT				
Ranges		0 to +2.56		V
Current Source	+5			mA
Sink		Internal Passive Pull-Down to Ground[2]		
OUTPUT SETTLING TIME[3]		0.8	1.5	μs
FULL SCALE ACCURACY[4]				
@25°C		±1.5	±2.5	LSB
T_{min} to T_{max}		±2.5	±4.0	LSB
ZERO ERROR				
@25°C			±1	LSB
T_{min} to T_{max}			±3	LSB
MONOTONICITY[5]				
T_{min} to T_{max}		**Guaranteed**		
DIGITAL INPUTS				
T_{min} to T_{max}				
Input Current			±100	μA
Data Inputs, Voltage				
Bit On – Logic "1"	2.0			V
Bit On – Logic "0"	0		0.8	V
Control Inputs, Voltage				
On – Logic "1"	2.0			V
On – Logic "0"	0		0.8	V
Input Capacitance		4		pF
TIMING[6]				
t_W Strobe Pulse Width	225			ns
T_{min} to T_{max}	**300**			ns
t_{DH} Data Hold Time	10			ns
T_{min} to T_{max}	**10**			ns
t_{DS} Data Setup Time	225			ns
T_{min} to T_{max}	**300**			ns
POWER SUPPLY				
Operating Voltage Range (V_{CC})				
2.56 Volt Range	+4.5		+5.5	V
Current (I_{CC})		15	25	mA
Rejection Ratio			**0.03**	%/%
POWER DISSIPATION, V_{CC} = 5V		75	125	mW
OPERATING TEMPERATURE RANGE	0		+70	°C

NOTES
[1]Relative Accuracy is defined as the deviation of the code transition points from the ideal transfer point on a straight line from the offset to the full scale of the device. See "Measuring Offset Error" on AD558 data sheet.
[2]Passive pull-down resistance is 2kΩ.
[3]Settling time is specified for a positive-going full-scale step to ±1/2LSB. Negative-going steps to zero are slower, but can be improved with an external pull-down.
[4]The full-scale output voltage is 2.55V and is guaranteed with a +5V supply.
[5]A monotonic converter has a maximum differential linearity error of ±1LSB.
[6]See Figure 7.
Specifications shown in **boldface** are tested on all production units at final electrical test.
Specifications subject to change without notice.

PIN CONFIGURATIONS

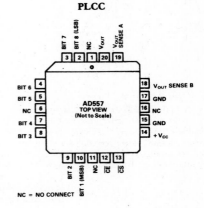

AD557 ORDERING GUIDE

Model	Package Options*	Temperature
AD557JN	Plastic (N-16)	0 to +70°C
AD557JP	PLCC (P-20A)	0 to +70°C

*See Section 14 for package outline information.

ABSOLUTE MAXIMUM RATINGS*

V_{CC} to Ground . . . . 0V to +18V
Digital Inputs (Pins 1-10) . . . . 0 to +7.0V
V_{OUT} . . . . Indefinite Short to Ground
Momentary Short to V_{CC}
Power Dissipation 450mW
Storage Temperature Range
N/P (Plastic) Packages . . . . –25°C to +100°C
Lead Temperature (soldering, 10 sec) . . . . 300°C

Thermal Resistance
Junction to Ambient/Junction to Case
N/P (Plastic) Packages . . . . 140/55°C/W

*Stresses above those listed under "Absolute Maximum Ratings" may cause permanent damage to the device. This is a stress rating only and functional operation of the device at these or any other conditions above those indicated in the operational sections of this specification is not implied. Exposure to absolute maximum rating conditions for extended periods may affect device reliability.

CIRCUIT DESCRIPTION

The AD557 consists of four major functional blocks fabricated on a single monolithic chip (see Figure 1). The main D/A converter section uses eight equally weighted laser-trimmed current sources switched into a silicon-chromium thin-film R/2R resistor ladder network to give a direct but unbuffered 0mV to 400mV output range. The transistors that form the DAC switches are PNPs; this allows direct positive-voltage logic interface and a zero-based output range.

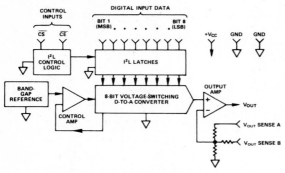

Figure 1. Functional Block Diagram

The high-speed output buffer amplifier is operated in the noninverting mode with gain determined by the user-connections at the output range select pin. The gain-setting application resistors are thin film laser trimmed to match and track the DAC resistors and to assure precise initial calibration of the output range, 0V to 2.56V. The amplifier output stage is an NPN transistor with passive pull-down for zero-based output capability with a single power supply.

The internal precision voltage reference is of the patented band-gap type. This design produces a reference voltage of 1.2V and thus, unlike 6.3V temperature-compensated zeners, may be operated from a single, low-voltage logic power supply. The microprocessor interface logic consists of an 8-bit data latch and control circuitry. Low power, small geometry and high speed are advantages of the I²L design as applied to this section. I²L is bipolar process compatible so that the performance of the analog sections need not be compromised to provide on-chip logic capabilities. The control logic allows the latches to be operated from a decoded microprocessor address and write signal. If the application does not involve a μP or data bus, wiring $\overline{CS}$ and $\overline{CE}$ to ground renders the latches "transparent" for direct DAC access.

Digital Input Code			Output
Binary	Hexadecimal	Decimal	Voltage
0000 0000	00	0	0
0000 0001	01	1	0.010V
0000 0010	02	2	0.020V
0000 1111	0F	15	0.150V
0001 0000	10	16	0.160V
0111 1111	7F	127	1.270V
1000 0000	80	128	1.280V
1100 0000	C0	192	1.920V
1111 1111	FF	255	2.55V

CONNECTING THE AD557

The AD557 has been configured for low cost and ease of application. All reference, output amplifier and logic connections are made internally. In addition, all calibration trims are performed at the factory assuring specified accuracy without user trims. The only connection decision to be made by the user is whether the output range desired is unipolar or bipolar. Clean circuit board layout is facilitated by isolating all digital bit inputs on one side of the package; analog outputs are on the opposite side.

UNIPOLAR 0 TO +2.56V OUTPUT RANGE

Figure 2 shows the configuration for the 0 to +2.56V full-scale output range. Because of its precise factory calibration, the AD557 is intended to be operated without user trims for gain and offset; therefore, no provisions have been made for such user trims. If a small increase in scale is required, however, it may be accomplished by slightly altering the effective gain of the output buffer. A resistor in series with V_{OUT} SENSE will increase the output range. Note that decreasing the scale by putting a resistor in series with GND will not work properly due to the code-dependent currents in GND. Adjusting offset by injecting dc at GND is not recommended for the same reason.

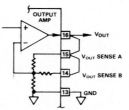

Figure 2. 0 to 2.56V Output Range

BIPOLAR −1.28V TO +1.28V OUTPUT RANGE

The AD557 was designed for operation from a single power supply and is thus capable of providing only a unipolar 0 to +2.56V output range. If a negative supply is available, bipolar output ranges may be achieved by suitable output offsetting and scaling. Figure 3 shows how a ±1.28V output range may be achieved when a −5V power supply is available. The offset is provided by the AD589 precision 1.2V reference which will operate from a +5V supply. The AD711 output amplifier can provide the necessary ±1.28V output swing from ±5V supplies. Coding is complementary offset binary.

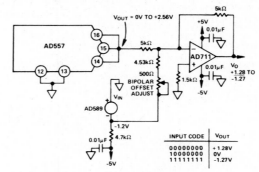

Figure 3. Bipolar Operation of AD557 from ±5V Supplies

Applications

GROUNDING AND BYPASSING

All precision converter products require careful application of good grounding practices to maintain full rated performance. Because the AD557 is intended for application in microcomputer systems where digital noise is prevalent, special care must be taken to assure that its inherent precision is realized.

The AD557 has two ground (common) pins; this minimizes ground drops and noise in the analog signal path. Figure 4 shows how the ground connections should be made.

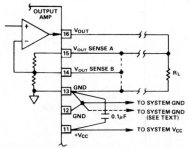

Figure 4. Recommended Grounding and Bypassing

It is often advisable to maintain separate analog and digital grounds throughout a complete system, tying them common in one place only. If the common tie-point is remote and accidental disconnection of that one common tie-point occurs due to card removal with power on, a large differential voltage between the two commons could develop. To protect devices that interface to both digital and analog parts of the system, such as the AD557, it is recommended that common ground tie-points should be provided at *each* such device. If only one system ground can be connected directly to the AD557, it is recommended that analog common be selected.

USING A "FALSE" GROUND

Many applications, such as disk drives, require servo control voltages that swing on either side of a "false" ground. This ground is usually created by dividing the + 12V supply equally and calling the midpoint voltage "ground."

Figure 5 shows an easy and inexpensive way to implement this. The AD586 is used to provide a stable 5V reference from the system's + 12V supply. The op amp shown likewise operates from a single (+ 12V) supply available in the system. The resulting output at the V_{OUT} node is ± 2.5V around the "false" ground point of 5V. AD557 input code vs. V_{OUT} is shown in Figure 6.

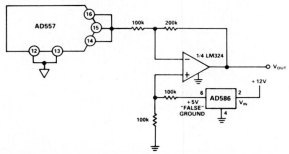

Figure 5. Level Shifting the AD557 Output Around a "False" Ground

TIMING AND CONTROL

The AD557 has data input latches that simplify interface to 8- and 16-bit data buses. These latches are controlled by Chip Enable ($\overline{CE}$) and Chip Select ($\overline{CS}$) inputs. $\overline{CE}$ and $\overline{CS}$ are internally "NORed" so that the latches transmit input data to the DAC section when both $\overline{CE}$ and $\overline{CS}$ are at Logic "0". If the application does not involve a data bus, a "00" condition allows for direct operation of the DAC. When either $\overline{CE}$ or $\overline{CS}$ go to Logic "1," the input data is latched into the registers and held until both $\overline{CE}$ and $\overline{CS}$ return to "0." (Unused $\overline{CE}$ or $\overline{CS}$ inputs should be tied to ground.) The truth table is given in Table I. The logic function is also shown in Figure 6.

Input Data	$\overline{CE}$	$\overline{CS}$	DAC Data	Latch Condition
0	0	0	0	"transparent"
1	0	0	1	"transparent"
0	ʃ	0	0	latching
1	ʃ	0	1	latching
0	0	ʃ	0	latching
1	0	ʃ	1	latching
X	1	X	previous data	latched
X	X	1	previous data	latched

Notes: X = Does not matter
ʃ = Logic Threshold at Positive-Going Transition

Table I. AD557 Control Logic Truth Table

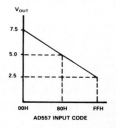

Figure 6. AD557 Input Code vs. Level Shifted Output in "False" Ground Configuration

In a level-triggered latch such as that used in the AD557, there is an interaction between the data setup and hold times and the width of the enable pulse. In an effort to reduce the time required to test all possible combinations in production, the AD557 is tested with $T_{DS} = T_W = 225$ns at 25°C and 300ns at T_{min} and T_{max}, with $T_{DH} = 10$ns at all temperatures. Failure to comply with these specifications may result in data not being latched properly.

Figure 7 shows the timing for the data and control signals, $\overline{CE}$ and $\overline{CS}$ are identical in timing as well as in function.

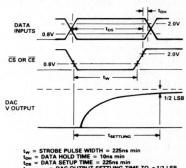

t_W = STROBE PULSE WIDTH = 225ns min
t_{DH} = DATA HOLD TIME = 10ns min
t_{DS} = DATA SETUP TIME = 225ns min
$t_{SETTLING}$ = DAC OUTPUT SETTLING TIME TO ±1/2 LSB

Figure 7. AD557 Timing

GAL®16V8A
GAL®20V8A

Generic Array Logic™
U.S. Patents 4,761,768 and 4,766,569

FEATURES

- **HIGH PERFORMANCE E²CMOS™ TECHNOLOGY**
  — 10 ns Maximum Propagation Delay
  — Fmax = 62.5 MHz
  — 8 ns Maximum from Clock Input to Data Output
  — TTL Compatible 24 mA Outputs
  — UltraMOS® III Advanced CMOS Technology

- **50% REDUCTION IN POWER**
  — 75mA Typ I_{cc}

- **E² CELL TECHNOLOGY**
  — Reconfigurable Logic
  — Reprogrammable Cells
  — 100% Tested/Guaranteed 100% Yields
  — High Speed Electrical Erasure (<50ms)
  — 20 Year Data Retention

- **EIGHT OUTPUT LOGIC MACROCELLS**
  — Maximum Flexibility for Complex Logic Designs
  — Programmable Output Polarity
  — GAL16V8A Emulates 20-pin PAL® Devices with Full Function/Fuse Map/Parametric Compatibility
  — GAL20V8A Emulates 24-pin PAL® Devices with Full Function/Fuse Map/Parametric Compatibility

- **PRELOAD AND POWER-ON RESET OF ALL REGISTERS**
  — 100% Functional Testability

- **ELECTRONIC SIGNATURE FOR IDENTIFICATION**

DESCRIPTION

The GAL16V8A and GAL20V8A, at 10 ns maximum propagation delay time, combine a high performance CMOS process with Electrically Erasable (E²) floating gate technology to provide the highest speed performance available in the PLD market. CMOS circuitry allows the GAL16V8A and GAL20V8A to consume just 75mA typical I_{cc} which represents a 50% savings in power when compared to their bipolar counterparts. The E² technology offers high speed (50ms) erase times, providing the ability to reprogram or reconfigure the devices quickly and efficiently.

The generic architecture provides maximum design flexibility by allowing the Output Logic Macrocell (OLMC) to be configured by the user. The GAL16V8A and GAL20V8A are capable of emulating standard 20 and 24-pin PAL® devices. The GAL16V8A is capable of emulating standard 20-pin PAL architectures with full function/fuse map/parametric compatibility. The GAL20V8A is capable of emulating standard 24-pin PAL architectures with full function/fuse map/parametric compatibility. On the right is a table listing the PAL architectures that the GAL16V8A and GAL20V8A can replace.

Unique test circuitry and reprogrammable cells allow complete AC, DC, and functional testing during manufacture. Therefore, Lattice guarantees 100% field programmability and functionality of all GAL products. Lattice also guarantees 100 erase/rewrite cycles and that data retention exceeds 20 years.

GAL16V8A / GAL20V8A BLOCK DIAGRAM

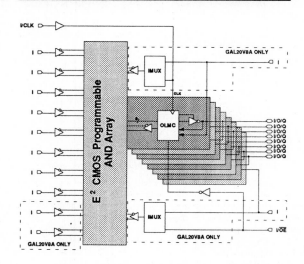

GAL16V8A / GAL20V8A ARCHITECTURE EMULATION

GAL20V8A PAL Architecture Emulation	GAL16V8A PAL Architecture Emulation
20L8	16L8
20H8	16H8
20R8	16R8
20R6	16R6
20R4	16R4
20P8	16P8
20RP8	16RP8
20RP6	16RP6
20RP4	16RP4
14L8	10L8
16L6	12L6
18L4	14L4
20L2	16L2
14H8	10H8
16H6	12H6
18H4	14H4
20H2	16H2
14P8	10P8
16P6	12P6
18P4	14P4
20P2	16P2

LATTICE SEMICONDUCTOR CORP., PO BOX 2500, PORTLAND, OREGON 97208-2500, U.S.A.
Tel. (503) 681-0118; 1-800-FASTGAL; FAX (503) 681-3037

May 1989

GAL16V8A BLOCK DIAGRAM

GAL16V8A
E²CMOS
Programmable
AND Array
(64 X 32)

GAL20V8A BLOCK DIAGRAM

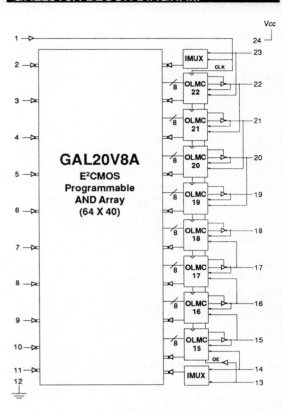

GAL20V8A
E²CMOS
Programmable
AND Array
(64 X 40)

GAL16V8A PIN CONFIGURATION

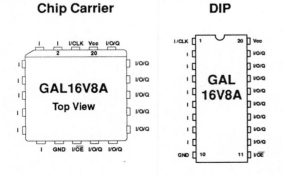

Chip Carrier

GAL16V8A
Top View

DIP

GAL
16V8A

GAL20V8A PIN CONFIGURATION

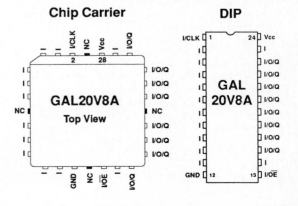

Chip Carrier

GAL20V8A
Top View

DIP

GAL
20V8A

GAL16V8A LOGIC DIAGRAM

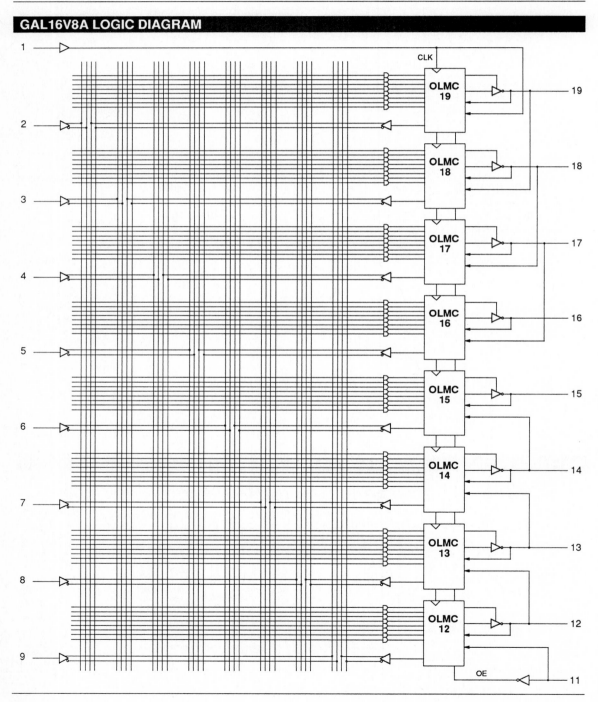

OUTPUT LOGIC MACROCELL (OLMC)

The following discussion pertains to configuring the output logic macrocell. It should be noted that actual implementation is accomplished by development software/hardware and is completely transparent to the user.

There are three OLMC configuration modes possible: registered, complex, and simple. These are illustrated in the diagrams on the following pages. You cannot mix modes, either all OLMCs are simple, complex, or registered (in registered mode the output can be combinational or registered).

The outputs of the AND array are fed into an OLMC, where each output can be individually set to active high or active low, with either combinational (asynchronous) or registered (synchronous)

configurations. A common output enable is connected to all registered outputs; or a product term can be used to provide individual output enable control for combinational outputs in the registered mode or combinational outputs in the complex mode. There is no output enable control in the small mode. The output logic macrocell provides the designer with maximum output flexibility in matching signal requirements, thus providing more functionality than possible with existing 20 and 24-pin PAL® devices.

The six valid macrocell configurations, two configurations per mode, are shown in each of the macrocell equivalent diagrams. Pin and macrocell functions are detailed in the following diagrams.

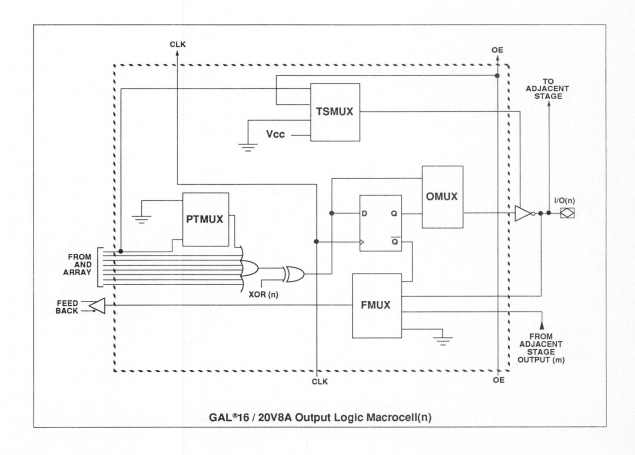

GAL®16 / 20V8A Output Logic Macrocell(n)

 **Lattice**
Semiconductor
Corporation™

REGISTERED MODE

In the Registered architecture mode macrocells are configured as dedicated, registered outputs or as I/O functions.

Architecture configurations available in this mode are similar to the common 16R8, 20R6 and 16RP4 devices with various permutations of polarity, I/O and register placement.

All registered macrocells share common clock and $\overline{OE}$ control pins. Any macrocell can be configured as registered or I/O. Up to 8 registers or up to 8 I/O's are possible in this mode. Dedicated input or output functions can be implemented as sub-sets of the I/O function.

Registered outputs have 8 data product terms per output. I/O's have 7 data product terms per output.

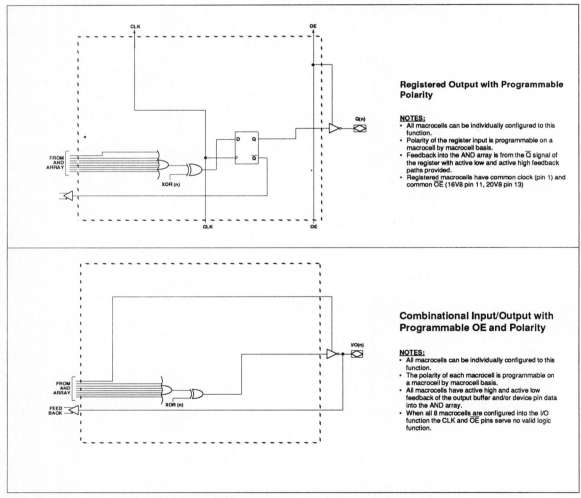

Registered Output with Programmable Polarity

NOTES:
• All macrocells can be individually configured to this function.
• Polarity of the register input is programmable on a macrocell by macrocell basis.
• Feedback into the AND array is from the $\overline{Q}$ signal of the register with active low and active high feedback paths provided.
• Registered macrocells have common clock (pin 1) and common $\overline{OE}$ (16V8 pin 11, 20V8 pin 13)

Combinational Input/Output with Programmable OE and Polarity

NOTES:
• All macrocells can be individually configured to this function.
• The polarity of each macrocell is programmable on a macrocell by macrocell basis.
• All macrocells have active high and active low feedback of the output buffer and/or device pin data into the AND array.
• When all 8 macrocells are configured into the I/O function the CLK and $\overline{OE}$ pins serve no valid logic function.

Note: The development software configures all of the architecture control bits and checks for proper pin usage automatically.

COMPLEX MODE

In the Complex architecture mode macrocells are configured as output only or I/O functions.

Architecture configurations available in this mode are similar to the common 16L8, 20L8 and 16P8 devices with programmable polarity in each macrocell.

Up to 6 I/O's are possible in this mode. Dedicated inputs or out-puts can be implemented as sub-sets of the I/O function. The two "outboard" macrocells do not have input capability. Designs requiring 8 I/O's can be implemented in the Registered mode.

All macrocells have 7 data product terms per output. One product term is used for programmable OE control. Pins 1 and 11 on a GAL16V8, and pins 1 and 13 on a GAL20V8, are always available as data inputs into the AND array.

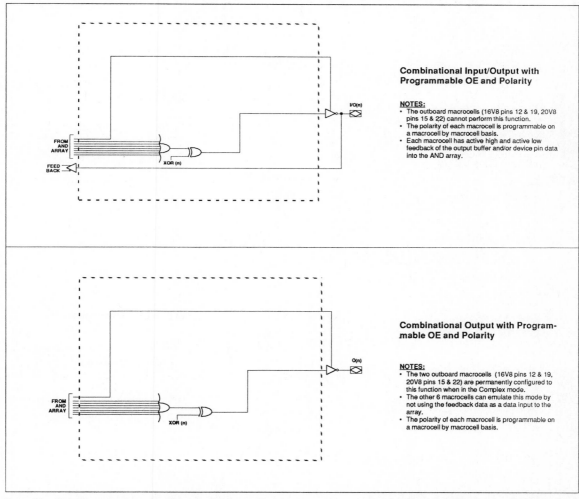

Combinational Input/Output with Programmable OE and Polarity

NOTES:
- The outboard macrocells (16V8 pins 12 & 19, 20V8 pins 15 & 22) cannot perform this function.
- The polarity of each macrocell is programmable on a macrocell by macrocell basis.
- Each macrocell has active high and active low feedback of the output buffer and/or device pin data into the AND array.

Combinational Output with Programmable OE and Polarity

NOTES:
- The two outboard macrocells (16V8 pins 12 & 19, 20V8 pins 15 & 22) are permanently configured to this function when in the Complex mode.
- The other 6 macrocells can emulate this mode by not using the feedback data as a data input to the array.
- The polarity of each macrocell is programmable on a macrocell by macrocell basis.

Note: The development software configures all of the architecture control bits and checks for proper pin usage automatically.

SIMPLE MODE

In the Simple architecture mode pins are configured as dedicated inputs or as dedicated, always active, combinational outputs.

Architecture configurations available in this mode are similar to the common 10L8, 18H4 and 16P6 devices with many permutations of generic polarity output or input choices.

All ouputs are associated with 8 data product terms. In addition, each output has programmable polarity.

Pins 1 and 11 on a GAL16V8, and pins 1 and 13 on a GAL20V8, are always available as data inputs into the AND array. The "center" two macrocells (GAL16V8 pins 15 & 16, GAL20V8 pins 18 & 19) cannot be used in the input configuration.

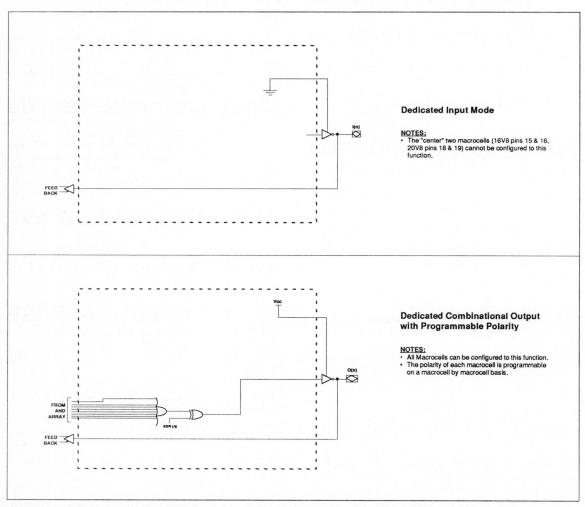

Dedicated Input Mode

NOTES:
• The "center" two macrocells (16V8 pins 15 & 16, 20V8 pins 18 & 19) cannot be configured to this function.

Dedicated Combinational Output with Programmable Polarity

NOTES:
• All Macrocells can be configured to this function.
• The polarity of each macrocell is programmable on a macrocell by macrocell basis.

Note: The development software configures all of the architecture control bits and checks for proper pin usage automatically.

ELECTRONIC SIGNATURE

An electronic signature (ES) is provided with every GAL16V8A and GAL20V8A device. It contains 64 bits of reprogrammable memory that can contain user defined data. Some uses include user ID codes, revision numbers, or inventory control. The signature data is always available to the user independent of the state of the security cell.

NOTE: The ES is included in checksum calculations. Changing the ES will alter the checksum.

SECURITY CELL

A security cell is provided with every GAL16V8A and GAL20V8A device as a deterrent to unauthorized copying of the array patterns. Once programmed, this cell prevents further read access to the AND array. This cell can be erased only during a bulk erase cycle, so the original configuration can never be examined once this cell is programmed. The Electronic Signature is always available to the user, regardless of the state of this control cell.

INPUT BUFFERS

GAL16V8A and GAL20V8A devices are designed with TTL level compatible input buffers. These buffers, with their characteristically high impedance, load driving logic much less than traditional bipolar devices. This allows for a greater fan out from the driving logic.

GAL16V8A and GAL20V8A devices do not possess active pull-ups within their input structures. As a result, Lattice recommends that all unused inputs and tri-stated I/O pins be connected to another active input, V_{cc}, or GND. Doing this will tend to improve noise immunity and reduce I_{cc} for the device.

OUTPUT REGISTER PRELOAD

When testing state machine designs, all possible states and state transitions must be verified in the design, not just those required in the normal machine operations. This is because in system operation, certain events occur that may throw the logic into an illegal state (power-up, line voltage glitches, brown-outs, etc.). To test a design for proper treatment of these conditions, a way must be provided to break the feedback paths, and force any desired (i.e., illegal) state into the registers. Then the machine can be sequenced and the outputs tested for correct next state conditions.

GAL16V8A and GAL20V8A devices include circuitry that allows each registered output to be synchronously set either high or low. Thus, any present state condition can be forced for test sequencing. If necessary, approved GAL programmers capable of executing test vectors perform output register preload automatically.

LATCH-UP PROTECTION

GAL16V8A and GAL20V8A devices are designed with an on-board charge pump to negatively bias the substrate. The negative bias is of sufficient magnitude to prevent input undershoots from causing the circuitry to latch. Additionally, outputs are designed with n-channel pull-up instead of the traditional p-channel pullups to eliminate any possibility of SCR induced latching.

BULK ERASE MODE

Before writing a new pattern into a previously programmed part, the old pattern must first be erased. This erasure is done automatically by the programming hardware as part of the programming cycle and takes only 50 milliseconds.

POWER-UP RESET

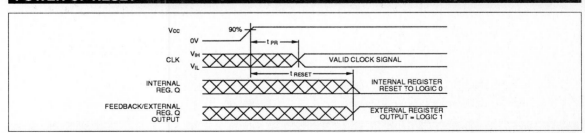

Circuitry within the GAL16V8A and GAL20V8A provides a reset signal to all registers during power-up. All internal registers will have their Q outputs set low after a specified time (t $_{RESET}$, 45µs MAX). As a result, the state on the registered output pins (if they are enabled through $\overline{OE}$) will always be high on power-up, regardless of the programmed polarity of the output pins. This feature can greatly simplify state machine design by providing a known state on power-up.

The timing diagram for power-up is shown above. Because of asynchronous nature of system power-up, some conditions must be met to guarantee a valid power-up reset of the GAL16V8A and GAL20V8A. First, the V_{cc} rise must be monotonic. Second, the clock input must become a proper TTL level within the specified time (t $_{PR}$, 100ns MAX). The registers will reset within a maximum of t $_{RESET}$ time. As in normal system operation, avoid clocking the device until all input and feedback path setup times have been met.

ABSOLUTE MAXIMUM RATINGS[1]

Supply voltage V_{CC} ....–.5 to +7V
Input voltage applied ....–2.5 to V_{CC} +1.0V
Off-state output voltage applied ....–2.5 to V_{CC} +1.0V
Storage Temperature ....–65 to 125°C

1. Stresses above those listed under the "Absolute Maximum Ratings" may cause permanent damage to the device. These are stress only ratings and functional operation of the device at these or at any other conditions above those indicated in the operational sections of this specification is not implied (while programming, follow the programming specifications).

SWITCHING TEST CONDITIONS

Input Pulse Levels	GND to 3.0V
Input Rise and Fall Times	3ns 10% – 90%
Input Timing Reference Levels	1.5V
Output Timing Reference Levels	1.5V
Output Load	See Figure

Tri-state levels are measured 0.5V from steady-state active level.

COMMERCIAL DEVICES
Refer to AC Test Conditions:
$R_2 = 390\Omega$
1) $R_1 = 200\Omega$ and $C_L = 50pF$
2) Active High $R_1 = \infty$; Active Low $R_1 = 200\Omega$ $C_L = 50pF$
3) Active High $R_1 = \infty$; Active Low $R_1 = 200\Omega$ $C_L = 5pF$

MILITARY DEVICES
Refer to AC Test Conditions:
$R_2 = 750\Omega$
1) $R_1 = 390\Omega$ and $C_L = 50pF$
2) Active High $R_1 = \infty$; Active Low $R_1 = 390\Omega$ $C_L = 50pF$
3) Active High $R_1 = \infty$; Active Low $R_1 = 390\Omega$ $C_L = 5pF$

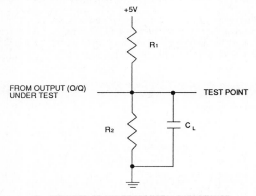

C_L INCLUDES JIG AND PROBE TOTAL CAPACITANCE

CAPACITANCE ($T_A = 25°C$, f = 1.0 MHz)

SYMBOL	PARAMETER	MAXIMUM*	UNITS	TEST CONDITIONS
C_I	Input Capacitance	8	pF	$V_{CC} = 5.0V$, $V_I = 2.0V$
$C_{I/O/Q}$	I/O/Q Capacitance	10	pF	$V_{CC} = 5.0V$, $V_{I/O/Q} = 2.0V$

*Guaranteed but not 100% tested.

 **Lattice**
Semiconductor
Corporation™

ELECTRICAL CHARACTERISTICS   **GAL16 / 20V8A-25L** Commercial

Over Recommended Operating Conditions (Unless Otherwise Specified)

SYMBOL	PARAMETER	CONDITION	MIN.	TYP.	MAX.	UNITS
V_{OL}	Output Low Voltage		—	—	0.5	V
V_{OH}	Output High Voltage		2.4	—	—	V
I_{IL}, I_{IH}	Input Leakage Current		—	—	±10	µA
$I_{I/O/Q}$	Bidirectional Pin Leakage Current		—	—	±10	µA
I_{OS}[1]	Output Short Circuit Current	$V_{CC} = 5V$ $V_{OUT} = Gnd$	–30	—	–150	mA
I_{CC}	Operating Power Supply Current	$V_{IL} = 0.5V$ $V_{IH} = 3.0V$ $f_{toggle} = 15MHz$	—	75	90	mA

1) One output at a time for a maximum duration of one second.

DC RECOMMENDED OPERATING CONDITIONS   **GAL16 / 20V8A-25L** Commercial

SYMBOL	PARAMETER	MIN.	MAX.	UNITS
T_A	Ambient Temperature	0	75	°C
V_{CC}	Supply Voltage	4.75	5.25	V
V_{IL}	Input Low Voltage	$V_{SS} - 0.5$	0.8	V
V_{IH}	Input High Voltage	2.0	$V_{CC}+1$	V
I_{OL}	Low Level Output Current	—	24	mA
I_{OH}	High Level Output Current	—	–3.2	mA

SWITCHING CHARACTERISTICS — GAL16 / 20V8A-25L Commercial

Over Recommended Operating Conditions

PARAMETER	#	FROM	TO	DESCRIPTION	TEST COND.[1]	MIN.	MAX.	UNITS
t_{pd}	1	I, I/O	O	Combinational Propagation Delay	1	3	25	ns
	2	CLK	Q	Clock to Output Delay	1	2	15	ns
t_{en}	3	I, I/O	O	Output Enable, Z → O	2	—	25	ns
	4	$\overline{OE}$	Q	Output Register Enable, Z → Q	2	—	20	ns
t_{dis}	5	I, I/O	O	Output Disable, O → Z	3	—	25	ns
	6	$\overline{OE}$	Q	Output Register Disable, Q → Z	3	—	20	ns

1) Refer to **Switching Test Conditions** section.

AC RECOMMENDED OPERATING CONDITIONS — GAL16 / 20V8A-25L Commercial

PARAMETER	#	DESCRIPTION	TEST COND.	MIN.	MAX.	UNITS
f_{clk}	7	Clock Frequency without Feedback	1	0	33.3	MHz
	8	Clock Frequency with Feedback	1	0	28.5	MHz
t_{su}	9	Setup Time, Input or Feedback, before CLK ↑	—	20	—	ns
t_h	10	Hold Time, Input or Feedback, after CLK ↑	—	0	—	ns
t_w	11	Clock Pulse Duration, High	—	15	—	ns
	12	Clock Pulse Duration, Low	—	15	—	ns

SWITCHING WAVEFORMS

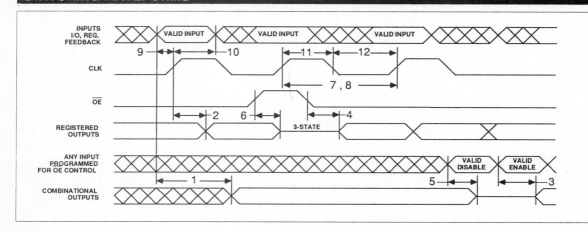

PARTS DIRECTORY

LOGIC GATES:

74LS00	Quad 2-input NAND
74HC00	Quad 2-input NAND (CMOS)
74LS02	Quad 2-input NOR
74LS04	Hex INVERTERS
74LS08	Quad 2-input AND
74LS10	Triple 3-input NAND
74LS14	Hex Schmitt-Trigger INVERTERS
74LS20	Dual 4-input NAND
74LS27	Triple 3-input NOR
74LS32	Quad 2-input OR
74LS86A	Quad 2-input EXCLUSIVE-OR
74LS244	Octal 3-State BUFFER
74S260	Dual 5-input NOR

MSI COMBINATIONAL FUNCTIONS:

74LS47	BCD-to-7-Segment DECODER/DRIVER
74LS83A	4-bit Binary FULL ADDER (or 74LS283)
74LS85	4-bit MAGNITUDE COMPARATOR
74LS138	3-line-to-8-line DECODER/DEMULTIPLEXER
74LS148	8-line-to-3-line Priority ENCODER
74150	1-of-16 MULTIPLEXER
74LS151	1-of-8 MULTIPLEXER

FLIP-FLOPS:

74LS112A	Dual JK Negative-Edge Triggered FLIP-FLOPS

COUNTERS:

74LS90	Decade COUNTER
74LS160A	Synchronous Decade COUNTER
74LS190	Synchronous Up/Down Decade COUNTER
74LS393	Dual 4-bit Binary COUNTER

REGISTERS:

74LS164	8-bit Serial-In Parallel-Out SHIFT REGISTER
74LS166A	8-bit Parallel-In Serial-Out SHIFT REGISTER
74LS373	Octal D-type LATCH (PIPO REGISTER)

MISCELLANEOUS DIGITAL ICS:

74184	BCD-to-Binary CONVERTER
74LS221	Dual MONOSTABLE MULTIVIBRATOR
2114	Static RAM (1K x 4)
GAL16V8A	Electrically Erasable Prog. Logic Device

LINEAR INTEGRATED CIRCUITS:

NE555	Timer
AD557	8-bit Digital-to-Analog Converter
ADC0804	8-bit Analog-to-Digital Converter

MISCELLANEOUS COMPONENTS:

MAN72   Common-Anode 7-segment LED Display
330, 1K, 3.3K, 10K, 27K, 33K, 47K, 68K, 82KŌ Resistors
10μ, 0.01μ, 0.001μ, 0.0047μ, 150pfarads Capacitors
10K, 50K ohms Potentiometers